# LONG LIVE THE KING

By

Brian Boughton

British Library Cataloguing in Publication Data
A CIP record of this book is available from the British Library
First Publication
ISBN 978-0-9540019-3-3
Brian Boughton's right to be identified as the author of this book has been asserted
by him in accordance with the Copyright, Designs and Patents Act 1988.

Illustrations by Wikimedia Commons.

*To Elizabeth.*

# CONTENTS

# FOREWORD

The kings and queens of England are some of the most important figures in history and scholars have written about them at length. But with one or two exceptions; their illnesses have been ignored or overlooked and this book seeks to redress this.

Sometimes the medical interest in a monarch is confined to the circumstances of his or her death and how it affected the successor. In others, illness dominated their reigns and the consequences were wide reaching.

In addition, the medical history of the monarchy is one of the best records of changing disease patterns over the centuries. As examples, Sweating Sickness appeared for the first time in 1485 before the Battle of Bosworth Field and killed many more than in the battle. It recurred at intervals but disappeared without apparent reason in 1578 and was never seen again. In a similar way, Smallpox decimated the Stuart courts but was then eradicated by vaccination. And tobacco smoking was unknown in Europe before 1528 but became the most important hazard to public health and killed all the monarchs of the modern era.

The same sources also give a special insight into how the practice of medicine changed over the centuries from black magic and religious superstition into modern science.

Our monarchs had many enemies and if their deaths were unexplained, foul play was often alleged. But this was rarely supported by any evidence and I have tried to limit speculation about this.

There are no surviving medical records before medieval times and the clinical details of our current monarch are not in the public domain. As a result, the period described is from 1047 to 1952.

For the sake of continuity I have given the more detailed medical descriptions in a separate appendix. And since almost everything can now be accessed on the Internet, the biography is short.

*Brian Boughton*

*London, January 2017.*

# INTRODUCTION

"The king is dead, long live the king" is the proclamation which announces the accession of a new monarch. In England it goes back to 1272 when Henry III died and his son, Edward I, was away on Crusade. And it has been used since then to avoid a power vacuum and ensure the throne is never vacant.

England has been ruled by 42 monarchs and two Lord Protectors, and these dominated the events of their time. Different personalities ruled England and their styles varied. Some, like Henry II and Elizabeth I were extraordinary, but others like Mary I and James II were a menace. Some, like Queen Anne were ineffectual and others like Richard II, Henry VI, and George III went insane.

Victoria reigned for 64 years, George III for 60, and Elizabeth I for 45 years. On the other hand Edward V, Richard Cromwell and Edward VIII ruled for less than a year and Jane Grey for just nine days. Richard II and Edward III began their reigns as children ruled over by Regents, but others like William IV and Edward VII were old men by the time they became king.

Our English monarchs led public lives which historians have studied and described at length. But their illnesses have been relatively overlooked, and this book attempts to shed more light on them.

Their diseases included rare inherited disorders about which royal physicians knew nothing and which were often made worse by medical intervention. Acute Porphyria afflicted the royal family for 500 years and there is now good evidence that it affected the 15 generations from 1512 – 1972. And Haemophilia was passed by the English monarchy into the royal houses of Europe where it significantly influenced events such as the Bolshevik revolution in Russia.

Monarchs and heirs to the throne used to lead their armies on the battlefield and were sometimes killed in battle. Others liked dangerous sports and were seriously injured or killed whilst hunting or jousting. Yet others were killed horse riding or were drowned at sea as they criss-crossed their empires.

Some died of fevers they contracted in squalid military camps and yet others from infections in the food prepared in filthy kitchens.

And all were as susceptible as their subjects to epidemics of Plague, Smallpox, or Influenza, which sometimes killed half the population of Europe. For centuries our kings and queens feared assassination and most of them experienced attempts to kill them.

Victoria was called the most shot-at monarch in history and her son Edward VII escaped a remarkable shooting attempt from point-blank range. Poisoning was always feared and often alleged, and some monarchs went to extraordinary lengths to avoid poisoning. One had the breast milk from his son's wet nurse tested, and a hapless royal cook who tried to poison the king was threatened with being boiled alive before his sentence was commuted to being hanged, drawn, and quartered.

The transition to a constitutional monarchy took a thousand years, but before this era our kings and queens wielded supreme power and many are regarded today as psychopaths. Some found the energy to rule their empires because they had Bipolar Disorder. Others became psychotic and were deposed and murdered.

Arranged royal marriages normally fulfilled a wider purpose and some of the spouses grew to dislike or even loathe each other. And with their dynastic duties done, they drifted apart or divorced or took up with lovers and mistresses and fathered illegitimate children. The record number of illegitimate children for an English king was 25, and since some cohabited with common prostitutes it is not surprising that some of them contracted venereal diseases.

Royal childbirth was the domain of the queen's ladies in waiting, but these had little or no experience and were much more dangerous than busy village midwives. As a result, childbirth frequently claimed the lives of royal women and it was one of the reasons why Elizabeth I never married. And it wasn't until Queen Victoria's reign that improvements in hygiene eradicated Puerperal Fever, and anaesthesia permitted trained obstetricians to manage the complications of labour.

The power and freedom of kingship often led to overindulgence with food, alcohol, tobacco, and sex. And these led to obesity, liver cirrhosis, heart disease, strokes, cancer, and venereal disease. Marijuana was used by Queen Victoria for her menstrual period pains 100 years before the general public had heard of marijuana, and it probably caused her long episodes of depression and her son's Attention Deficit Disorder. Many kings were attended by quack doctors, and at least one monarch was dispatched to his maker with a euthanasia syringe. Most monarchs were courageous in the face of death and the medical profession strived to serve them as best it could. But others charged exorbitant fees and some of the Pipe Rolls show vast sums of money spent on medical bills and Parliament's reluctance to pay them.

Until modern times, royal physicians had no real understanding of what they were treating, and often did more harm than good. As a result, most monarchs kept them at arm's length. On the other hand, royal physicians were never allowed to question or examine the monarch and the first time an accurate diagnosis was possible was often at autopsy. In addition, the consequences of an error could be serious and royal physicians were cautious about making diagnoses or predicting outcomes, and attended the king in a group to seek safety in numbers.

The tombs of English kings and queens are mostly in the great cathedrals where they generated a vast income for the church. There was often competition to bury a king's corpse and in some cases different bits are in different cathedrals or even different countries. Sometimes mistakes were made and the bodies ended up in the wrong place. And when kings and queens were executed or defeated in battle their bodies were quickly buried away from the public gaze.

In most instances a dead monarch was embalmed and lay in state for the public to recognise that an era had ended and another was beginning. Some bodies were transported many miles to reach their intended destination, and in one instance memorial crosses were built at the end of each day's march to Westminster Abbey. Some royal funerals were controversial and caused public riots and there was one example which closed London for a week.

Some royal tombs were later desecrated and in the case of William the Conqueror only one leg bone remains. And the corpse of Oliver Cromwell was exhumed and paraded publicly, and then hanged and beheaded in a symbolic act of revenge. In Cromwell's case his final resting place was lost from the records, but the mystery of Richard III was solved in 2012 and the lost grave of Henry I at Reading Abbey is undergoing investigation. State funerals are important opportunities for international diplomacy and often produced the biggest crowds ever seen. As a result, the funeral of Queen Victoria was attended by rulers from as far away as Siam, and the funeral of George V was broadcast on the radio all around the world.

# THE NORMANS

# 1066-1154

*William I*          *William Rufus*          *Henry I*

*Matilda*          *Stephen*

# *William I*

William I was the son of Robert Duke of Normandy, and a tanner's daughter called Harlotte. He was born illegitimately in 1027, became King of England in 1066, reigned for 21 years and died of alcoholism and a riding accident at the age of 60.

He was the cousin of England's last Saxon monarch, King Edward the Confessor, and his French mother dreamed of a tree growing from her belly with its branches extending across the sea to England. He soon became his father's favourite and inherited the Dukedom of Normandy at the age of seven when his father died on Crusade.

William was a man of fair stature with a fierce countenance and strong arms. And when his femur was examined in modern times, it was calculated he stood 5' 10" tall. He enjoyed excellent health and could shoot a bow from a horse at full gallop.

In 1053 he married his cousin, Matilda of Flanders, and they had four sons and six daughters. In addition, he had an illegitimate son called William Peverel. He went down in history as William the Conqueror, but his enemies called him William the Bastard. And when the residents of a besieged city hung animal skins from the city walls to mock his mother's lowly origins, William ordered their hands and feet cut off and their eyes gouged out. It was a violent era and after one wedding feast a Norman lord returned home minus his ears, eyes, and genitals and ended his days as a monk.

In 1066, Edward the Confessor, the last Saxon king of England, died childless, and William thrust himself into the dispute for the throne against Harold Godwinson Earl of Wessex, Sven II of Denmark, and Harald Hadrada, King of Norway. By this time Viking culture had permeated much of Europe and these contenders were all Viking descendants or Viking allies.

Edward the Confessor had lived in Normandy during the Danish occupation of England, and had promised the English throne to William. William had also rescued Harold Godwinson from a shipwreck in 1064 and Harold had pledged him allegiance. But in 1066, Edward underwent an alleged deathbed change of heart, and his Saxon council, the Witenagemot, advised that Harold should succeed as king. William submitted his counter claim to Pope Alexander II, and in return for promises of English lands and titles, he amassed an invasion force of 600 ships and 7,000 men to fight under a papal battle flag.

In England, Harold Godwinson assembled an army on the south coast and a fleet of ships to guard the English Channel. But then Harald Hadrada landed an army in Yorkshire, and Harold marched north and defeated him at the Battle of Stamford Bridge. At this point William's fleet crossed the Channel and landed in Pevensey Bay. Here he famously slipped and fell on the shingle beach but avoiding a bad omen, he grabbed a handful of pebbles and rose, shouting, "By the splendour of God I have taken possession of England." At Hastings he erected wooden forts and waited for Harold's return.

With Halley's Comet in the night sky Harold marched his army back to the south coast and covered 250 miles in just 12 days. When William heard of his approach he left for Senlac Ridge seven miles from Hastings, where Harold's weary foot soldiers faced a rested, well-fed, disciplined Norman force of archers, infantry, and cavalry. In a nine-hour battle, William's army was thrown back with heavy casualties and at one point he removed his helmet to quell a rumour that he had been killed. The Normans counter-attacked with cavalry and under fire from Norman archers Harold was killed by an arrow to the eye. And with him, his two brothers, Gyrth and Leofwine Godwinson were killed too.

Harold did not survive to receive the reinforcements which may have sealed his victory next day, and his army fled. It was said his right leg and half his left leg were hacked off, and his mutilated body was only recognised by his mistress, Edith Swan Neck, by what she called secret marks upon it. The altar at Battle Abbey marks the spot where he fell and where his heart was buried. His other remains were interred in the chancel of the manor church at Bosham near Chichester.

Some Saxon supporters declared for Edward Etheling, but when William reached Berkhamsted they surrendered. At his coronation in Westminster Abbey on Christmas Day he was crowned by Archbishop Aldred, but when the assembled lords cried out allegiance, the Norman troops outside panicked and set fire to the outbuildings.

During the first years of his reign, he suppressed revolts in England and Wales and when resistance continued between the Humber and the Tees, he sowed the fields with salt, and the land did not recover its fertility for a hundred years. He eliminated the English nobility, and their estates were handed to the Norman noblemen who had fought for William. He also turned 36 parishes in Hampshire into the New Forest to support his love of hunting.

After 1072 he spent 11 years in Normandy. Family disputes followed and his elder son, Robert, led a rebellion against him. In 1079 William was unhorsed and wounded, and Robert only lowered his sword after recognising his father's face. In 1080, Queen Matilda reconciled father and son, and William restored Robert's inheritance.

He brought England under his central control and replaced the Saxon earldoms with Norman counties. But his costs escalated and in 1085 he commissioned a national tax ledger. It became known as the Doomsday Book because it was like the Day of Judgement and there was no appeal against it. It legalised the transfer of Saxon lands to Norman landowners who in turn were subject to the king. When completed, William owned 20% of English land, the church another 20%, Norman barons 55%, and only 5% remained in English hands. In return for the Pope's support, he replaced the English bishops with papal counterparts. And to enforce his rule he built castles throughout England and replaced English with Norman French as the language of the ruling classes. He was in good health until 1087 when he developed abdominal swelling and Philip of France likened him to a pregnant woman. He gave up eating to lose weight and survived only on alcohol, and he almost certainly had liver cirrhosis[1] with fluid ascites in the abdomen. In this condition and on campaign against Philip of France in 1087, his horse reared at the sight of a blazing house and threw him against the iron pommel of the saddle.

He collapsed in pain and the chroniclers said he had burst his bowels. But he survived for ten days, which was not possible if his bowel had perforated, and since he passed blood in his urine he had more probably ruptured his bladder. He was taken to the Priory of St Gervais in Rouen but could not be helped. On his deathbed, he regretted his violent life and directed his treasure be used to build churches and assist the poor.

In Saxon times, any royal prince could be elected as the next king by the Witan council, but William overruled this. And since his second son Richard had been killed in a hunting accident, William granted Normandy to his eldest son Robert and the throne of England to his third son William Rufus.

When he died the servants plundered everything they could carry and left his naked body on the floor. This was shipped down the River Seine to the monastery of St Stephen in Caen, where a knight called Ascelin demanded a levy of 60 shillings for him to be buried there. With these delays his body swelled too large for the stone coffin and it had to be forced in with disastrous results. His remains were placed in a shrine built by William Rufus and this lay undisturbed until it was examined in 1552.

In 1562 Calvinists scattered his remains, but a thigh bone survived and was interred in a new shrine. This was destroyed during riots in

---

[1] See Medical Appendix – 16. Liver Cirrhosis, page 339.

1783 and replaced by a simple stone memorial. The thigh bone next escaped the allied bombing of Caen in 1944, and in 1987 it was reinterred beneath a simple memorial in the Abbey of St Etienne.

*William I memorial in Caen*

# William II

Born sometime between 1056 and 1060, William II was the third son of William I and Mathilda of Flanders. He was King of England for 13 years and was killed in a stag hunt in 1100.

His hair was yellow and because of a red face he was known as Rufus. He had different coloured eyes due to an inherited characteristic called heterochromia iridis, and he had a tendency to stutter. He was a flamboyant character, but the church denounced his court as dissolute and questioned his sexuality. He did not marry and he had no children.

His oldest brother, Richard, was killed in a stag hunt and when their father died, William succeeded in England and his brother, Robert, in Normandy. Their youngest brother, Henry, inherited nothing and the result was family split. In a revolt in 1088 William bribed many of his nobles and invaded Normandy where he defeated

Robert's army. The two then reconciled their differences and William helped Robert recover lands he had lost to France.

After the death of Archbishop Lanfranc, William confiscated his church lands. In 1093, he nominated Anselm of Bec as the new archbishop, but animosity followed and in 1097 Anselm was exiled and William claimed his church lands as well.

He brutally controlled his Norman nobles and when William of Eu was accused of treachery, he was blinded and castrated. In 1091 William defeated an invasion by King Malcolm III of Scotland, and in 1092 he built a castle at Carlisle to control Cumbria. Malcolm next invaded Northumbria but at the Battle of Alnwick in 1093, he was overwhelmed by William's forces and Malcolm and his son Edward were killed.

In 1096 Robert joined the First Crusade and pledged Normandy to William in return for funding the venture.

William raised the money with a levy from the whole of England and he ruled Normandy as Robert's regent from 1097 to 1099.

The most memorable event in William's life was his death in 1100. His hunting party in the New Forest had spread out to chase a stag, and William and Walter Tyrell, Lord of Poix, became separated from the others. It was the last time he was seen alive and he was found the next day by a group of peasants, lying dead in the woods with an arrow in his chest. With an eye on the approval of Henry I, the next king, the chroniclers concocted a tragic accident. Their reports said that Walter let loose an arrow which glanced off a tree and struck William in the chest. On receiving the wound the king was silent but broke off the arrow and fell to the ground. Walter tried to help him but there was nothing he could do, and fearing he would be charged with murder, he fled to France where for the rest of his life he denied killing the king either intentionally or accidentally.

William's body was abandoned and the other nobles in the hunting party fled to secure their own interests. The chroniclers wrote that William's brother Henry was in the hunting party and immediately after William's death he sped to Winchester to secure the royal treasure. Thence to London where he was crowned before his older brother Robert could return from the crusade.

The bad relationship between William and Henry had deteriorated at times to open conflict, so there was always a suspicion that William had been murdered. Indeed, the later chroniclers pointed out that Walter was an accomplished archer and was unlikely to have fired so dangerously.

Legend has it that local peasants dealt with the king's body, and a charcoal burner named Purkis conveyed it to Winchester on a cart. He was buried in a church which predated the cathedral where his remains are now scattered under the south presbytery screen, among the mortuary chests of more ancient kings and queens. In the New Forest a memorial stone now stands on the spot where he was struck down close to the A31 near the village of Minstead.

*The Rufus Stone*

# Henry I

Henry was born in Selby in 1068 and was the fourth son of William I and Mathilda of Flanders. He became King of England in 1100 and ruled for 35 years. He died of food poisoning in 1135 aged 67.

In 1100 he married Edith, the daughter of King Malcolm III of Scotland, and who later changed her name to Matilda. Henry had two children from this marriage but many mistresses and 25 illegitimate children. He later married Adela of Louvain but there were no children by this marriage. He died near Rouen in 1135 at the age of 67 and is buried at an unknown location in what was Reading Abbey.

He was William I's youngest son and expecting to become a bishop, he was given more schooling than his brothers. As a result he was called Beauclerc and was the first King of England to read and write.

His oldest brother, Richard, was killed in 1081 in a stag hunt. As a result their father bequeathed Normandy to his son, Robert, and England to William Rufus. Henry was excluded and the two brothers signed an agreement to exclude him in the event that one of them died without issue.

But in 1100, William Rufus was killed hunting in the New Forest and Robert was away at the First Crusade. Henry seized the Royal Treasury at Winchester and was accepted as king by leading barons.

He then secured their loyalty by a Charter of Liberties which was the forerunner of Magna Carta.

In 1101 Robert returned home from the crusade with a wife and mounted a rebellion against Henry. But in 1106 Henry defeated him at the Battle of Tinchebray in Normandy and Robert spent the last 28 years of his life in virtual imprisonment. In the Treaty of Alton, Robert recognised Henry as King of England in return for an annual settlement of 2,000 silver marks.

Henry's learning was tinged with ruthlessness and he is remembered for throwing a burgher named Conan Pilatus from a tower of Rouen and for blinding his own granddaughter.

*William Adelin*

In 1120, his heir, William Adelin, was drowned in the *White Ship* disaster. This was a new vessel which Thomas Fitz Stephen offered to transport Henry's retinue from Harfleur. But Henry had his own transport and his nephew, the future King Stephen had a stomach bug. As a result these two didn't travel on the *White Ship* and it saved their lives. But the 17-year-old William Adelin and 300 noblemen were aboard it and many bodies dressed in rich clothes were later washed up along the shores of Harfleur. According to a chronicler the crew drank a great deal of wine and the boat was very overcrowded. So much so that some travellers thought twice and disembarked. The captain was urged by the revellers to overtake the king's ship which had already set sail. But setting off in the dark with too much sail hoisted, it struck a submerged rock called the *Quillebœuf* and quickly capsized. William Adelin boarded a small boat and could have escaped, but he turned back to rescue his half-sister and his boat was swamped by swimmers trying to save themselves. Only two survived by clinging to the rock all night.

When William Adelin died, Henry's daughter Matilda was married to Geoffrey, Count of Anjou, and Henry forced the barons to accept her as his heir. The prospect of a female ruler, however, led to civil war and ushered in 300 years of Angevin rule.

In 1135 Henry was aged 67 when he visited Matilda and his grandchildren in Lyons-la-Forêt in Normandy. Here he died of food poisoning after eating "a surfeit of lampreys". These are slimy, eel-like creatures which grow up to three feet in length and migrate from the sea to breed in freshwater rivers. They breathe through gills and have sucking stoma which they attach to fish in order to feed off their flesh. They were a common delicacy but not poisonous, and Henry's fatal food poisoning must have been caused by the unhygienic preparation of the meal. Friends advised him not to eat it so it might have smelled unwholesome, but Henry disagreed and paid the price.

His body was sewn into the hide of a bull to preserve it on the journey back to England and he was buried in front of the altar in Reading Abbey, which he had founded. The Abbey was destroyed during the Protestant Reformation and some believe Henry's remains were stolen. No trace of the original tomb has been detected so far, and its probable site in Forbury Gardens adjoining St James' School is marked by a plaque and is subject to ongoing excavations.

Henry's legacies included the Curia Regis which formed the basis for Parliament, and the Royal Taxation which became the future Exchequer. He also introduced the practice of the Royal Touch in which the king "cured" patients with Scrofulous Skin Tuberculosis by touching or stroking them, and which was a practice that lasted until the reign of Queen Anne.

*Henry I's memorial at Reading Abbey*

# *Matilda*

Matilda was the daughter of Henry I of England and Edith of Scotland and was born at Sutton Courtenay in 1102. She inherited the throne in 1120 when her brother was drowned in the *White Ship* disaster, and she died in Rouen of unknown causes at the age of 65.

As a child, Matilda was educated by nuns at Wilton Abbey and she was betrothed to Henry, the Holy Roman Emperor. She was sent to Germany aged eight with a dowry of 10,000 silver marks and was a young stranger in a foreign court. Her English retinue was dismissed and she was forced to learn German, and at St Peter's basilica in Rome she was crowned Queen of Germany, Italy, and the Holy Roman Empire.

When she was 16, the emperor travelled to Lotharingia and she acted as his regent in Italy. But the marriage was childless and the emperor died in 1125, leaving Matilda a widow at the age of 23. She was summoned back to England by her father Henry I but the laws of succession were unclear and the custom was to name a pool of legitimate heirs and let them challenge each other for the throne. Against this background her cousin Stephen of Blois was made to swear allegiance to Matilda but the barons were divided in their support.

Her father next arranged for her to marry Geoffrey of Anjou but she viewed Geoffrey as entirely beneath her and was outraged. Nonetheless, he was handsome and intelligent, and the marriage took place in 1128 at Le Mans. It was a tempestuous union, and a year after the wedding Matilda left Geoffrey and returned to England. But the Great Council ordered her back to her husband and in 1133, she gave birth to their first child. In 1134, the couple's second son was born and Matilda nearly died of haemorrhage and infection.

When her father died in 1135, Matilda was in Anjou and far from the unfolding events in England. Her cousin Stephen rushed to England to seize the crown and was supported by barons who did not approve of female rulers. But Matilda and Geoffrey planned to reclaim her inheritance and by 1139 she commanded sufficient military strength to challenge Stephen. Her greatest triumph came in 1141, when her forces defeated and captured him at the Battle of Lincoln. But her advantage lasted only a few months and when she arrived in London, the city did not support her when she refused to lower taxes.

Stephen was freed in exchange for Mathilda's half-brother, Robert of Gloucester, and a year later the tables were turned when Matilda was besieged at Oxford. She escaped by fleeing across the snow-covered countryside in a white cape. Defeated again in Devizes in 1141, she escaped by disguising herself as a corpse being carried away for burial.

Matilda and her son Henry returned to Normandy where he began to show the signs of potential kingship. In 1147 when he was 14, he accompanied Matilda on a second invasion of England and in 1153, Stephen's own son Eustace died suddenly. Stephen's grief was combined with the arrival of another army led by Henry, and without the will to resist further, he acknowledged Henry as heir to the English throne.

Matilda retired to Rouen in Normandy where she ran her independent court. She intervened in family quarrels and in the later disputes between Henry II and Archbishop Becket. She died at Notre Dame du Pré near Rouen in 1167 but the cause of her death is unknown. She was buried in the Abbey of Bec-Hellouin but her tomb was destroyed by an English army in 1421. In 1684 some of her bones were identified and reburied at Bec-Hellouin in a new coffin. This was lost again after the destruction of the church by Napoleon, but was found and transferred to Rouen Cathedral.

As the founder of the Plantagenet dynasty, her epitaph reads:

*Great by Birth*
*Greater by Marriage*
*Greatest in her Offspring*
*Here lies Matilda*
*the daughter, wife, and mother of Henry.*

*Matilda's grave in Rouen Cathedral*

# Stephen

Stephen was the grandson of William I and was born at Blois in 1097. He became King of England in 1135, ruled except for one short break for 19 years, and died at Dover at the age of age of 57.

He was raised at the English court of King Henry I, and in 1125 married Matilda of Boulogne. She was an active participant in his struggles for the English crown and they had three sons and two daughters.

*Mathilda of Boulogne*

England came to dominate the cross-Channel trade and Stephen became the richest man in England. But law and order broke down among the baronial classes.

Following the death of William Adelin, Henry I named Matilda as heir and made the barons swear allegiance to her. But she was in Normandy when Henry died, and Stephen claimed that on his deathbed Henry changed his mind about the succession. He sped from Normandy to take control of the royal treasure in Winchester, and he used this to buy support among the barons.

During the first years of his reign Cumberland and Westmorland were lost to the Scots, and Normandy fell to one of Henry I's illegitimate sons. By 1139, England sank into civil war. He was captured by the Matilda's forces at Lincoln and imprisoned in Bristol.

Matilda, the former empress, was on the verge of being crowned queen when her tax proposals caused Londoners to rebel. She was forced out of London and with the capture of her half-brother the Earl of Gloucester, she was obliged to restore Stephen to the throne. In 1142 she was besieged at Oxford but managed to escape, and in 1147, her teenage son, the future King Henry II, raised an army in Normandy and invaded England. Stephen's eldest son Eustace was born in 1129 and was a golden child, for whom everyone had high hopes. Stephen asked the Pope to crown Eustace as his living heir but the Pope refused. And in Cambridge Castle, Eustace dined on food taken from a nearby monastery and he collapsed in pain. Some accounts say he died immediately whilst others that he died a week later. Many suspected poison and others said he choked. Whatever the cause Stephen lost the will to oppose Matilda and Henry, and in 1154 at Dover Priory Stephen developed acute abdominal pain. This was described as an iliac passion and is what we now call acute appendicitis. He died and was buried in Faversham Abbey in Kent alongside his son Eustace and his wife Matilda, and with his second son William excluded from the throne, his cousin Matilda's son succeeded as Henry II. The tombs were destroyed during the dissolution of the monasteries and no trace remains.

*Faversham Abbey before its destruction*

# THE PLANTAGENETS

## 1154-1485

*Henry II*    *Richard I*    *John*    *Henry III*    *Edward I*

*Edward II*    *Edward III*

*Richard II*    *Henry IV*    *Henry V*    *Henry VI*    *Edward IV*

*Edward V*    *Richard III*

# Henry II

Henry II was born in Le Mans in 1133 and became king in 1154. He ruled for 35 years and died in Chinon of a pelvic abscess caused by horse riding. His family name came from their broom (Plante genesta) cap badge and his dynasty ruled England for 331 years.

His mother, Mathilda, was the daughter of Henry I and was briefly Queen of England. She was the widow of the German Holy Roman Emperor and had three daughters before she married Henry's father, Geoffrey of Anjou. His grandfather had married the Queen of Jerusalem, and according to myth an ancestor called Melusine, was a witch called Satan's daughter. As a result the Plantagenets were sometimes called the devil's brood.

Henry became a contender for the English throne when William Adelin drowned in the *White Ship* disaster. Henry's mother, Matilda, invaded England against her cousin King Stephen and in the civil war that followed the Angevins grew in strength. When Stephen's son Eustace died at Bury St Edmund's, Stephen lost the will to resist Henry, and the Treaty of Wallingford determined that Henry would become the next king. In 1154, Stephen died in Dover and Henry succeeded to the throne.

He was a formidable, restless, stocky man with a lion face, a freckled complexion, grey eyes, and a harsh cracked voice. He had a large round head, close-cropped tawny hair, a bull neck, and a powerful frame. And his first act as king was to cross the English Channel in a storm to secure the royal treasure at Winchester.

With a natural tendency to corpulence, he was always dieting. He had no interest in finery but dressed in hunting clothes which he repaired himself. He often wore a short riding cloak and his nickname was Henry Curtmantle. His hands were rough from not wearing gloves and he never sat down except when riding a horse or eating a meal. He worked from dawn to dusk, rode five times the distances of other men, and stayed up all night arguing. He was self-assured, articulate, intelligent, and literate. But he was depressive as well as manic and it seems likely that he had Bipolar Disorder[2]. He held regular conferences about law and administration and he commissioned Glanville, which was the foundation of the modern Common Law and replaced trial by duel with trial by jury. He was schooled by brilliant scholars, had an excellent memory, and he knew by heart the history of the world. He had little difficulty with languages and he knew something of every tongue from Scotland to the Pyrenees.

He was only distracted from work by the prospect of a good day's hunting or hawking, and he was by nature wary and had only a small circle of friends. He was normally approachable and friendly and full of wit and charm, and he remembered faces and past events with what seems to have been a photographic memory. He rarely delegated important tasks to others and in matters of state he was cynical, caustic, and frequently broke his word. His temper was spectacular and he could roll around on the floor in a purple fury. If possible he avoided war but on the battlefield he was an able general. And in middle age he bequeathed different parts of his empire to his sons but was careful to retain the real power to himself.

---

[2] See Medical Appendix – 21. Mental Illness, page 350.

He became Lord of Normandy in 1150, Count of Anjou in 1151, and in 1152 at the age of 19 he married Eleanor of Aquitaine. She was the daughter of William Duke of Aquitaine, and Aenor de Chatellerault, and she was the greatest heiress in Europe. She was ten years older than Henry and a formidable woman who loved poetry and music and ran the most cultured court in Europe. She led an independent life which included an adventurous crusade to the Holy Land. And in a world where women were expected to be chaste and could be ostracised and even executed for behaving otherwise, she had many love affairs, one of which was with Henry's own father.

*Eleanor of Aquitaine*

Her previous marriage to Louis VII of France produced only daughters, and an annulment by the Pope was sought. In contrast, she and Henry parented William, Henry, Geoffrey, Joanna, Mathilda, Richard, Eleanor, Philip, and John. The marriage created a vast empire but after parenting their children Henry and Eleanor drifted apart. Henry had numerous illegitimate children and it was said that Eleanor noticed how the barons kept their wives and daughters away from the king's gaze. And when Eleanor was under house arrest in

Winchester, Henry struck up a famous romance with Rosamund de Clifford. These two lived openly together but when Henry's attempt to divorce Eleanor failed, Rosamund retired to Godstow Abbey in Oxford where she died in 1176. Denied a divorce by the Pope, Henry scandalously took up a last romance with Princess Alys of France when she was already betrothed to Henry's own son, Richard.

As a European emperor Henry reigned in Anjou, Maine, Touraine, Poiteau, Guienne, and Gascony, as well as Normandy and England. By the age of 21 he was the richest man in Europe and he travelled from Scotland to Spain on campaigns to destroy the power of disloyal barons. It was said his method was to gouge out men's eyes, cut off their limbs, rape their women, and raze their castles to the ground. To invade Ireland he borrowed fortunes from the Geraldini bankers in Florence who were the predecessors of the Medicis and Ireland's modern-day FitzGeralds. On his travels he could suddenly change his mind and stay in a wayside tavern for the night, and his courtiers were left to their own devices and sleep in barns or pig sties.

The church was another matter. Thomas Becket was Henry's closest friend and became his chancellor in 1154.

Hints of a homosexual relationship between Henry and Becket lack evidence, and in those days, men shared the same bed out of necessity. A power struggle existed between Henry, the French king, Henry's barons, his wife Eleanor, their sons, and the church. And when in 1162 Henry sought to control the church's revenues and courts, he appointed Becket as archbishop to carry this out. But Becket had been raised by Archbishop Theobold and when he was forced to choose between the church and the king, he chose the church.

A struggle ensued in which Becket excommunicated supporters of Henry, and Henry exiled Becket's family to Flanders. Attempted reconciliations failed and when Becket preached a controversial sermon, three of Henry's knights took what they thought was a signal from the king and travelled to England and murdered Becket on the altar steps in Canterbury Cathedral. News of the murder reverberated around Europe and Henry took to his chamber for six weeks and only narrowly escaped excommunication. The Pope canonised Becket and when miracles were reported at his shrine in Canterbury Cathedral, a fabulously wealthy pilgrimage was born.

Henry lived an itinerant life and in just one year in 1158 he and Eleanor visited every part of their empire and travelled 3,500 miles on horseback. They were accompanied by a court of 250 people and stayed nowhere long. It was said he wore out his garments and broke his body and his beasts. Everyone including the queen rode on horseback and no one bathed regularly. Indeed, his son John once astonished everyone by having eight baths in as many months. The chamber pots stank and the food and the wine recorded in the Pipe Rolls were horrid. Vitamin deficiency diseases such as scurvy were common in winter and in 1158 Henry's army was decimated by Dysentery[3] and he had to cease campaigning.

But his worst enemies were his own family, who spied and rebelled against him. It was inevitable the vast empire would be divided after his death and Henry preferred his son Young Henry to succeed him in England and crowned him during his own lifetime. But he was no more than Henry's regent, and Eleanor preferred her other son Richard. When rebellions broke out in 1173, Henry had to campaign against them, and at Limoge, Richard's archers aimed at Henry and nearly killed him.

*Henry the Young King*

---

[3] See Medical Appendix – 11. Dysentery, page 328.

In 1183 his son, Henry the Young King of England, died of Dysentery. He was 28 and childless and this left Richard heir to the English throne. Henry II was now 50 and looked older than his years. He was grey haired, corpulent, bow legged, lame in one leg from being kicked by a horse, and he was no longer a tower of physical strength. His legs were swollen and he had horrid ingrown toenails.

In 1189 on campaign, his army went down with Dysentery and many died by the roadside. Henry became ill and was unable to travel further. His men held him upright in the saddle whilst he bargained with Philip of France and he had to be carried back to Chinon in a litter. He could not stand or walk and a perianal abscess caused by horse riding progressed to a pelvic abscess and blood poisoning. He was forced to rest with the Knights Templar at Ballou, and lapsing into a delirium, he was nursed to death by one of his illegitimate sons. His attendants stole everything including his clothes, and when Richard visited the body next day he was horrified when blood trickled from the dead king's nostrils. At the time this was taken to signify the dead king's displeasure at Richard's presence, but a modern explanation is the now well-described anticoagulant effect of blood poisoning.

He was buried in Fontevrault Abbey where his tomb bears the inscription:

*I am Henry the King*
*To me divers realms were subject*
*I was Duke and Count of many provinces*
*Eight feet of ground is now enough for me*
*Whom many kingdoms failed to satisfy*
*Who reads these lines let him reflect*
*Upon the narrowness of death*
*And in my case behold*
*The image of our mortal lot*
*This scanty tomb doth now suffice*
*For whom the earth was not enough.*

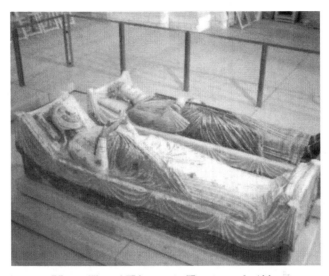

*Henry II and Eleanor in Fontevraud Abbey*

Eleanor survived into the reigns of her sons Richard and John, and in widowhood she travelled across Europe to match make important marriages. On one journey she was imprisoned by her Lusigan relatives, and on another she was besieged in Mirebeau until freed by Richard. In 1204 she died at the age of 80 and was buried next to Henry II in Fontevraud Abbey.

# Richard I

Richard I was the third son of Henry II and Eleanor of Aquitaine and was born in 1157 at Beaumont Palace in Oxford. He became king in 1189 and was killed on military campaign in France at the age of 42.

He was six feet five inches tall, had red hair, blue eyes, and a pale complexion. His mother idolised him and as a youth he lived at her court in Aquitaine which was famous for its storytelling and troubadours. He read and composed poetry in Limousin and French but he spoke no English.

He was a warrior king who became known as Coeur de Lion, and he had the exact talents to succeed his father. He was a great general but was cruel and greatly feared.

In total he spent just ten months of his ten-year reign in England and he appointed Hubert Walter, the Archbishop of Canterbury, to run the country for him. He regarded England as a source of revenue for his crusades and many felt he bled the country dry. On one occasion he declared he would sell London if he could find a buyer.

He was betrothed to Princess Alys of France but she had affairs with her own brother Philip II, and with Richard's father Henry II, and Richard eventually refused to marry her. On crusade in Cyprus in 1191 he met and married Princess Beregeria of Navarre and she became the only English queen never to visit England.

*Beregeria of Navarre*

Some questioned why they had no children as Richard had publicly confessed to sins against nature. This may not have meant sodomy but heterosexual sex outside marriage or unnatural sex with women. And though he often shared a bed with men, this was commonplace and did not infer he was bisexual. He was in fact extremely promiscuous with women and once threatened to burn down an abbey if the abbot would not allow him to sleep with a nun.

Richard's coronation at Westminster in 1189 was a lavish festival but women were excluded and Jews were publicly flogged for attending without invitations. And as anti-Semitism became rife, 150 were burned to death in York.

In 1190 he went on crusade to Jerusalem with Philip II of France and visited his sister Joanna, the Queen of Sicily. Christians were regarded by Arabs as brutish, lank haired, smelly, uncivilised people, and after the victory in Acre against Saladin, Richard beheaded 3,000 Turks and went down in Arab history as Malik Ric (Evil Richard). The siege of Jerusalem failed, and worn out with Malaria, Richard set off to return home. He landed in Trieste and travelled overland through Hungary and Austria where he was captured and imprisoned by Duke Leopold in the fortresses at Durnstein and Wurzburg.

Here he was handed over to the Holy Roman Emperor and ransomed for 34 tons of silver. To pay this, all England's medieval church plate was collected and melted down by the Benedictines at Peterborough Cathedral, and none of it now survives.

He returned with his mother to Anjou but was soon on campaign against Philip of France. He never set foot in England again but was reconciled with his brother John. He returned to Jerusalem a second time where he was infected with Malaria and Dysentery but survived.

In 1199 he was back in the Limousin besieging the lightly defended castle of Châlus-Chabrol because a peasant had uncovered a treasure trove of Roman gold which Richard claimed as feudal overlord. He was walking around the castle not wearing chainmail to inspect his sappers, who were undermining the castle wall, when a defender on the walls amused him, crossbow in one hand and clutching a frying pan in the other to beat off missiles. He aimed at the king but missed and Richard applauded; however, a second bowman then struck Richard in the shoulder.

His surgeon Mercadeus failed to remove the crossbow bolt and mangled the king's arm which became infected and gangrenous. The crossbow man, Bertrand de Gourdon, was brought before Richard and claimed Richard had killed his father. Richard forgave him and sent him away with 100 shillings. He then set his affairs in order, bequeathed England to his brother John, and died in the arms of his mother. As soon as he was dead, the crossbow man was flayed and hanged. Richard's heart was buried at Rouen and when this was analysed by modern scientists they found it had been embalmed with frankincense. His entrails were interred in Châlus and his body at Fontevraud Abbey in Anjou at the feet of his father. In 1232 the Bishop of Rochester announced that Richard had spent 33 years in purgatory and was now ascended to Heaven. His remains in Fontevraud, however, were desecrated during the French Revolution.

After his death Berengeria lived out her days in religious piety and when she died she was buried at Le Mans.

# *John*

John was the youngest son of Henry II and Eleanor of Aquitaine and was born at Beaumont Palace in Oxford in 1166. He became king at the age of 32, ruled for 18 years and died of Dysentery whilst on military campaign in Newark at the age of 50.

He was crowned in Westminster Abbey in 1199 and married Isabelle of Gloucester. But this childless marriage was dissolved by the Pope and allowed John to marry Isabella of Angouleme. They had three daughters and two sons, the oldest of whom became Henry III.

*Isabella of Angouleme*

John was red haired and five feet five inches tall, with a powerful, barrel-chested body like his father. He was intelligent and well educated and he owned a travelling library of books. He liked music, became a connoisseur of jewellery and was famous for fashionable clothes. He was an industrious administrator, an able general and he enjoyed backgammon, hawking, and hunting. He could be genial, witty, generous and hospitable, but at other times, petty, jealous, cruel and prone to fits of rage. It was said he could never be trusted and he famously gnawed his fingers.

In 1170 Henry II bequeathed England to John's brother, who was crowned Young Henry of England. John's brothers Richard and Geoffrey became Count of Aquitaine and Duke of Brittany and since John was to inherit nothing, he was nicknamed "Lackland". But when Henry II needed peace with Humbert III of Savoy, he betrothed John to Humbert's daughter, Princess Alais, and promised John the Savoy lands in Chinon and Loudun. But Alais then died whilst crossing the Alps, and John was left again with no inheritance.

But his opportunity came in 1173 when his brothers and their mother rose in revolt against Henry II. Henry the Young King of England allied himself with Louis VII of France and Queen Eleanor encouraged Richard and Geoffrey to join him in Paris. But Henry II defeated this coalition, and Eleanor was imprisoned for her role in it. During the fighting John travelled with his father and was rewarded with possessions across the empire and was created King of Ireland.

John's brothers William, Henry, and Geoffrey, died of natural causes and it was Richard who succeeded their father in England in 1189. Two years later Richard left for the crusade to the Holy Land, and it was John who ruled England as regent. He was popular with the people but quarrelled with Richard's Sicilian administrators. And when Richard was imprisoned in Wurtzburg, John had it rumoured that he was dead.

Richard was killed in 1199 on campaign in France, and his heir to the throne was his 12-year-old nephew, Arthur of Brittany. Norman law favoured John as heir and Angevin law favoured Arthur, and this split the nobility who fell into open conflict. John was supported by the English and Norman nobles and when he was crowned at Westminster in 1199 he was also backed by his mother. The conflict with Arthur's supporters in Anjou, Brittany, and France continued until John defeated them at the Battle of Mirebeau in 1202. Arthur was taken prisoner and eventually murdered in Falaise Castle, some said by John's own hand, and his body was thrown into the River Seine.

John lacked religious conviction and his atheism became a very serious issue. His anti-religious habits included failing to take communion, making blasphemous remarks, and telling scandalous jokes about the Resurrection. As a result his relationships with the church were bad and the Pope suspended his royal church revenues and excommunicated him.

His peripatetic court involved itself in aspects of local governance which had previously been delegated to local nobles. And the royal court became based on close friends of the king who travelled with him, gained favours, married wealthy heiresses, and had debts remitted. In addition John became suspicious and vindictive towards barons with sufficient wealth to challenge him.

In 1200 he ran out of money and divorced his first wife to marry the wealthy Isabella of Angoulême. It was usual for the kings of this period to keep mistresses, but chroniclers complained that John's mistresses were married noble women, and the five illegitimate children during his first marriage were unacceptable. When he married his second wife Isabella of Angoulême she was nine years old, but they eventually had five children including John's heir, Henry III.

Wars broke out in Scotland, Wales, and Ireland and in 1215 disaffected barons forced John to hold a council at Runnymede to discuss reforms. The resulting Magna Carta was drafted by the Archbishop of Canterbury and was to be implemented by a council of barons. But John merely regarded it as a time-saving device and only agreed to it under duress. It replaced the king's arbitrary rule with the rule of law, to which every man including the king was subject. It promised church rights, protection from illegal imprisonment, access to swift justice, and limitations on feudal payments to the Crown. But neither side stood by their commitments, and within three months the charter was annulled by the Pope. After John's death, the regency government of his infant son Henry III, reissued the document, and stripped it of some of its radical content. Short of funds, however, Henry III re-issued the charter in 1225 in exchange for a grant of new taxes; and his son, Edward I, repeated the exercise in 1297 and confirmed it as part of England's law. There are four parchment copies of Magna Carta which survived the next 800 years and remain the foundation of common law in Britain and around the world.

At war again with his barons, John attacked their northern lands. They responded by inviting Philip II of France to invade the south of England and on campaign at King's Lynn, John contracted Dysentery[4]. Crossing the tidal estuary of the Wash, he lost his baggage train, and the Crown Jewels were sucked into the quicksand.

His bloody flux grew worse and by the time he reached Newark he could travel no further. Here he died and dubious accounts were circulated that he had been poisoned by a surfeit of peaches and cider. His body was escorted by mercenaries and was buried in Worcester Cathedral at the altar of St Wulfstan.

After John died, Isabella arranged the speedy coronation of their nine-year-old son Henry III in Gloucester. She then left him in the care of William Marshal, Earl of Pembroke, and returned to France to secure her own inheritance at Angoulême. In 1220, she married Hugh X of Lusignan but without the consent of the King's Council in England, and a dispute followed. When she died in 1246 she was

---

[4] See Medical Appendix – 11. Dysentery, page 328.

buried in the churchyard at Fontevraud Abbey until Henry III ordered her body be moved beside Henry II and Eleanor of Aquitaine.

# Henry III

Henry III was the son of King John and Isabella of Angoulême and was born in Winchester in 1207. He became king at the age of nine and ruled initially under the regency of William Marshal. His reign lasted 56 years and he died of a stroke in London in 1272.

He was five feet six inches tall but powerfully built like his grandfather, and he had a squint in one eye which would have led to monocular blindness.

He became king during the first Baron's War and his mother was keen for him to be crowned promptly. So his coronation in Gloucester Cathedral was attended by just a handful of noblemen, and in the absence of a crown a simple golden band was placed on the young boy's head. Four years later a second coronation in Westminster Abbey was ordered by the Pope who considered the first ceremony had not been carried out correctly.

Henry was excessively pious, gave over generously to charity, and publicly washed the feet of lepers. He had a collection of religious relics and church ceremonies could reduce him to tears. He adopted

Edward the Confessor as his patron saint and turned Westminster Abbey into an Angevin mausoleum to replace Fontevraud Abbey. He extracted huge sums of money from the Jewish community who he segregated and forced to wear yellow badges.

He failed to control Wales and Ireland but was successful in Scotland after Alexander II married Henry's sister. He tried unsuccessfully to elect his brother as Holy Roman Emperor and succeed the King of Sicily. He became unpopular because of high taxes and the English resented his Lusignan relatives who had undue influence at court. He spent much of his reign fighting the barons over royal rights and his military campaigns in Normandy, Anjou, and Aquitaine were a debacle.

The English barons were led by Simon de Montfort, the Earl of Leicester, who was married to Henry's sister and led factions who wanted Henry to surrender power to a baronial council. In 1258, seven of their leaders abolished Henry's absolute powers, and reintroduced Magna Carta to give power to a baronial council and a parliament which met three times a year.

In 1264 De Montfort defeated Henry and his son Edward at the Battle of Lewes and Henry was reduced to a figurehead. Henry was forced to call a parliament controlled by de Montfort but when the monarchy itself came under threat some barons feared De Montfort had gone too far. In 1265 Prince Edward was freed and defeated De Montfort at the Battle of Evesham. De Montfort was executed and his severed head and testicles, and his hands and feet, were exhibited as a warning to Henry's enemies.

In 1272 Henry had a premonition that his end was near when he suffered a series of strokes. There are several possible causes, the commonest of which is high blood pressure. And Henry died of natural causes in London at the age of 65 with his wife by his bedside. His body was buried in Westminster Abbey in the tomb of Edward the Confessor until 1290 when his son returned from crusade and built a new brass sarcophagus which is there today.

*Henry III's tomb in Canterbury Cathedral*

# Edward I

Edward I was the son of Henry III and Eleanor of Provence and was born in 1239. He became king at the age of 33 and died of Dysentery whilst on military campaign in Carlisle at the age of 65.

As a boy there were concerns about his health but he grew so tall as to tower over others and his contemporaries called him Edward Langshanks. When his tomb was opened in 1774 his skeleton measured 6'2" and it was clothed in purple robes. He was a fair-haired man who spoke with a lisp and he had a drooping eyelid. In 1272 he was on crusade in Cyprus when he heard of the death of his father and succeeded him as king. But it took him two years to return to England to be crowned, and during this time England was ruled by a royal council. In 1254 he married Eleanor of Castile and they had fourteen children, of whom six survived. And in 1299 he married Margaret of France and had two more children. He was interested in Arthurian myths and held Round Table events at court. But he was overinfluenced by his mother's French family and was accused of favouritism towards her relatives. In the Song of Lewes it says that when he was cornered he promised anything and when he escaped he went back on his word. Concerned about his son's homosexuality, he married him in 1308 to Isabella of France and exiled his male lover, Piers Gaveston, from court.

*Eleanor of Castile*

Edward overhauled the judicial system and re-introduced Magna Carta. But gradually he reverted to preserving his royal supremacy and rebuilding his prestige. He was the only monarch to survive being struck by lightning and the first English king to exploit the French practice of the Royal Touch[5].

He was dragged into his father's war against Simon de Montford the wealthy Earl of Leicester. There were sieges of Gloucester and Leicester, and Edward and his father were defeated at the Battle of Lewes in 1264 but were victorious at the Battle of Evesham a year later.

---

[5] See Medical Appendix – 1. Two Millennia, page 284.

To pay for these wars the nobility paid swingeing taxes and Edward borrowed heavily from the Frescobaldi bankers in Florence and from the Jews. But he then outlawed further money lending, and in Lincoln, York, and London hanged 300 Jews, expelled 3,000 more and compelled the remainder to wear yellow badges. One of his captains also marooned a ship full of Jews on a tidal sandbank and left them all to drown. Edward was a charismatic but ruthless personality and during one of his Plantagenet fits of rage, a Dean of St Pauls fell dead from fear. After the Battle of Evesham against de Montford in 1265 he slaughtered all the wounded rebels and publicly displayed de Montfort's amputated limbs and genitals.

After bloody campaigns he incorporated Wales as an English principality and built massive castles at Harlech, Carnarvon, and Conwy. And he instructed his son, the future Edward II, be born in Carnarvon as the first Prince of Wales. Problems had arisen with the Scottish succession, and Edward's nomination of John Balliol did not work well. When war followed Edward defeated the Scots at the Battle of Falkirk, after which he executed William Wallace by having him disembowelled alive. He confiscated the Scottish Coronation throne, the Stone of Destiny, and brought it to Westminster. But then Robert the Bruce emerged as a military match and defeated him at the Battle of Bannockburn. Despite all this violence Edward was forced to accept many of the provisions of Magna Carta which secured the Common Law for posterity and established a permanent parliament.

Despite his ruthlessness, Edward was a devoted husband and when Eleanor died in Lincoln in 1290 her funeral cortege to London stopped each evening for him to erect a cross in her memory. There are Eleanor crosses at Lincoln, Grantham, Stamford, Geddington, Northampton, Stony Stratford, Woburn, Dunstable, St. Albans, Waltham, Cheapside, and Charing, which was then a little village near Westminster. She was buried in Westminster Abbey, and Edward later married Margaret of France and had two more sons. The Hailes Abbey Chronicle also indicates that Edward had an illegitimate son called John Botetourt.

*Charing Cross, London*

Later in his reign Edward tried unsuccessfully to broker peace with France and unite Europe for another crusade, and he spent three years in Gascony before ceding it to Philip IV of France.

He was on military campaign in the north of England when he fell ill on Burgh marshes on the Solway Firth. Having seen Dysentery[6] many times, he knew what to expect when he developed bloody diarrhoea. He made his will and charged the Earls of Lincoln and Warwick to protect his son. And he decreed that his son's lover, Piers Gaveston should never be allowed back to England. In Carlisle, on taking him his breakfast the servants found him moribund and he died in their arms.

His body was brought south and lay in state at Waltham Abbey before burial in Westminster Abbey in a tomb inscribed, "Edward the First, Hammer of the Scots". He decreed that his heart be taken on crusade to the Holy Land and his bones boiled white and carried into battle against the Scots. But these instructions were never carried out.

---

[6] See Medical Appendix – 11. Dysentery, page 328.

# Edward II

Edward II was born in Carnarvon in 1284 and became king in 1307. He was the son of Edward I and Eleanor of Provence and was the first Prince of Wales. He was deposed and murdered in 1327 at the age of 43.

In 1308 his father became concerned at Edward's bisexuality and married him to Isabella of France the daughter of King Philip IV. She was 12 years old and for the first years of their marriage Edward kept older mistresses. He and Isabella then had four children, the oldest of whom became Edward III.

*Isabella of France*

During his reign, the Scots pillaged the north and defeated Edward at the Battle of Bannockburn. There were high taxes and famine, and after the birth of the future Edward III, Isabella was allowed to return to France where she attracted exiles and became a focus of plotting. There she took Roger Mortimer as a lover and they invaded England in 1326 against little resistance. Edward's favouritism at court focussed on the homosexual Piers Gaveston, and this enraged Isabella who was the daughter of the King of France and a she-wolf by temperament. When Edward attempted to make Gaveston Earl of Cornwall and Duke of Poitiers it provoked widespread anger and Gaveston was exiled and eventually murdered.

Male and female homosexuality was tolerated openly in Greco-Roman times when the ruling classes had house slaves to gratify their sexual pleasures. But when Christianity spread across Europe the Church imposed biblical teachings about sodomy which was made sinful and against natural law. In the Old Testament, Leviticus 20:13 says, "If a man also lie with mankind, as he lieth with a woman, both of them have committed an abomination: they shall surely be put to death; their blood *shall be* upon them." And in the New Testament, I Corinthians 6:9 says, "neither fornicators nor idolaters shall inherit the kingdom of God... nor adulterers nor effeminate nor abusers of themselves with mankind".

In medieval times individuals and entire organisations like the Knights Templar were tried for sins against natural law and if found guilty their estates were forfeited and they were ordered to do penance. If they persisted they were castrated or dismembered and if this failed they were executed. Homosexuals were burned at the stake until 1638 when conviction for sodomy was commuted to hanging or beheading. It remained a capital crime until 1861 and homosexual acts short of sodomy were only legalised in 1867. But sodomy remained punishable by imprisonment until ten years after the Wolfenden report in 1957. Edward was running serious risks, and when he gave Welsh lands to the homosexual members of the Despenser family they were hunted down and murdered.

When Roger Mortimer, the queen's lover, invaded England in 1327, Edward's rule collapsed and he was imprisoned in Berkley Castle. A rescue attempt failed and he was murdered by Thomas Gurney and William Ogle in favour of his son, the future Edward III. Some accounts of Edward's death are gruesome and his screams were heard a mile away. It was said he was pinioned with a door and killed with a red hot poker in his rectum, using a cow's horn to insert it into his anus. But a red hot poker was the usual medieval method to seal the body orifices after death and this may have been distorted in later accounts.

Another version is that Edward was kept naked in a pool of floating corpses until he starved to death. Either way he died in captivity and was buried in St Peter's Abbey, the predecessor of Gloucester Cathedral, where a fine tomb was erected by his son Edward III. His fate has been the subject of speculation ever since and another version is that he was not murdered at all and his so-called dead body was the substituted body of a murdered porter at Berkley Castle. Another was that Edward was held in Corfe Castle in Dorset and then in Ireland and later in Germany where he met Pope John XXII. It was even said his son Edward III later met him in disguise in Koblenz and that he died there in 1341.

*Edward II's tomb in Gloucester Cathedral*

Mortimer ruled as co-regent with Isabella until her son came of age and was crowned Edward III. Mortimer then fell out with others at court and was deprived of his lands and imprisoned. And following Edward III's marriage to the 16-year-old Phillippa of France, Mortimer was hanged at Tyburn. Queen Isabella retired with a generous pension and lived out her life at Castle Rising in Norfolk where she doted on her grandchildren. She died in 1358 aged 63 and was buried opposite St Paul's Cathedral in Christ Church in London, leaving her estates to her favourite grandson, Edward the Black Prince.

# Edward III

Edward was the son of Edward II and Isabella of France and was born at Windsor in 1312. He was crowned king at the age of 14, reigned for 50 years, and dying of a stroke at the age of 64 he was succeeded by his grandson.

When his birth was announced Londoners sang and danced in the streets. He became king after his father was murdered by Queen Isabella and her lover Roger Mortimer, who ruled in Edward's name until he was 18. Then, while Mortimer and Isabella slept in Nottingham Castle, a group loyal to Edward entered the fortress through a secret passage and arrested Mortimer in the queen's bedroom. He was executed and Isabella was retired to Norfolk where she miscarried Mortimer's child and eventually died in 1358.

Edward married Phillipa of Hainault and their 30-year marriage produced nine children. His oldest son, Edward the Black Prince, predeceased him, and when Edward's more able son John of Gaunt was passed over for the throne this became a factor in the Wars of the Roses. When Queen Philippa fell ill with dropsy, Edward took a 15-year-old lady in waiting called Alice Perrers as a mistress. After Philippa's death in 1369, Edward fell increasingly under the influence of Perrers, who had three of his illegitimate children but was corrupt and grasping. Contemptuous courtiers also said she infected the king with venereal disease.

Edward claimed the French throne through his mother's lineage and with increasing tensions over international trade he began the Hundred Years War with France in 1337, and some say he became England's greatest military commander.

To finance his campaigns he borrowed from Italian bankers and through his use of the English longbow and new artillery weapons, he won a famous victory at Crecy against a far larger French army. His son, the Black Prince, was victorious at Poitiers and the French King Philip and his son Prince John were captured and only released in return for Edward's claims in France.

French towns were burned to the ground, meat and grain stores were robbed, and when he abandoned the laws of chivalry and executed thousands of French prisoners he became hated in France. In 1348, the Black Death killed half of the population of Europe but in 1369, the war restarted. Edward was now older and his son, John of Gaunt, led the campaign. But this failed, and in 1375, the English possessions in France were reduced to the coastal towns of Calais, Bordeaux, and Bayonne.

Edward enjoyed unprecedented English popularity in his early reign and he involved the nobility extensively in waging war and running the country. He adopted St George as his patron saint and introduced the title of duke for his close relatives. In addition, he created the Order of the Garter modelled on the legend of the Round Table. An apocryphal story is that when the Countess of Salisbury accidentally dropped her garter at a ball in Calais, and Edward tied it around his knee and adopted *honi soit qui mal y pense* as the motto of the Order of the Garter.

The fear of French invasion united Edward's nobility against France and he made the most of this threat and introduced the English language into the law courts and to Parliament. He revived

English through the works of Geoffrey Chaucer. But military failure abroad and the costs of campaigning led to political discontent. This came to a head in the Parliament of 1376, which was called to levy taxes but encountered grievances and led to the dismissal of Edward's advisors.

His last years were marked by disappointments and strife, in which his failing health played an important part. He became a shadow of his former self and living to what was then old age, his friends died and the new generation became aligned to his sons.

As these became more powerful Edward's family conflicts worsened and in 1376 his heir, the Black Prince, visited England from Aquitaine and died at the age of just 46 from what seems to have been Tuberculosis[7].

*Edward the Black Prince*

That same year Edward fell ill with an abscess and he died at Sheen following a seizure. His death mask shows the sagging jaw of a stroke victim, and it is likely that this and his senile dementia were due to cerebrovascular disease. It was said that Alice Perrers stripped the gold rings from his fingers before his body was cold.

---

[7] See Medical Appendix – 5. Tuberculosis, page 311.

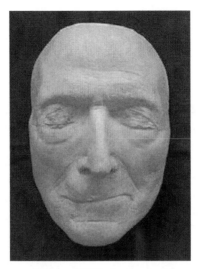

*Edward III's death mask*

After a long reign his legacy led to civil war between the members of his large family of Lancastrians and Yorkists. In Edward's dotage, it was John of Gaunt who ran the country and expected to become king.

Edward gambled seriously when he named his infant grandson as heir, and allowed the nobility to become powerful enough to wage civil war. And when the next king fell mentally ill, the result was regicide and an end to the 331-year Plantagenet dynasty.

# Richard II

Richard was the son of Edward, Prince of Wales, and grandson of Edward III. His mother was Joan of Kent and he was born in 1367 in Bordeaux. He became king of England at the age of ten and was murdered in Pontefract Castle in 1400 at the age of 33.

When his father, the Prince of Wales, died prematurely from Tuberculosis, his grandfather, Edward III, named Richard as heir. The king's most able son, John of Gaunt, was running the country but was overlooked. And as a result chroniclers were aghast at the prospect of a child king and predicted disaster.

Richard grew to be six feet tall, with blue eyes and handsome features. He was physically strong and once rode all night from London to Daventry to lead an army on the battlefield. He had a French tutor, owned a library of French books, and was a patron of Chaucer. He was a connoisseur of architecture, sculpture, music and painting, and his palaces were lavish. He became the nation's leader in fashion and his master chefs compiled the first ever cookery book, the Forme of Cury, which contained 196 recipes.

In 1382 at the age of 12 he married Ann of Bohemia, the daughter of the Holy Roman Emperor. But the marriage was childless and when Ann died from the Plague[8] he married an eight-year-old child bride, Isabella of France, in what was a romantic make-believe.

There were no children by either marriage and there were rumours of Richard's homosexual relationships with the courtiers Robert de Vere and Michael de la Pole.

*Anne of Bohemia*            *Isabella of France*

After Anne's death his mental health deteriorated and he became melancholic and disorganised. He could only focus on his own personal needs and demanded constant praise. He was also obsessed with symbolism and adopted the White Hart as a family symbol and designed his own extravagant tomb in Westminster Abbey.

---

[8] See Medical Appendix – 6. Plague, page 314.

In addition, he became naïve and fell into the old mistake of rewarding only favourites. Unlike his father and grandfather, he was not at ease with the great men of the kingdom, especially his uncle, John of Gaunt. And as his narcissism became more awkward he eventually lost touch with reality and is now thought to have been schizophrenic[9].

When sane he was a sophisticated man and his lasting achievements included support for Geoffrey Chaucer and John Wycliffe. He also commissioned Hugh Herland to build the hammer beam ceiling of Westminster Hall.

But gradually he became a solitary figure and his mental state was an increasing cause for concern. In one fit of paranoia he set up a rival court in Cheshire which was despised in London. In addition, he maintained England's first standing army and was not able to reduce taxes when many thought he could afford to.

In 1397 he mishandled threats to his authority by confiscating estates and by judicial and extrajudicial executions. Food prices rose, the Pope in Avignon imposed higher taxes, and Lollards murmured the first hints of English nonconformism. John Ball travelled the country preaching sedition and cities like Canterbury built walls around themselves. In addition, the nobility had formed powerful armies during the reign of Edward III and the country was full of trained mercenaries.

The poll tax of 1380 led to serious unrest, and Wat Tyler and Jack Straw led a Peasants Revolt which marched on London. They burned manor houses, beheaded prisoners and eventually reached Black Heath just outside the capital. The 14-year-old king faced down their 60,000-strong armed mob. But when he met them a second time at Mile End they were drunk, and when Tyler insulted the king a fight broke out and Tyler was killed. The archers drew their longbows and history hung in the balance, until Richard, who had won his spurs at Crecy, rode forward and defused the crisis. He agreed to all their demands and persuaded the rebels to disperse. He then brought in an army to defend the capital, revoked the promised pardons and all the leaders were tried at St Albans and hanged, drawn, and quartered.

But these examples of kingsmanship became scarce and violence

---

[9] See Medical Appendix – 21. Mental Illness, page 350.

spread across the kingdom. Plots to assassinate him were uncovered and John of Gaunt was arrested. Richard's mother had been a mediator in family quarrels but in 1385 she died. As a result the family tensions increased, the Duke of Gloucester was denounced as a traitor, and Richard marched his army against Gaunt's son Henry Bolingbroke.

Richard's army included elite Cheshire archers and Welsh pikemen, but many of the barons had their own private armies and conspiracy and treason were everywhere. Richard's court was dominated by deceit and he was widely unpopular and desperately short of money. Enemies bought pardons to escape execution, and when Gaunt died in 1399 Richard fatally blundered when he confiscated Henry Bolingbroke's inheritance. Bolingbroke was exiled to France, and in England the nobles began to take sides. Bolingbroke invaded England and landed at Ravenspur in Yorkshire. He captured and imprisoned Richard in the Tower of London where he agreed to writs for a new parliament and betrayed close friends to be executed. A commission then found against Richard's rights of succession, and Parliament formally deposed him and crowned Bolingbrook as Henry IV. Richard was then transferred to Pontefract Castle and murdered. Stories of him being brutally killed were not borne out by Dean Stanley's examination of the skeleton in 1871 and it seems probable that he was poisoned[10] or suffocated.

Henry Bolingbroke was a good propagandist and had Richard's body borne to London to be viewed publicly in St Paul's Cathedral. It was buried in the priory at Kings Langley in Hertfordshire but in 1413 Henry V transferred it to an elaborate tomb in Westminster Abbey. Years later Richard's court double and probable illegitimate son, Richard Maudelyn, was beheaded for pretending to be the king, and a priest was executed for spreading the rumour that Richard had been seen alive in Scotland.

---

[10] See Medical Appendix – 23. Poison, page 359.

# Henry IV

Henry IV was born at Bolingbroke Castle in Lincolnshire in 1367 and became king in 1399. His father was John of Gaunt, the most able son of Edward III, and his mother was Blanche of Lancaster, the country's richest heiress. He died of epilepsy in 1413 at the age of 46.

*John of Gaunt and Blanche of Lancaster*

He was stocky, vigorous, devout, well read and musical, and he excelled at martial arts. He first married Mary de Bohun and they had six children including his successor, Henry V. And when Mary died in childbirth he married Joan of Brittany.

*Mary de Bohun*

From 1390-92 he campaigned with the Teutonic Knights in Lithuania, and in 1393 he journeyed to Jerusalem and visited countries where his gift for languages gained him an international reputation.

Amid accusations of treason, Henry was banished by Richard II to six years' exile, but when he was in Paris in 1398 his father died and Richard II claimed Henry's vast inheritance and extended his banishment to life. But in 1399 Richard II was in Ireland when Henry invaded England. And when he was declared king he claimed that Richard had abdicated of his own free will and died in prison of an illness. In reality Richard had abdicated to save his life and was then murdered.

Henry was always short of the money he needed to run the country, and Parliament accused him of mismanagement and extended its powers over his royal purse. He hosted a visit from Manuel II of Palaeologus, who was the only Byzantine emperor ever to visit England, and in 1406 he captured and kept hostage the future James I of Scotland. Then, in 1400, there was a revolt by Owain Glyndwr who declared himself Prince of Wales. In the last years of his reign the fable of a living Richard II was revived, and a living impostor was found. Spies from Scotland infiltrated English towns and declared Richard was in the Scottish Court, waiting for a signal to recover his throne.

At this stage Henry developed a disfiguring skin disease which was almost certainly Psoriasis and was probably related to stress.

Even more seriously, he developed epileptic seizures[11] during which he fell unconscious, foamed at the mouth, bit his tongue, shook with convulsions and vomited, urinated, and soiled himself. These often occurred without warning and for the king it was devastating and he was forced to transfer royal powers to his son.

In those days epilepsy was usually fatal and the victims often choked to death after vomiting during a seizure. He had always dreamed of going on Crusade and it was predicted by a soothsayer that he would die in Jerusalem. And as it turned out, he died in the Jerusalem chamber at the residence of the Abbot of Westminster.

---

[11] See Medical Appendix – 20. Epilepsy, page 348.

The cult of Thomas Becket was enjoying a renaissance at that time and as a result Henry chose to be buried in Canterbury Cathedral, not Westminster Abbey. The tomb was examined in 1832 and his embalmed body was well preserved.

# Henry V

Henry V was the son of Henry IV and Mary de Bohun and was born in Monmouth in 1386. He became King of England at the age of 27, and died of Dysentery in France at the age of 36. After the Battle of Agincourt in 1415 he married Catherine, the daughter of King Charles VI of France, and their son became Henry VI.

He was 6' 3" tall, with dark hair cropped in a ring above the ears. He possessed extraordinary energy and it was said his eyes flashed with the mildness of a dove and the brilliance of a lion. During his father's exile in 1398, Henry was 12 and he lived in the royal court in England where Richard II treated him kindly.

When his father became king, Henry studied at Oxford University where his uncle was Chancellor. At the age of 16 he was in the royal army at Shrewsbury fighting against the rebellion of Harry Hotspur. At the head of his troops he lifted his helmet visor and was struck in the face with an arrow. Powerful arrow storms from trained archers with long bows were the decisive weapons of the age and the tempered arrow heads were forged to penetrate plate armour. A direct strike would have passed through Henry's skull and killed him instantly. So the arrow that entered his face had probably ricocheted from another object and had spent much of its energy. Even so, it penetrated six inches into Henry's cheek bones but somehow managed to miss the vital structures at the base of his skull.

He was taken to a place of safety but his life was in mortal danger. His medical attendants attempted to remove the arrow but succeeded only in breaking the wooden shaft. With the metal bodkin lodged deeply inside his skull, bleeding, infection, and death were inevitable, but at that point a London surgeon called John Bradmore was summoned and performed a remarkable operation. First he fashioned probes from elder pith and clean linen infused with rose honey, which he used to widen the wound and gain access to the arrow head inside the king's skull. He then forged a set of metal tongs with a clasp screw and inserted these into the wound to grip the arrow head and secure it firmly. Then by moving it to and fro he pulled out the bodkin. The gaping wound was irrigated with white wine and dressed for 20 days with an antiseptic of honey, barley flour, and flax. This was centuries ahead of its time and when Henry's portraits were painted in later life he was depicted in profile to hide the ugly scar on the right side of his face. Bradmore's life-saving surgery changed the course of history, and he was paid 40 shillings, awarded an annuity of 10 marks, and appointed Searcher of the Port of London.

When Henry's father developed epilepsy the young Henry carried out much of the country's administration under the watchful eyes of his uncles, Henry and Thomas Beaufort. When his father died in 1413, Henry was crowned in Westminster Abbey and declared his intention to rule England at the head of a united nation. The body of the murdered Richard II was moved to Westminster Abbey and those who suffered in the previous reigns were restored to their titles and estates. Henry's gravest domestic danger was Lollard discontent towards Catholic Church doctrine and in Saint Giles's Fields, a thousand protestors were dispersed and forty executed.

In 1415 Henry was forced into war by French support for Owain Glyndwr. And with a generous subsidy from Parliament he sailed from Southampton with 8,000 troops. He captured Harfleur but was threatened by the French army and was desperate to reach the defences of Calais. He marched his men to the point of exhaustion but the French then intercepted them on the River Somme at Agincourt. His men had run out of food, and thousands had died of Dysentery from eating contaminated shellfish in Harfleur. Others suffered with St Anthony's Fire from eating grain contaminated with ergot, and the forth coming battle was a grim prospect for the English. Vast numbers of French peasants had volunteered to fight but the French nobility were fearful to arm them. Nevertheless, Henry still faced a much larger French army which bristled with pikemen and mounted knights in armour.

But Charles VI of France was a schizophrenic who they called the lunatic king. Amid his delusions his knights could not agree a chain of command and what emerged was a flawed battle plan dominated by heavily armoured knights on horseback. The French army was 25,000 strong and outnumbered the English at least four to one. But Henry's army included skilled archers who for many years had trained at archery butts in villages across England, and could shoot their longbows more rapidly and with a longer range than the French crossbowmen. They were lightly clad with canvas bags and broadswords, some were mounted, and they were extremely mobile on the field of battle. Added to which the French were fighting out of duty to feudal overlords whereas the English had been paid 6d a day and as much loot as they could steal and carry. These were elite soldiers and when they died in old age, parish churches up and down the country commemorated them with pride.

Henry's manoeuvres on the battlefield denied space for the French cavalry to outflank him, and the French fell into the trap of launching a full-frontal cavalry charge at the English archers. On a narrow front in knee-deep mud they were struck down by a storm of arrows which blackened the sky. And they sank into the mud among their fallen horses and were slaughtered. The French sustained 8,000 casualties compared to the 500 English dead. And contrary to the rules of chivalry another 2,000 French prisoners were executed to prevent them rejoining the battle. The brutality was extreme and the battlefield was strewn with severed heads and limbs. The surgeons used Opium and Hemlock for pain relief, and rabbit fur and egg white to staunch the bleeding. But cautery with hot irons, and amputation with an axe were the mainstays of treatment and few survived the infections which inevitably followed.

After Agincourt, the Holy Roman Emperor acknowledged Henry's claims to France and ended the 100 Years War. And in 1419 Henry married Catherine, the French king's daughter, and they were crowned in Westminster Abbey. In 1421 he returned to France but did not live long enough to be crowned there. At Meaux he developed Dysentery[12] and was weakened so much he could not ride and had to be carried on a litter. Lying ill for three weeks, he made arrangements for the government of his two kingdoms after his death, and when he died at Chateau de Vincennes he was only 36.

His body was carried in procession across France and returned to England where it was buried at Westminster Abbey in a tomb inscribed: "Henry V, Hammer of the Gauls, lies here". The tomb's silver was stolen in 1546 and a sword, found in the Abbey triforium in 1869, is thought to have been part of its decorative armour.

*Catherine de Valois*

---

[12] See Medical Appendix – 11. Dysentery, page 328.

His widow, Catherine de Valois, later fell scandalously in love with a commoner, Owen Tudor, and one of their five sons, Edmund, Earl of Richmond, was the grandfather of Henry VII. But with her fall from grace, she ended her days in Bermondsey Abbey where she was ill with the schizophrenia[13] she inherited from her father, and passed on to her son Henry VI.

She died in 1437 and was buried in the Lady Chapel at Westminster. But Henry VII later pulled down her tomb to build his own chapel and Catherine's body was placed in an unburied open coffin of loose boards near to the tomb of Henry V. It remained there for 200 years and Samuel Pepys saw her remains in 1669 and was even allowed to kiss them. Her body was buried in 1778 and a century later Dean Stanley re-buried it permanently under the altar in Henry V's chantry.

---

[13] See Medical Appendix – 21. Mental Illness, page 350.

# Henry VI

Henry VI was born at Windsor in 1421 and became King of England at the age of nine months. He was the son of Henry V and Catherine of Valois and he reigned from 1422-61 and again from 1470-71. He was the only monarch to be crowned king of England and France and he was murdered in the Tower of London at the age of 50.

His father died on campaign in France and after her liaison with a Welsh squire called Owen Tudor, Henry saw little of his schizophrenic mother. In 1423 a regency council was established to rule for the two-year-old boy king. Richard Beauchamp, Earl of Warwick, was his guardian, the Duke of Bedford led the war in France, and the Duke of Gloucester ran the government. Aged 24, he married Margaret of Anjou when she was 16. They had one son who was executed by Edward IV at the Battle of Tewkesbury and from then on they were childless.

Among his achievements he founded Eton College and King's College Cambridge. But he was prudish and sanctimonious and preferred reading holy scriptures to dealing with the business of state. He delegated this to his wife who surrounded herself with a clique of courtiers and stoked factional unrest between the Dukes of Beaufort, Suffolk, Gloucester, and York. Henry wore dreary clothes and when forced to wear the crown on feast days he did penance next day by wearing a hair shirt.

*Margaret of Anjou*

After Joan of Arc's victories in France and her eventual execution, the English nobility clashed over the French war and Henry became deeply unpopular because of the territories which were lost to France. The Duke of Suffolk was scapegoated and in 1447; on his way into exile his ship was intercepted and he was beheaded. His body was later washed up on a beach at Dover. By 1449, the French had overrun the whole of Normandy. The English troops returning home had not been paid and became lawless, and Jack Cade (John Mortimer) led a rebellion in Kent. Henry came to London with an army but Cade triumphed and went on to occupy the capital for a period. Guyenne and Bordeaux were then lost to the French, and by 1451 only Calais remained English.

Like his mother and grandfather, Charles VI of France, Henry suffered from schizophrenia[14]. At the age of 31, he had a complete mental breakdown and was unaware of what was going on around him. He had often had an odd demeanour and commoners had been sent for trial for merely commenting about this.

But among the growing storm clouds his schizophrenia worsened and he became babylike and sat silent in fixed postures for long periods. He spent much time isolated at his hunting lodge in Clarendon in Wiltshire, and at one point he had a hysterical fugue and forgot how to walk. He sometimes lost his memory and speech and he failed even to respond to the birth of his son. He was extremely prudish about nudity and sex and he declared the baby must have been fathered by the Holy Ghost. A deputation of 12 Lords Spiritual and Temporal from the Privy Council examined Henry but he declined to answer their questions and was carried back to bed. They instructed his physicians to moderate his diet and administer powders. But whatever these were, he was seriously ill for a year and Richard Duke of York was appointed Protector of the Realm.

With London teaming with armed men and Queen Margaret running the country, the disaffected nobles endorsed the claims of the House of York. Pitched battles were fought in the north of England and a great council made things worse when Queen Margaret sided against the Yorkists.

The rival factions converged at St Albans and on 22nd May 1455 Henry's battle standard was unfurled to signify that he was at war with any subjects who opposed him, and the 30-year Wars of the Roses began. He was struck by an arrow and four of his close aides were killed. But he was taken back to London as king where he fell into a state of indifference and his mental state worsened. The Commons demanded the appointment of a Regent but Queen Margaret nursed him back to sanity. In this way he became her puppet and increasingly she managed his affairs in her name and in the name of their son. In one of the battles Henry sat under a tree watching her direct their army whilst he was laughing and singing. In

---

[14] See Medical Appendix – 21. Mental Illness, page 350.

1461 Henry began a nine-year imprisonment in the Tower of London which he spent in relative comfort and holy contemplation.

At the instigation of the Earl of Warwick, and to the fury of Queen Margaret, Edward Duke of York was crowned Edward IV. In 1470 Henry was released by Warwick and became his puppet. He fled to France and returned next year to regain the throne. But he was now "mute as a crowned calf" and when Warwick was killed at the Battle of Barnet Henry was deposed for a second time, and Edward IV was reinstated.

In 1471 Henry's teenage son, Edward, was killed at the Battle of Tewkesbury and soon after this Henry died in mysterious circumstances in the Tower of London. According to the Arrivall Chronicle his death was due to melancholy on hearing news of his son's death. However, it was widely accepted that Edward IV and his brother Richard of Gloucester had murdered him.

His body was displayed in public and he was originally buried in Chertsey Abbey. But in 1485, his body was moved to St George's Chapel in Windsor Castle and in death he achieved the saintly martyrdom he might have hoped for. Miracles were attributed to his shrine and when this was examined in 1910 it revealed a wooden box containing dismembered bones, including a skull which was much broken and covered in blood. Queen Margaret was taken prisoner after the Battle Tewkesbury and in 1475 she was ransomed to her cousin, King Louis XI of France. She lived in France as his poor relation and died there at the age of 52.

# Edward IV

Edward IV was the son of Richard Duke of York and Cecily Neville, and he was born in Rouen in 1442. He was king of England from 1461-1470 and again from 1471-1483. He died of a heart attack in London at the age of 41.

As the Earl of March he spent his youth in Ludlow, and when his father and brother were killed at the Battle of Wakefield he became Duke of York and third in line to the throne.

He was 6'4" tall and handsome but an insatiable womaniser whose many lovers included married women. He had three illegitimate children, one of whom was Perkin Warbeck, one of the Pretenders to Richard III.

He was easy in the company of all kinds of men and he had a prodigious memory for names. In 1461 the entire kingdom celebrated his coronation and he quickly won the support of Parliament. He operated networks of informers and ruthlessly executed opponents including Henry VI, Edward Prince of Wales, and George Duke of Clarence. He refused to allow his troops to carouse in towns before a battle and he usually ordered no quarter to the enemy and dragged them out of churches to be executed.

But his claim to the throne was vigorously opposed by Henry VI's Queen Margaret, and in 1464 he lost the important support of the Earl of Warwick. Warwick had been intent on peace with France and wanted Edward to marry into the French royal family, but Edward secretly married Elizabeth Woodville and Warwick withdrew his allegiance. She came from a landed but not a noble family and it was said she was too poor for a king's wife but too rich for a harlot. Worse still, she was the widow of Sir John Grey and she swamped her court with his Lancastrian supporters.

*Elizabeth Woodville*

Her marriage to Edward produced ten children, including the princes who were murdered in the Tower and Elizabeth of York, the future queen of Henry VII.

The rivalry between York and Lancaster broke into open conflict and in 1455 the first Battle of St Albans signalled the beginning of the Wars of the Roses. Civil war was fought across the country for 15 years and both sides suffered defeats and used French support to invade England. On the Lancastrian side Warwick was killed at the Battle of Barnet and the Prince of Wales at the Battle of Tewksbury. Henry VI completely lost his sanity and was murdered in the Tower of London and his wife, Queen Margaret, retired to France.

On the Yorkist side Edward's father became Lord Protector of England but was killed at the Battle of Wakefield. Edward replaced him as Duke of York and in 1461 he was proclaimed king.

With the Lancastrian line virtually extinguished, Edward's only rival was Henry Tudor and he was living in exile. In 1478 Edward's brother George, Duke of Clarence, was found guilty of treason and executed, according to Shakespeare by drowning in a butt of Malmsey wine. And free of family feuding, Edward could at last concentrate on running the country. He placed crown lands in the hands of skilled managers, promoted foreign trade, paid off the national debt and controlled the expenses of the court. He built St George's Chapel at Windsor and his books became the foundation of the British Library. He supported the printer William Caxton and he owned a copy of the first printed English book, *The Dictes and Sayenges of the Philosophers.*

But he grew fat and in 1481 he delegated the pacification of the Scottish borders to his brother Richard. His health began to fail and his womanising focussed on a favourite called Jane Shore, a mercer's wife. Some blamed his early death on his unhealthy over eating and in 1483, at the age of 41, he fell ill at Westminster with chest pains. He survived long enough to add codicils to his will, and when he died of a heart attack his body was buried at Windsor in the St George's Chapel. He was succeeded by his 12-year-old son, but fatally he trusted the boy's safety to Richard of Gloucester and within a year the boy and his brother were murdered.

# Edward V

Edward V was the older son of Edward IV and Elizabeth Woodville and he was born in 1470. He became king at the age of 12 and was murdered in the Tower of London in 1483.

Along with his younger brother Richard, Duke of York, Edward was one of the Princes in the Tower, who disappeared after being imprisoned there by their uncle, Richard of Gloucester, ostensibly for their own safety. The events have remained controversial for centuries but Edward was never crowned king and reigned for less than a year.

He was born in the Abbots House in Westminster Abbey where his mother had sought refuge from the Lancastrians who had deposed her husband. Following Edward IV's restoration in 1471 the young Edward was created Prince of Wales, and was established at Ludlow Castle. As a child he was under the guardianship of Earl Rivers, a noted scholar. And in a letter to Rivers, Edward IV set down precise conditions for the education of his son and the management of his household. "The prince was to rise every morning at a convenient hour, according to his age. His day would begin with Matins and then Mass, which he was to receive uninterrupted. After breakfast, the business of educating the prince began with virtuous learning. Dinner was served from ten in the morning, and then the prince was to be read noble stories of virtue, honour, cunning, wisdom, and of deeds of worship, but of nothing that should move or stir him to vice".

Perhaps aware of his own shortcomings, Edward IV was keen to safeguard his son's morals, and he instructed Rivers "to ensure that no one in the prince's household was a habitual swearer, brawler, backbiter, common hazarder, adulterer, or user of words of ribaldry. After further study, in the afternoon before Evensong the prince was to engage in sporting activities suitable for his class. Supper was served from four, and the curtains were to be drawn at eight. Following this, the prince's attendants were to enforce themselves to make him merry and joyous towards his bed. They would then watch over him as he slept."

Dominic Mancini, an Italian visitor to the court, reported "that in word and deed the young Edward gave many proofs of his liberal education, and of polite and scholarly attainments beyond his age. He had such dignity in his whole person, and in his face such charm, that however much they might gaze, he never wearied the eyes of beholders."

His father planned a prestigious marriage for the boy, and in 1480 agreed for the ten-year-old to be betrothed to the Duke of Brittany's four-year-old daughter, Anne. There were two stages for royal marriages in the middle ages, which were the betrothal and the wedding proper. The usual age for betrothals was six for a girl and eight for a boy, followed by marriage at 12 and 14 respectively. The betrothal was more festive than the wedding and was an early marriage contract drawn up between the families on behalf of their children. Planned marriage was important among noble landowners, and entailed an initial exchange of property between couples' families and the payment of the bridal dowry. The betrothal festivities might entail the future groom offering a ring, a pair of sandals, or a kiss to the bride-to-be. Then the couple might share a glass of wine and a fruit to symbolise the forthcoming union. And during the betrothal ceremony, the children would take vows in a similar way to the wedding. In Edward's case the transfer of vast estates of Brittany required a papal dispensation and stated that his first child would become Prince of Wales and his second, Duke of Brittany.

But at Ludlow, whilst still awaiting his marriage, in 1483 the prince received news of his father's sudden death. Edward IV's will nominated his brother, Richard, Duke of Gloucester, as Protector of his son. And when the boy king and his party set out for London they were intercepted at Stony Stratford by his new guardian. Rivers and Grey, the boy's guardians at Ludlow, and Thomas Vaughan, the boy's chamberlain, were arrested and sent north where they were eventually executed. Edward's protests were dismissed and Richard escorted him to London. The boy's mother Elizabeth Woodville fled to sanctuary in Westminster Abbey with her daughters and her younger son, Richard, Duke of York and she unsuccessfully set about getting Richard of Gloucester's regency annulled and a regency council set up with her as head.

Gloucester and Buckingham entered London with the young king and a large body of armed men, and an atmosphere of coup d'état gripped the city. While the grasping Woodvilles had been unpopular, King Edward IV was much loved by Londoners, and most were loyal to his son. But Richard of Gloucester eased their fears by explaining he was countering a Woodville conspiracy and this was gradually accepted and the city was calmed. Edward was lodged in the Tower of London with his Woodville uncles to await his coronation, and this was not sinister as the Tower was also a royal residence. When his coronation date was fixed Elizabeth Woodville was relaxed enough to send Edward's ten-year-old brother Richard, Duke of York, to join him. But then the coronation was postponed and a prominent theologian Ralph Shaam, presented evidence that Edward IV was already contracted to marry Lady Eleanor Butler before he married Elizabeth Woodville. As a result Edward IV's marriage to Elizabeth was invalid and their children were illegitimate. The children of Richard's executed older brother George, Duke of Clarence, were then barred from the throne, and in a Titulus Regius which was read out at St Paul's Cathedral, Parliament declared Richard was the legitimate king. The following day he acceded to the throne as King Richard III and every peer in England attended the coronation on 6th July.

Edward reverted from being called King Edward V to Prince Edward and he and his brother were seen less often within the Tower. The two were seen publicly playing bows and arrows in the Tower gardens for the last time in September, and the final person to see Edward alive was his physician, Dr Argentine, who found him in a state of melancholy. The fate of the brothers has always remained unclear, but it is generally accepted they were murdered and that Richard ordered it. In 1486 the Croyland Chronicle reported that the sons of King Edward IV had died a violent death, and in later years Thomas More wrote that the princes were smothered with pillows. This version appeared in William Shakespeare's play, in which Sir James Tyrrell murdered the princes on Richard's orders. Thomas More wrote how Richard ordered a John Green to carry a letter to Sir Robert Brackenbury, the Constable of the Tower, to kill the children. But Brackenbury refused and the king then approached Sir James Tyrrell, who was more receptive. Richard sent him to the Tower with an order that the keys be surrendered to him. And Thomas More told how Tyrell employed a Miles Forest and John Dighton to carry out the deed. In 1502 during the reign of Henry VII Tyrrell confessed to the murders prior to being hanged and implicated the two other men. However, Tyrrell's confession was extracted under torture and he was unable to locate the bodies which he claimed had been moved.

The other possible architects of the murders were Henry Stafford, Duke of Buckingham, or Henry Tudor's mother, Margaret Beaufort, but the evidence incriminating them has never been substantiated. There was no funeral for the two princes and the two bodies were reportedly buried "at a stair foot meetly deep in the ground, under a great heap of stones."

*The stairwell in the White Tower*

In 1674 the bones of two children in an elm chest were discovered at a depth of 10 feet by workmen rebuilding the stairwell to the chapel in the White Tower. One report was that and they fitted the ages of two brothers and they were found with "pieces of velvet about them. The skull of one was intact but the other was broken, as were many of the other bones." Charles II, the reigning monarch in 1674 was convinced and asked Sir Christopher Wren to design a marble urn bearing the names of Edward and Richard. And the bones were buried next to the tomb of their sister, Elizabeth of York, in the Henry VII chapel in Westminster Abbey.

In 1933, this grave was opened and the skeletons were determined to be those of two children, aged 7 to 11 and 11 to 13. These had been interred carelessly among animal bones, and many of the human bones were missing or broken by the workmen. From the examination of photographs of this exhumation it was not possible to determine the sex of children's skeletons and no modern scientific examination has been conducted to determine their carbon dating and DNA analysis.

The mystery of Edward V did not end with his death and during the reign of Henry VII there were a number of Pretenders. Edward himself was too well known to be impersonated but this was not true of his younger brother Richard. The main Pretender was Perkin Warbeck, who some said was the illegitimate son of Edward IV, but who Henry VII declared was a Flemish imposter. Warbeck gained support outside England and instigated foreign invasions of Cornwall, Ireland, and Scotland which Henry VII suppressed. Eventually Warbeck was captured and held in the Tower and was then drawn to Tyburn where he read out a confession and was hanged.

The second Pretender, Lambert Simnel, was born around 1477. His real name is not known and there are different claims that his father was a baker or an organ builder. At the age of 10, he became a pupil of an Oxford priest called Richard Simon who tutored the boy in courtly manners. Simon noticed a striking resemblance between Simnel and the murdered sons of Edward IV.

And Yorkists who were still determined on an uprising took Simnel to Ireland to head an Irish government as the Earl of Kildare. In 1487, the 10-year-old was crowned in Dublin as King Edward VI and raised an army to invade England. Flemish and Irish mercenaries landed on Piel Island in Lancashire and were joined by English supporters. But they were defeated by Henry VII at the Battle of Stoke Field and Simons was imprisoned. Henry VII pardoned Simnel and employed him in the royal kitchens as a spit-turner, and when he grew older, he became a falconer and he died around 1525.

# Richard III

Richard was the second son of Richard Duke of York and Lady Cecily Neville. He was born at Fotheringay Castle in 1452, became king in 1483 and was killed two years later at the Battle of Bosworth Field. In 1472 he married Ann Neville, the daughter of the Earl of Warwick, and their only son died aged 10.

*Ann Neville*

His claim to the throne became possible when his father and older brother were killed at the Battle of Wakefield. And as the last Yorkist, his defeat at Bosworth Field was the decisive battle of the Wars of the Roses and the end of the Plantagenet dynasty.

Richard was a physically deformed hunchback and throughout history hunchbacks were regarded as evil. In some cultures they were put to death and Victor Hugo's Quasimodo was only safe from the mob in the great cathedral of Notre Dame. The withered arm, deformed spine, and the limping gait of "Richard Crookback" were once thought to have been Tudor propaganda invented by Thomas More and William Shakespeare, as none of Richard's portraits suggest a deformity and on the battlefield he was a fearsome warrior. But x-rays of one his portraits show that a normal shoulder was painted in at a later date, and the recent discovery of his skeletal remains have confirmed a severe spinal kypho-scoliosis[15] which he concealed with cleverly cut clothing. He spent his youth at Middleham Castle with his cousin Richard Neville, the Earl of Warwick. And when his father and brother were killed at the Battle of Wakefield, the 8-year-old Richard, was sent to the Low Countries beyond the reach of Henry

---

[15] See Medical Appendix – 19. Kypho-scoliosis, page 338.

VI's vengeful Queen Margaret. He became involved in treacherous politics from the age of 11 when his brother Edward IV appointed him Commissioner of the Western Counties. Edward owed much to Richard for pacifying the north and they fled together to Burgundy in 1470 when Warwick defected to the Lancastrians and restored Henry VI. But they reinvaded England and after the battles of Barnet and Tewkesbury in 1471 he married Warwick's daughter, Anne Neville. Her first husband, the Prince of Wales, had been killed at Tewkesbury, and Richard and Anne had only one son, Edward of Middleham, who died of natural causes.

During the reign of his brother, Richard demonstrated skill as a military commander and as Governor North he became the richest nobleman in England. He and his brother George, Duke of Clarence, fell out over George's marriage to another of the Neville sisters and George was accused of treason and murdered in the Tower of London by drowning in a butt of Malmsey wine.

Richard was highly regarded in the north of England where he fought campaigns against Malcolm III of Scotland, endowed universities, and protected juries from intimidation.

But on the death of Edward IV in 1483, the king's son Edward V was aged only 12, and his brother Richard, was 9. Their mother quickly overturned Richard's guardianship of the two princes in Edward IV's will and set up a regency council with herself as head. Richard did not expect to survive if Edward was crowned king and when the council moved the boy from Ludlow, Richard intercepted the party and removed his guardians to Pontefract Castle where they were executed.

He then moved Edward to the Tower of London and set about discrediting his right to the throne. A bishop said he had betrothed the boy's father to Lady Eleanor Butler, and his marriage to Elizabeth Woodville was therefore illegal and the boy was not the rightful heir. And the boy's father was not even the rightful Duke of York because Lady Cicely Neville had testified that he was in France when Edward IV was conceived in 1441. Based on this evidence Parliament passed a Titulus Regius in support of Richard and in 1483 he was crowned in Westminster Abbey.

Richard has come down in history as a deformed man with a self-image problem, who trusted nobody and was prepared to sacrifice anyone for the throne. Even those who avoided his malevolence could not trust their futures and it was inevitable that eventually he would find himself isolated. The Lancastrian cause was almost exhausted by the time Henry Tudor landed in Wales in 1485, and his army was tiny and a military victory against Richard seemed unlikely. The traditional site of the final battle was under Ambion Hill near Market Bosworth. But drainage of the marshes in that area has confused the geography and modern excavations suggest the main battleground was two miles west on farm land off the Roman road from Atherstone to Leicester. Here at Fenn Lane Farm, medieval artillery has been unearthed, along with a silver boar badge which belonged to one of Richard's knights.

For Richard, the omens of the soothsayers were bad and he mistrusted the loyalty of the allies who advised him not to fight that day. He slept poorly the night before the battle but when he woke he celebrated Mass and was confident when he rode out from Leicester at the head of 5,000 troops which included mercenaries from Burgundy and Spain. In contrast Henry Tudor's army of 3,500 included Welshmen, Frenchmen, and Scots. Modern analysis suggests that Richard's tactics were flawed when he deployed Norfolk's men behind marshland where they could not engage the enemy.

He also misjudged the loyalty of Northumberland and the importance of holding hostage, Thomas Stanley's son, Lord Strange.

During the battle, Richard was abandoned by both these factions and the defection of Stanley's 6,000 troops changed the outcome. Unwilling to commit to Richard or Henry on the battlefield, Thomas Stanley ignored the threat to kill his son and held back until the outcome appeared more clear. As an excuse he said his troops were sick with a disease which came to be known as the Sweating Sickness[16] and had never been seen before. And after the battle the sickness followed Henry's victorious entourage to London where it proceeded to kill 15,000 people in six weeks which was more than ten times the 1,000 Yorkists and 100 Lancastrians who died at Bosworth.

Soon after the armies clashed, Richard saw it was possible to bring the battle to a quick conclusion by engaging Henry in personal combat and killing him. Not trusting the Stanleys, he ordered Lord

---

[16] See Medical Appendix – 8. Sweating Sickness, page 319.

Strange to be executed, but by then his troops were beginning to defect and they did not carry out the order. And disregarding advice he set off with 120 handpicked men to search out Henry Tudor. To kill him by his own hand was a Plantagenet impulse and it proved his undoing. He rode straight for Henry's bodyguard and killed Sir John Cheney with a lance. And with only a few yards to go he next killed Henry's standard bearer with a battle axe. But when he was within a sword's length of Henry, the Stanleys fell upon him, and Northumberland stood by and refused to deploy his troops against them.

Contemporary accounts describe how Richard was driven into the marsh, unhorsed, surrounded, and hacked to death. The battle then came to a halt and his naked body was dragged with a rope around his neck into Henry's presence. He was flung across a pack horse and ridden back to Leicester, and when his helmet with its ring of gold fell off the Stanleys placed it on Henry's head. Modern forensic examination of Richard's skeleton suggests he died from arrow injuries and multiple body blows, of which three to his head were fatal. It is also likely that his dead body received further insults as it was ridden into Leicester.

In the collegiate foundation of the Annunciation of Our Lady, the body was placed on public display until buried by the monks in an unmarked grave in the choir of Greyfriars Church.

Years later when Yorkist resistance had dissipated, Henry VII placed an alabaster memorial on the grave but the church was later destroyed during the dissolution of the monasteries. A legend from 1612 was that the cadaver was exhumed and thrown into the River Soar. But this was never substantiated and in 2012 excavations in Greyfriars public car park where the church once stood, unearthed a skeleton bearing an arrowhead and 10 wounds including a fractured skull.

The skeleton's identity has been confirmed by carbon dating and mitochondrial DNA comparison with Richard's Ibsen family descendants in Canada. The skeleton confirmed a severe kypho-scoliosis of the spine and modern CT scanning and computer-assisted facial reconstruction produced a close resemblance to Richard's contemporary portraits.

*Computer reconstruction vs original portrait*

After the excavations in Greyfriars car park in 2012, York Minster and Leicester Cathedral contested the right to provide a permanent resting place for the king's remains, and in 2014 the High Court decided in favour of Leicester. In 2015 his remains were carried through the city in an oak coffin made by his Canadian descendants, and thousands lined the streets when the cortege passed by. The modern trend is to rehabilitate Richard's reputation and Leicester University has been renamed King Richard University.

At Bosworth in 1485 Richard was the only English king to die on the battlefield since 1066, and his death ended of the Wars of the Roses, the Plantagenet dynasty and the middle ages.

*Greyfriars car park and Richard's remains*

*The 2015 funeral cortège in Leicester*

An underlying cause of the Wars of the Roses was the psychopathic character of the Plantagenets whose rule was based on fear and violence. The end began when Edward III outlived his heir, the Black Prince, and he named his infant grandson to succeed him as Richard II. In doing this Edward III overlooked his able, ambitious second son, John of Gaunt, and this was a mistake. Underage kings succeeded to the throne, and their appointed regents created colossal instability and murdered two anointed kings. In addition, Richard II and Henry VI were both schizophrenic and their bizarre behaviour destabilised the country and set the different factions at each other's throats. Another unwise decision was made when Gaunt died and his Lancastrian estates were confiscated from his son, Bolingbroke. England's vast possessions in France proved ungovernable by Edward III's successors, and after Henry V died, France became a refuge for English discontents and a seed bed of rebellion. Most of the Lancastrian Plantagenets were eventually killed in battle and when York dominated at last, war had become a way of life and they fought among themselves for supremacy. Under the brief reign of Richard III a sense of coup d'etat gripped the country and when Henry Tudor invaded from France the country was yearning for peace.

# THE TUDORS

## 1485-1603

*Henry VII*            *Henry VIII*            *Edward VI*

*Jane Grey*            *Mary I*            *Elizabeth I*

# Henry VII

Henry VII was the son of Edmund Tudor and Margaret Beaufort and he was born in 1457 at Pembroke Castle. He was 28 when he became king and he died of Tuberculosis at the age of 52.

Henry's grandfather, Owen Tudor, was a commoner from Anglesey. He became a Page to Henry V and when the king died, he became Groom to the Bedchamber of the King's schizophrenic widow, Catherine of Valois. There was a scandalous love affair, a secret marriage, and five children. And Owen was created Duke of Richmond but was beheaded after the Battle of Mortimer's Cross in 1461. Henry's father, Edmund Tudor, married Margaret Beaufort who was descended illegitimately from John of Gaunt and his mistress Catherine Swinford. Margaret was 13 years old when she gave birth to Henry and she survived three kings and died at the age of 66.

Henry's claim to the throne was extremely tenuous and his Tudor descendants never felt secure. But after the Battle of Bosworth Field this mattered little. Henry had killed a usurper monarch, he was recognised by Pope Innocent III, and he united the country's warring factions. In addition, England yearned for peace and he was its de facto king.

He was tall and athletic and rode well. He was also highly intelligent and extremely ambitious. He was introduced to the court of Henry VI but during the reign of Edward IV he fled to Brittany. It was there he fathered an illegitimate son, Roland de Velville, whose descendants returned to Anglesey and later served in the court of Elizabeth I. In 1471 he became head of the House of Lancaster and the target of Yorkist plots. But when Edward IV tried to extradite him from Brittany, Henry feigned illness and claimed the protection of the Church.

After Edward IV's death in 1484, Henry was persuaded to challenge Richard III for the crown. His claim to the throne was tenuous but the Wars of the Roses had killed most of the prominent Yorkists and Henry later executed the few who remained. His small army landed at Milford Haven but grew in strength as it marched across Wales.

Henry himself had no military training and at Bosworth Field he wisely placed the command of his army under the Earl of Oxford. Betrayed on the battlefield, the formidable Richard attempted to engage Henry in personal combat which Henry was lucky to avoid. But Richard fought his way towards him and was close enough to kill Henry's standard bearer before he was surrounded by Stanley's men and hacked down. During a reign which extended 24 years this was the closest Henry came to death. Six months after his coronation he married Elizabeth of York, and by uniting the Houses of York and Lancaster he ended the Wars of the Roses.

*Elizabeth of York, Queen of Hearts*

Elizabeth's credentials could hardly have been more illustrious. She was the daughter of Edward IV, sister of Edward V, niece of Richard III, and the Queen of Scotland and France. She was tall and elegant, and when card play was invented in 1486, her portrait appeared on every pack of cards.

She was 21 when she married Henry and her wedding robes were carefully cut to conceal the fact that she was already pregnant. But this was a critical marriage and her pregnancy was a prudent test of her fertility. In any case Henry and Elizabeth went on to develop a loving relationship and after she died in childbirth in 1503 he never re-married. The four surviving children of her eight pregnancies were Arthur Prince of Wales, Henry VIII of England, Margaret Queen of Scotland, and Mary Queen of France.

In his early reign, Henry was constantly threatened by rebellion. The Stafford and Lovell revolt in 1486 collapsed, but in 1487 Yorkists rebelled in support of Lambert Simnel, who was a boy they claimed was the Earl of Warwick. But they were defeated by Henry at the Battle of Stoke and Simnel was employed by Henry as a servant in the royal kitchens. In 1490, a young Dutchman called Perkin Warbeck claimed to be Richard, the younger of the two Princes killed in the Tower, and he won the support of Edward IV's sister, Margaret of Burgundy. He invaded Ireland in 1491 and England in 1495, and persuaded James IV of Scotland to invade England in

1496. But when Warbeck landed in Cornwall in 1497 to join 8,000 Cornishmen led by a blacksmith called Michael Joseph, Warbeck was captured and executed at Tyburn.

*Prince Arthur*            *Catherine of Aragon*

In 1501 Henry's son, Arthur, was married to Catherine of Aragon in St Paul's Cathedral. In a triumph of international diplomacy, there was a month of feasting in London before the Prince and Princess of Wales went to live at Ludlow Castle. Arthur was 15 and Catherine 16, and they conversed with each other in Latin. The teenagers slept together but the famous question as to whether they had sexual intercourse is debated to this day. The truth is shrouded by history but the balance of evidence suggests they did.

Within months of their arrival in Ludlow, however, an epidemic swept Wales. Catherine was the first to sicken but she survived. Arthur on the other hand became seriously ill and within days he died of pneumonia. His illness was called a Consumption and it was almost certainly Influenza. Because of the 30-year cycle of pandemics of Influenza[17] and the periodic lack of immunity in young people, it is common for the mortality to be high in this age group. And there is no evidence to support the theory that Arthur was poisoned in a remote backwater to make way for his glittering brother in London.

---

[17] See Medical Appendix – 7. Influenza, page 317.

Arthur's body was embalmed and after three weeks at Ludlow Castle it was removed to Ludlow Parish Church where the heart was buried. Henry VII ordered his son's body be buried in the nearest English cathedral, but this was in Hereford, and in appalling weather the cortege lost its way over the Clee Hills and ended up in Worcester. Bogged down in mud, it was dragged out with oxen, and accompanied through Bewdley and Tickenhill by monks in hoods and torch bearers. William Overdale, the Controller of the prince's household, rode ahead and after the arrival of the body in Worcester he closed the city.

At the funeral service, a white horse was ridden into the cathedral, local abbots followed a choir and more torch bearers, and three earls carried royal banners. Then, after a Mass of Nine Lessons there was a dole of groats to every poor man and woman. The gentlemen then removed the body to the south side of the altar and Overdale broke his staff of office and cast it into the grave. Henry VII, Queen Elizabeth, Henry the new Prince of Wales, and Catherine of Aragon did not attend the funeral, but this was the accepted royal custom. Centuries later during the republican inter regnum, the shrine was defaced. But archaeologists have since confirmed the presence of a skeleton in front of the altar and in 2002, a commemorative funeral pageant was held in the cathedral. Those wishing to examine the body, however, were denied access.

*Arthur's tomb in Worcester Cathedral*

After the death of Arthur, Henry's court became a gloomy place, and when Elizabeth died in childbirth, Henry became a recluse and saw few people except his second son. And despite proposed marriages to the Queen of Naples and the Archduchess of Austria, he never remarried.

Having experienced relative poverty during his years of exile, Henry paid great attention to the nation's accounts, and his parsimony was well known in the courts of Europe. He stamped out fraudulent book keeping in the national exchequer, audited his own accounts, and even took to collecting taxes himself. But such were the taxes he imposed, it is suggested that had he not died when he did, there would have been a rebellion. In contrast there is evidence of his generosity to the poor and to the Church.

He was an excellent judge of men and dealt ruthlessly with opposition. He ran every aspect of the affairs of state, and it was during his reign that England ceased to be medieval. He brought Welsh customs into line with England, and annexed the Principality. He avoided costly foreign wars, stabilised the country's economy, introduced a new system of weights and measures, and initiated exploration of the New World. England's wool merchants flourished, and Norfolk landowners drained the Fens and grew rich. Water pumps were used to drain coal and tin mines, and in Antwerp English wool was traded for German metal, Baltic canvas, Italian silk, and Portuguese spices. In prosperous households, pewter was replaced with silver, and in London there were 52 goldsmiths in Cheapside alone. Henry supported Oxford and Cambridge Universities, and when Erasmus visited England, he was impressed by the country's intellectual activity.

During his reign, Henry ran households at Westminster, Greenwich, and Richmond Palaces, and Royal manors at Windsor and Woodstock. He rebuilt the lady chapel in Westminster Abbey and when Sheen manor was destroyed by fire he built a Gothic palace on its site at Richmond. There are records of occasional lavish banquets and entertainments with music, dancing, masked balls and Spanish acrobats. But his court was not renowned for gaiety, and his famous Michael Sittow portrait depicts a king preoccupied with state affairs.

As his physician, Henry appointed Thomas Linacre who had studied medicine in Padua and founded the Royal College of

Physicians. And as he grew older, Henry was worn out but did not feel secure enough to retire. His eyesight deteriorated and he feared not being able to do the paperwork and being cheated. His physicians bathed his eyes with poultices of eyebright, fennel and rose water and he may have had cataracts, glaucoma, or conjunctivitis.

In 1509 he developed chest pains, a persistent cough, and loss of weight. Such wasting was usually due to Tuberculosis, for which there was no cure, and Henry would have known this and put his affairs in order. In his will he confessed his sins, paid for 10,000 Masses to be said, and left bequests to the poor and to religious and academic institutions. He became emaciated and was unable to celebrate Mass, and he died in the Palace of Whitehall in Holy Week.

People understood the contagious nature of infections and Henry's court had always moved if Plague or Sweating Sickness broke out in London. Strict rules of hygiene were kept in the court kitchens, but the king's Tuberculosis[18] was probably caught from a servant spitting or from raw, infected cow's milk.

His body was laid in state at Richmond, and at his funeral 600 torch bearers lit its way to a night-time burial in Westminster Abbey. He had built a chapel there to commemorate the murdered Henry VI, and commissioned the Florentine sculptor Pietro Torregiano to build a magnificent tomb of black marble and gilt bronze. And on his deathbed, he requisitioned this for himself and asked his son Henry to marry Catherine of Aragon in order to seal the Spanish alliance. But the nation felt heavily taxed and there was no outpouring of national grief when he died.

---

[18] See Medical Appendix – 5. Tuberculosis, page 311.

*Tomb of Henry VII and Elizabeth of York*

# Henry VIII

Henry was the second son of Henry VII and Elizabeth of York and was born in 1491 at Greenwich Palace. He became king at the age of 18, ruled England for 38 years, and died of a pulmonary embolism at the age of 53. His sisters, Margaret and Mary, married James IV of Scotland and Louis XII of France and in attempts to secure a male heir he had six wives. A son by Jane Seymour became Edward VI, a daughter by Catherine of Aragon became Queen Mary I, and a daughter by Ann Boleyn became Queen Elizabeth I.

Henry also had an illegitimate daughter by Mary Boleyn and an illegitimate son by Elizabeth Blount. The latter was Lady in Waiting to Catherine of Aragon and the boy became known as Henry Fitzroy. The king tried but failed to legitimise him as heir, and Fitzroy died of Consumption aged 17 and was buried in Framlingham Church.

When Henry VIII's skeleton was exhumed in 1818, it was 6'2" tall, and a suit of armour made for him when he was 21 indicated long limbs and a 21-inch waist. He was charismatic and physically athletic, restlessly energetic and terrifying when roused to anger. He was also likened a Greek god and was much admired by Machiavelli. He tried twice to have Cardinal Wolsey installed as Pope, placed Coverdale's Bible in all English churches, dissolved the monasteries, and brought the Church under secular law with himself as Defender of the Faith. This was carried out by his Chief Minister Thomas Cromwell and enriched Henry beyond his dreams. But it isolated him from Spain and France and led to his excommunication from the Catholic Church and to the Catholic rebellion known as the Pilgrimage of Grace.

He undertook the enclosures of the common land, promoted exploration of the New World, and built a royal navy of 80 warships which included the *Mary Rose* and the *Great Harry*. He quelled rebellion in Ireland, defeated James IV of Scotland and Francis I of France, and overcame complex marital problems to secure a male heir and ensure the survival of the dynasty.

In his youth he hunted, hawked, and jousted, and in middle age he wrote poetry and music and laid the foundation for Tudor literature. He was intellectual and before the death of his older brother he was destined for a life in the church. As a result, he knew enough theology to write a tract entitled *Defence of the Seven Sacraments*. He spoke Latin, French, and Italian, and was an international figure who staged a spectacular summit conference at the Field of the Cloth of Gold.

He was feared by foreign kings and loved by the common people but for much of his life, he was severely affected by illness. During Christmas 1514, he contracted Smallpox[19] for which there was no treatment and the mortality rate was 60%. His physicians feared for his life but he recovered and two months later he was back on military campaign in France. An entirely new disease had appeared in England, called the Sweating Sickness[20] and during a 1517 epidemic Henry moved his court to Richmond. Only the queen and Dr Linacre had access to him, and foreign ambassadors were forbidden to come to court. Henry would not accept household goods from towns with Sweating Sickness, and sent for safe supplies from Holland. At Richmond, Lord Grey, his Latin secretary, died of the disease, and Cardinal Wolsey fell ill with it and was lucky to survive. In response Henry fled to various secret houses, and let the country run itself.

---

[19] See Medical Appendix – 4. Smallpox, page 307.
[20] See Medical Appendix – 8. Sweating Sickness, page 319.

He appointed Thomas Linacre as Court Physician and six assistants to support him. They attended the court in royal livery, and Henry's Sergeant Surgeon, Thomas Vicary, was painted by Hans Holbein. They prescribed herbal remedies which were generally inert but Henry had a healthy scepticism and trained himself as an apothecary.

As a result he could prepare Feverfew to ward off fever, rhubarb pills and celandine roots for constipation, and eyebrights to relieve eye strain. And he was not slow to prescribe for his hapless courtiers.

Henry ate prodigious quantities of meat and suffered badly from constipation and painful piles. Another cause of these was his need to travel extensively on horseback. Piles are varicose veins in the rectum and in the age of horse transport the "bottom doctors" who specialised in piles made a lucrative living. When tobacco was introduced into England in 1578 one widely prescribed cure for constipation was tobacco enemas introduced into the rectum through a wooden tube. The haemorrhoidal creams which were also prescribed included camomile, yarrow, horsetail, elder leaves, blueberry, and oak bark. In addition, Henry's stools were inspected every morning by the Groom of the Stool who helped with his chamber pot arrangements and reported to the council each day on the king's stools and the colour of his urine. This was a lucrative office held in turn by Sir William Compton, Sir Henry Norris, and Sir Anthony Denny.

In 1525 on Hitchen Common, Henry's walking pole snapped when he tried to vault a ditch. He landed head first in deep mud, and his footman Edmund Moody, had to save him from drowning. The head injury turned out to be serious, and Henry started to suffer headaches which continued for the rest of his life, so he may have fractured his skull. Around this time he also suffered a urinary infection, which is unusual for a young man, except when due to kidney stones or venereal disease. Then a sore appeared on his leg which was treated by Thomas Vicary and gave rise to the theory that Henry had contracted Syphilis[21], and that Syphilitic madness was responsible for his irritable behaviour in later life.

Syphilis had reached Europe around 1493 and as a young man

[21] See Medical Appendix – 10. Syphilis, page 325.

Henry was extremely promiscuous and could easily have contracted the infection. He had shared the sexual favours of Mary Boleyn with Francis I of France who went on to die from the Great Pox. And when Henry returned from France in 1514 he developed a rash which some thought was due to Syphilis. Wolsey's physician, Augustine Agostini, said that Wolsey and Henry had both contracted it, and a portrait of Henry at Hever Castle, shows a collapsed nose, which is an important sign of the disease. But no other portraits showed the same feature and whilst Henry's leg ulcer and the headaches could have been Syphilitic in origin, the infection is known as the "great mimic" and almost any symptoms can be wrongly attributed to it. The repeated miscarriages of Catherine of Aragon and Ann Boleyn are also sometimes blamed on the Great Pox, but the women would have had to be infected too and there was there is no evidence of this.

In 1525 whilst hunting at Hanworth, Henry went down with toothache and for the first time he developed gout. It seems likely that a surfeit of alcohol, game, and rich meat were the cause of this, and it was destined to return at intervals. The same year he sustained a serious leg injury whilst jousting, and this caused recurrent leg ulcers which were to dog the rest of his life.

In addition, he turned into a tiresome hypochondriac, and with a worsening temper, he became a very difficult patient for his doctors. In 1528 the Sweating Sickness returned to London, where there were 40,000 deaths. When three members of the Privy Council became victims, Henry's court fled the capital, and when Ann Boleyn and her father fell ill, Henry sent Dr William Butt to attend them and they recovered. But then Henry developed headaches, and in the panic which followed, a tour of the north was cancelled. But he recovered and attributed this to pills which were first concocted in Persia by the famous physician Al Rhaze and contained vitriol, copper, sal ammoniac, gold leaf, chalk, clay, coral, pearl, and tar.

Jousting was a favourite but dangerous sport of kings, and Henry II of France had been killed jousting. But in 1536 Henry's career in the lists came to an abrupt end when in full armour he was unhorsed and the steed fell on top of him. He was unconscious for two hours and Queen Anne was informed he was dead. But he survived and contemporary witnesses said that his unpredictability was much worse after this injury. His leg ulcers worsened and may have caused osteomyelitis and a deep venous thrombosis. His temper became even more frightening and he told Lord Norfolk that a humour had befallen his legs and the physicians had advised him not to go out in the heat of the day. With increasing immobility, he began to gain weight and he was particularly fond of the sweet potatoes recently discovered in the New World. He suffered agonies from leg ulcers, and his bad temper kept getting worse.

Lightning pains due to Syphilitic Tabes Dorsalis have been suggested as the cause of his leg pains but postphlebitic syndrome from a venous thrombosis is the more likely explanation. Lord Montague predicted grimly that the affliction would eventually kill him, and at times his Fool, Will Somers, was the only one who could keep him happy. Court jesters were permitted familiarities without regard for deference, and Sommers possessed a shrewd wit. However, he occasionally overstepped the mark and in 1535, he called Queen Anne "a ribald" and the Princess Elizabeth "a bastard", and Henry threatened to kill him with his own hands.

In 1538 an attempt was made on Henry's life by poisoning[22] but he was always paranoid about this possibility and the plot was foiled. The cook was merely hanged, drawn, and quartered, but Henry's rage was such that he at first ordered him to be boiled alive. Later that year he was well enough to take Queen Jane on a pilgrimage to Canterbury, but in May his leg became infected, and a clot broke loose and blocked his lung. This must have been a pulmonary embolism since he was speechless with pain, and so cyanosed, his face turned black. Depending on the size of a pulmonary embolus patients either fall dead instantly, develop chest pain due to a gangrenous lung, or develop high blood pressure and die of heart failure. For 12 days Henry was expected to die, but he defied predictions and a month later he was well. From then on the surgeons were careful not to allow the leg to fester and they repeatedly drained it using cautery. By this time Henry lost his good looks and his armour had increased from a chest size of 37 to 54 inches. He wore spectacles for short eye sight, and with the smell of his leg ulcers he was no longer attractive to women. But in 1540 he fell hopelessly for Catherine Howard and was rejuvenated like a

---

[22] See Medical Appendix – 23. Poison, page 359.

young man. That year he was ill with a Malarial fever[23] and had a further deep vein thrombosis and pulmonary embolism. His leg "became clogged again and his face turned black". The surgeons once more drained the abscess and he again survived.

After the execution of Catherine Howard, Henry grew much fatter, and a special 7'6" long and 7" wide bed was made for him. In 1544 his legs became yet worse and the apothecaries prescribed liquorice pastilles, cinnamon comfits, and various plasters and sponges. He became so weak he was unable to stand and his temper was foul. Despite his Malaria fevers and his infected legs, he appeared in 1546 as Commander in Chief at the head of an army which invaded France.

But from then on, he became progressively incapacitated and kept to his private lodgings. He had two wooden invalid trams constructed but concealed these from public view.

With a specially constructed ramp he was still able to mount a horse, but he became unable to climb stairs and was let up and down from his bed chamber with the help of an engine which acted as a stair lift.

In 1546 he ceased to take exercise and the court began to jockey for control of his son, Edward. As the surgical cautery of his leg ulcers grew more frequent and more painful, his bills for sick room comforts rose from £1,500 to a staggering £7,500 a year. In 1548 he realised he was dying and discussed this with Catherine Parr and wrote to Francis I of France. The court musicians were dismissed, he received Holy Communion, and as an act of mercy he reprieved the Duke of Norfolk who he had condemned to death. Archbishop Cranmer was summoned but by the time he arrived Henry was unable to talk and when the Primate asked if he died in the faith of Christ, Henry was only able to clasp his hand in assent.

He died of a further pulmonary embolism and the death was kept secret for three days until the Privy Council could close the country's ports. The nation sensed the passing of a great monarch, and William Thomas caught the mood when he wrote, "I wot not in all the histories I have read, to find a king to equal him". His 28-stone body was embalmed for lying in state in Whitehall, and the coffin, topped

---

[23] See Medical Appendix – 9. Malaria, page 322.

with a wax effigy, was drawn by black horses to St George's Chapel at Windsor for burial with Jane Seymour. It took 16 men to lower the coffin into the vault, and the chief officers of the Royal household terminated their office by snapping their white staves and throwing them into the grave.

Henry had confiscated a black marble tombstone sarcophagus from Wolsey but the designs were changed several times. One hundred years later the tomb was desecrated by Roundheads, and the touchstone was reused in the 19th century for the tomb of Horatio Nelson in the crypt of St Paul's Cathedral.

*Henry VIII's touchstone on Nelson's tomb*

As regards his six wives, their historical importance was as baby machines who Henry needed to secure the Tudor dynasty, and the main interest in their medical history concerns their difficulty in providing him with a male heir.

*Catherine of Aragon*

Catherine was the daughter of Queen Isabella of Castile and King Ferdinand II of Aragon. At the age of three she was betrothed to Henry's brother Arthur, and she married him at the age of 16. When Arthur died five months later, she wished to return to Spain, but the importance of the Spanish alliance would not permit this and Henry VII proposed she married the 11-year-old future Henry VIII. But this required a papal dispensation and hinged on whether Arthur and Catherine's marriage had been consummated. The Council assumed that it had, since it postponed a decision in case she was carrying Arthur's child. A priest testified that Catherine had confessed the same story but her ladies in waiting swore otherwise, and when she was interviewed by Cardinal Campeggio, she told him that when she married Henry, she "was a true maid without touch of man".

In 1503, she was betrothed to marry Henry but there were years of delay and her mother died in Spain. Henry VII died in 1507 and in 1509 Henry VIII married Catherine at a private ceremony at Greenwich. She was 24 and quickly became pregnant, but the child was miscarried after three months. When Catherine's abdomen remained swollen, twins were suspected and everyone awaited the delivery of a second child. But then the swelling disappeared and she was humiliated.

In 1511 she was pregnant again, and when a full-term male infant was born he was christened Henry. Wine was given out for Londoners to celebrate and beacons were lit around the country. The baby was cosseted at Richmond with a wet nurse, a mistress, and four servants to rock his cradle, but after 52 days he died whilst asleep in his cot. Cot death, or sudden infant death syndrome (SIDS), is the sudden unexpected and unexplained death of an apparently healthy baby in its sleep. Nowadays about 1 in 3,000 babies die of it each year in the UK and though most cases are still unexplained the commonest cause is suffocation due to the baby sleeping on its face. There is some evidence that the babies have brain stem abnormalities which prevent them responding normally to asphyxiation, and mothers are now routinely given advice on how to ensure their babies sleep as safely as possible by not sleeping on their faces, and not sleeping in a bed with adults.

The royal couple and the Council were devastated and the little boy's death had a profound effect on English history. Even nowadays some cot deaths are investigated as murder and it is curious that the nursery attendants were not blamed.

In 1513, during the battle of Flodden Moor Catherine gave birth prematurely to another child which did not survive. And at this time, Henry's mistress Mary Boleyn was said to have delivered an illegitimate daughter who looked like Henry. As for Catherine, she wrote to Henry in Calais, that she was about to take a "pilgrimage to Walsingham" which was their coded phrase for "pregnant again". In 1514 another full-term live boy was delivered, but again the baby only survived a few hours. And then in 1516 she delivered a baby girl, Mary, who was to be her only surviving child. At the age of 30 she had a further miscarriage, and then a full-term child who died a few days after birth. After this she became infertile or more likely, slept apart from the king.

In 1519, Henry had an illegitimate son by Elizabeth Blount who he later attempted to legitimise and appoint to the Privy Council. But by 1525 it was clear that Queen Catherine would not provide a legitimate male heir, and Henry was made aware by Wolsey of the passage in Leviticus XX "that if a man shall take his brother's wife, it shall be an unclean thing, and they shall be childless". Since Henry had a daughter, Wolsey convinced Henry that "childless" meant "no son", and the machinery for divorce was set in motion. After 22 years of marriage Henry expelled Catherine from court, and refused to address her as Queen. But a royal divorce required papal dispensation and Pope Clement VII was a prisoner of the Holy Roman Emperor who was Catherine's uncle. Despite the gloomy prospects of success, the royal divorce was referred to Rome by Thomas Cromwell and under pressure, the Pope sent Cardinal Campeggio to England with instructions to prolong the negotiations and agree nothing. Campeggio did the Pope's bidding and used the excuse of recurrent gout to postpone meetings. In 1535, Catherine was confined to Kimbolt Castle where she feared being poisoned and had her maids taste all her food. Rumours abounded of poisoning attempts by the Boleyn faction and there was a real risk that during one of his fits of rage Henry would execute her for disobedience.

For some time she had "a dropsy" (swollen ankles commonly caused by heart failure) but when she died in 1536, it was said it was of heartache which was a euphemism for breast cancer. In her last letter to Henry, she pardoned him of his sins and begged him to care for their daughter. Finally, she told Henry that her eyes still desired him above all others, but she defiantly signed it "Catherine the Queen". But he did not reply and when he appeared in public after her death he was dressed from head to foot in resplendent yellow.

At her embalming the heart was entirely blackened and when the chandler cut it in two, he found a black object clinging to the core which modern pathologists say is a rare tumour of the heart called a melanotic sarcoma.

*Catherine's tomb in Peterborough Cathedral*

She was buried in a quiet ceremony in Peterborough Cathedral where her grave is marked with a simple memorial stone at which Spanish ambassadors still pay their respects.

Her successor, Ann Boleyn, was the daughter of Thomas Boleyn, Earl of Wiltshire, and Lady Elizabeth Howard. She was introduced to Henry's household in 1523, when Henry was having an affair with her sister, Mary, and she was pursued by Henry during the years it took him to divorce Catherine of Aragon.

*Ann Boleyn*

She had polydactyly of the left hand and this congenital sixth finger may also have affected her daughter, Elizabeth. It is sometimes associated with congenital abnormalities of the internal organs, but it is more often harmless and is usually removed in infancy.

She was vivacious and flirtatious and much hated by the women at court, who called her a sorceress and a whore. But she was also beautiful and highly intelligent, and was much admired by Lord Percy, to whom she was secretly betrothed, and by the poet Thomas Wyatt. Henry's love letters to her often ended: "HR seeks AB and no other", and to her admirers Ann wrote in Latin, "Noli me tangere, ego Caesaribus" – "Do not touch me for Caesar's I am".

Some have suggested that Ann slept with Henry as soon as the divorce from Catherine was approved by Cranmer, and that she conceived the Princess Elizabeth out of wedlock. But the private wedding took place on 14th November 1532, and a public ceremony followed on 25th January 1533. And since Princess Elizabeth was born on 7th September 1533, she was not conceived outside of marriage. Ann told Henry she had a great desire to eat apples and the king told her this was a sign. But the birth of a female was a disappointment to Henry, though he changed the laws of succession in favour of the Protestant baby girl, and plans were made to marry her stepsister to a Catholic foreigner.

Ann soon became pregnant a second time but miscarried at three months. In 1513 she had a further stillbirth, and then a final pregnancy in which a stillborn boy was born. Fatally, she flirted at court and was indiscreet enough to let it be known, that Henry "was no good in bed". And when Henry became convinced he would have no sons by her, there followed accusations of adultery with two of her admirers, Francis Dereham and Thomas Culpepper, and incest with her brother George. To some extent these accusations arose from the personal feud between Ann and Thomas Cromwell, and the prime witness at Ann's trial was Jane Boleyn. She was the wife of Ann's allegedly incestuous brother and when she was executed after the Catherine Howard trial, she recanted her evidence against Ann.

*Ann Boleyn's grave in the Tower of London*

She was executed by a French swordsman with a single blow and her body was placed in an arrow chest and buried in the Tower Chapel of St Peter ad Vincula.

*Jane Seymour*

The youthful Jane Seymour was the daughter of Sir John Seymour and Margery Wentworth. She was a descendant of King Edward III and she and Henry were distant cousins.

She was quite different from Catherine of Aragon and Ann Boleyn and whilst she could read and write a little, she was much better at needlework and household management. Just 10 days after Ann Boleyn's execution, Jane married Henry in the Palace of Whitehall and quickly became pregnant. When she went into labour, prayers were said for her safety, but the delivery dragged on for two days before she presented Henry with the son he had always needed. Her Seymour relatives were ecstatic, and for Henry, it had taken him 30 years of marriage to produce a healthy son.

But the difficult labour had taken its toll on the young mother. Her accoucheurs may have washed their hands but more likely they did not, and she had been draped for the delivery in animal furs which by modern medical standards were filthy. It was not surprising therefore that any bruised and injured tissues should become infected, and it was not until 1847 that Semmelweiss described how labour room cleanliness could reduce Puerperal Fever[24].

---

[24] See Medical Appendix – 13. Puerperal Fever, page 333.

In Tudor times child bed fever was a deadly complication which claimed the lives of countless young mothers, and over a period of two weeks, Jane slipped into a coma and died. Anti-Henricians falsely put it about that Jane had undergone a caesarean section to save the life of the child, and when he was asked, Henry had said, "Save the child by all means for other wives can always be found." In truth Henry was devastated and when he himself died it was Jane with whom he was buried in St George's chapel at Windsor.

*Anne of Cleves*

Henry was now 46 and he needed more than one son to guarantee the Tudor dynasty. Thomas Cromwell trawled the courts of Europe, but suitable princesses were wary of Henry's reputation and eventually Henry had to settle for Anne of Cleves. The Holbein portrait of the princess which Cromwell commissioned was over flattering, and when she arrived in England, Henry "liked her not for she was heavy and lumpen", she spoke only German, and her manners were frankly rural.

Henry accused Cromwell of trickery and tried to escape the marriage by raising the question of her previous betrothal to the Duke of Lorraine. But he was trapped and conceded, "I must needs against my will, put my head into the noose." On their marriage night they were undressed by their attendants and the marriage bed was blessed. But Henry, who himself was obese, was repulsed by her fat body and in the nights that followed he began to cross the river to visit the apartments of a Lady in Waiting called Catherine Howard.

At first Anne had no idea that her husband was displeased with her. She told her ladies, "Why, when he comes to bed he kisseth me, and taketh me by the hand, and biddeth me 'Good night, sweetheart.'" But her lady, Eleanor Paston, had to tell her that this wasn't enough to make a pregnancy and her ladies later confirmed that the marriage was never consummated. An agreement was hammered out for an annulment and Ann was given Richmond Palace, Hever Castle, and Ann of Cleves' house in Lewes. For a time she continued to attend court "as Henry's sister" and even ate with Henry and his new attraction, the pretty teenager Catherine Howard. Ann remained in England, isolated from her family in Flanders, and she outlived all of Henry's remaining wives.

*Catherine Howard*

Catherine Howard was a daughter of Lord Edmund Howard and Joyce Culpeper, and was a cousin of Ann Boleyn. She lived across the river in the Norfolk family's Lambeth residence and was secretly married to Henry at Oaklands. As a giddy teenager she was a pawn in the dangerous game of power politics, and she was over fond of presents and handsome young men. Henry genuinely seemed to believe that this strip of a girl could be attracted to an obese, smelly, bad-tempered old man, and he may have known nothing of her previous admirers or her keen eye for young men. She did not become pregnant by Henry.

When he fell ill again she unwisely took up with one of her former lovers and started to lock her bedroom door to servants. Soon the opponents of the Howards began to spy, and when the truth came out Catherine confessed, and Henry threatened to kill the entire Howard family. Under torture two young men, Francis Dereham and Thomas Culpepper, were forced to admit to making love to her and they were hanged, drawn, and quartered. Catherine admitted her crimes, was convicted of treason, and was promptly deserted by her terrified family. She died with great dignity on Tower Green, having practiced her execution with a wooden block the night before. Facing the executioner's axe, she declared she was dying a queen but would have preferred to die the wife of Thomas Culpepper. Her Lady in Waiting, Jane Boleyn, had helped in Catherine's adulteries and was also sentenced to death but had a mental breakdown. As a result Henry was forced to change the Insanity Laws so that her execution could proceed.

*Catherine Parr*

Henry's last wife, Catherine Parr was the eldest daughter of Sir Thomas Parr of Kendal in Westmorland, and Maud Green. Sir Thomas was a descendant of King Edward III, and the Parrs were a noble northern family.

She was twice as old as Catherine Howard, but not beyond child bearing when she married the 52-year-old Henry. She had been widowed after two previous marriages to Sir Edward Burroughs and Lord Latymer and was a mature, well-educated, blue-stocking woman who was amazed when Henry proposed to her. But by now he only needed a companion and she cared for him in the painful last years of his life and had no children by him. She published prayers and meditations and cleverly promoted the Protestant cause in a time of Catholic unrest. She also persuaded Henry to build Trinity College Cambridge and Christ College Oxford. When Henry was in France, he made her Regent and gave her custody of his three children – Edward, Mary, and Elizabeth. And after Henry's death she married Thomas Seymour and died of Puerperal Fever after giving birth to his son.

In summary, all of Henry's first three wives became pregnant by Henry but the last three marriages were probably not consummated. During her 22-year marriage to Henry, Catherine of Aragon had two stillbirths, two neonatal deaths, a cot death of a 52-day-old infant, and one child, Mary, who survived to adulthood. Ann Boleyn had two stillbirths, one neonatal death of a premature boy, and a daughter, Elizabeth, was the only surviving child. In modern parlance Catherine and Ann both suffered from habitual abortion[25]. Jane Seymour had one pregnancy and delivered a healthy son – Edward – but died of Puerperal Fever two weeks later. And none of the remaining three marriages produced any pregnancies but Henry kept numerous mistresses and had several illegitimate children, including a daughter by Mary Boleyn and a son by Ann Blount.

His first wives produced three surviving children from 11 pregnancies, which is an overall infant mortality of 73%. Such figures are high by modern standards but were not unusual at the time. And for comparison the famous Dean Colet was the only one of his

---

[25] See Medical Appendix – 14. Habitual Abortion, page 336.

mother's 22 children to survive the first year of life. Poor nutrition, hard physical work, and intercurrent disease accounted for high infant mortality in the poorer classes, but in the case of the king's wives, their habitual abortions would not have been due to this.

# *Edward VI*

Edward VI was the son of Henry VIII and Jane Seymour and was born in 1537 at Hampton Court. He was nine years old when he became king and he died in Greenwich of Tuberculosis at the age of 15.

There was as much rejoicing at the arrival of a male heir to the throne but his mother, Jane Seymour, died 12 days later from Puerperal Fever[26] and the joy turned to mourning. He was cared for by a dry nurse called Sybil Penn and a wet nurse called Mother Jack. And the king rewarded them with pearls and appointments and the status of his trusted fool, Will Sommers. The baby had four nursery

---

[26] See Medical Appendix – 13. Puerperal Fever, page 333.

maids to rock his cradle and a physician in full time attendance called Dr Owen. Queen Catherine Parr became his stepmother and Henry VIII allocated the modern equivalent of £2 million a year to his household at Hampton Court.

Henry had waited many years for a male heir and his conduct towards the child's welfare indicates a modern understanding of infectious diseases and the importance of hygiene. Edward was a frail infant and Henry would not allow him to be exposed to epidemics of infection. He removed him for long periods to Ashridge monastery where it was said the air was healthier and staff who fell ill were immediately dismissed. The baby's nursery was scrubbed three times every day and for fear of assassination no one was allowed to approach the child without permission from the king.

When Edward was breastfed his wet nurse was tested for poisons and after he was weaned his food was tasted before he ate it.

As a toddler he was showered with toys and entertained and with a girl called Jane Dormer, he learned to dance as soon as he could walk. At the age of six the women were taken from him and he was brought up in the adult world of homes in Hertfordshire and Bedfordshire. He was educated by Richard Cox and John Cheke, who were Cambridge humanists, and those closest to him remarked how he was full of promise. He grew into a healthy adolescent and was athletic, intelligent, and well educated. He was also a happy boy who was fond of playing games with his friends Barnaby Fitzpatrick, Henry Sidney, and his cousin Lady Jane Grey. But in the company of self-seeking adults he felt threatened and in their presence he could become haughty, arrogant, and spiteful.

When Henry VIII died in 1546 Edward was brought to London and crowned in Westminster Abbey. There were street entertainments along the coronation route and after a long ceremony there were banquets which went on late into the night. It was a long day for a 9-year-old but he survived the ordeal without falling asleep. He enjoyed reading *Aesop's Fables*, excelled in geography, French, and Latin, showed a precocious interest in astronomy and philosophy, and learned to play the lute. He read Aristotle's *Ethics* and translated Cicero's *De Philosophia* from Latin into Greek. He was made aware of the theological controversies of the day and he was raised a devout Protestant.

During his short reign clerics from around Europe were invited to England to revise the Bible and the Prayer Book into a Protestant format. In 1552 the Catholic doctrine of the Holy Communion was changed to a Protestant commemorative rite and he was taught to equate dishonest practices with Papistry and encouraged his bishops to preach against corruption. In addition, he founded 20 grammar schools which thrive to this day. Under the guidance of his stepmother Catherine Parr, he played with his stepsisters. It was said that Elizabeth repaired his shirts and wrote little notes to him in Latin, but Mary stayed cold and aloof and showed little affection.

As a teenager he became involved in state affairs and wrote treatises on economics in his daily journal. He became familiar with the navigational quadrant and was taught by Sebastian Cabot about the variation of the magnetic compass. He learned all the ports and safe havens in England, Scotland, and France, sent ships to trade with the Levant, and sponsored a ship called the *Edward Bonaventure* on Willoughby's expedition to Russia. But like most children who are overindulged he could be inclined to cruelty, and when he sent heretics such as Joan Boucher to be burned at the stake he lost no sleep about it.

As a 10-year-old king, he was easily misled into feeling that he ruled in person when in reality his so-called actions were the endorsements of his regency council. His father had foreseen this and in his will had made provisions in the Privy Council to balance the opposing factions. But the will contained loopholes which were overturned after Henry's death and the Duke of Somerset emerged as Protector of the Realm. Somerset was a liberal dreamer who tried to marry the young king to Mary Queen of Scots. But after the Battle of Pinkie, Mary escaped to France and married the Dauphin instead. Somerset seized church property, executed his own brother, built a palace in London and corrupted everyone. When revolts broke out against land enclosures he brought in foreign troops to suppress the peasants and he was widely hated and eventually fell from grace.

In 1549 in a last attempt to cling to power, he moved the king to the isolation of Windsor, but the boy became ill and some said it was this journey through bitter weather that broke the king's heath. In the meantime, the national debt grew, religious schism widened, and England wasted her time and energy fighting the Scots. Somerset was sentenced to death in 1552 and was replaced by the unpleasant but more capable Northumberland.

Edward enjoyed the life of his country houses. He loved musicians, dancers, tumblers, jugglers, tight rope walkers, greyhound races, archery, bear baiting, and dog fights. He played tennis and cards, lost money playing dice, and joined in military games on horseback, sometimes in full armour. He was his own captain of sport and developed a talent for organising barriers, jousts, tourneys, archery competitions, and even mock sea battles. His personal needs were met by eighteen gentlemen of the Chamber and he was always accompanied by a yeoman body guard.

In 1551 the Sweating Sickness broke out in Cambridge and two of Edward's friends died of it. But when he went on a long tour of the south he returned with a persistent cough and loss of weight. In 1553 he began to spit blood and Dr Owen recognised it was Tuberculosis[27] and persuaded him to rest at Greenwich. For a short time he benefitted from the change of air but when the "Rheum cough" returned Northumberland began to fear the worst. Worried that his Protestant ambitions would be undone by the succession of Mary, Northumberland decided that Lady Jane Grey should succeed the throne and in May she was married to Northumberland's son Guildford Dudley. This shameless tilt at power revealed Northumberland's ambitions and was a blunder. The 15-year-old king coughed incessantly and grew weaker, and his physicians reported a tumour on the lung and advised him to confine himself to his rooms. Northumberland now persuaded the king to exclude his sisters, Mary and Elizabeth, from the succession and to name the male children of his Protestant cousin Lady Jane Grey as heirs. The will was written in Edward's own handwriting and it is clear from the wording that he expected to survive his illness. But the Consumption worsened and when he became aware of the truth of his predicament, three further strokes of the quill named the childless Lady Jane Grey as his successor. The judiciary was aware of the implications but they and the bishops were forced to countersign the will and the army and navy were mobilised to deal with any backlash.

After June 11th Edward ate nothing and on the 14th he had a lung haemorrhage. In desperation, a common woman who boasted she

---

[27] See Medical Appendix – 5. Tuberculosis, page 311.

could cure the king was allowed to administer medicines to him. But these caused an eruption of scabs all over his skin, his hair fell out, his fingernails came off, and he developed kidney failure. This gave rise to rumours that Northumberland had hastened the king's demise with poison[28], and that he should be charged with the king's murder. The final symptoms could have been due to deliberate poisoning with Arsenic or Mercury, but an innocent overdose of medicinal tonic is more likely. As the king's renal failure worsened he ceased to pass urine and his head, abdomen, and legs became swollen. The physicians shaved his head to allow the application of plasters and on 4th July his face was seen at a window of Greenwich Palace for the last time. On 6th July, he was raised up in bed and he prayed for deliverance from a miserable life and for England to be saved from Papistry. And when he died in the arms of his best friend, Henry Sidney, he prayed, "Lord have mercy on me and take my spirit." The French ambassador who had arrived for a private audience was the first to be told the king was dead and was turned away.

That night a horseman rode to warn the Princess Mary that she must flee to safety and when Lord Robert Dudley arrived next day to take her to the Tower she had fled to the loyal Howard family in Norfolk.

Many royal deaths were accompanied by rumours of poison but the Privy Council ignored this possibility and announced the king had died of a Consumption. He thus suffered the same fate as his grandfather Henry VII and his stepbrother Henry Fitzroy, and modern opinion supports a diagnosis of Tuberculosis, with kidney failure due to Arsenic or Mercury.

Because of the political storm surrounding the succession his embalmed body was not buried for a month. He was taken to Westminster Abbey on a funeral chariot which bore his crowned wax effigy and was followed by choirs of young boys and a pageant of flags. And there were funeral services with Protestant and Catholic rites before he was buried in the Henry VII Chapel. This was destroyed during the Reformation, but when his vault was rediscovered in 1658 it was marked with a new memorial.

---

[28] See Medical Appendix – 23. Poison, page 359.

# Jane Grey

Lady Jane Grey was born at Bradgate in Leicestershire in 1537 and was the daughter of Henry Grey, the Duke of Suffolk, and Frances Brandon, the great-granddaughter of Henry VII. She reigned for just nine days and was executed in the Tower of London at the age of 17.

Frances Brandon was a cold-hearted mother who was soured by her feeble-minded husband who she treated as a non-entity. Their youngest daughter Mary failed to grow to adult stature and was mentally retarded, and a common cause of this was Cretinism due to dietary Iodine deficiency. At 5' 0" Jane was also petite and wore platform shoes to make herself look taller. But despite being manoeuvred in the treacherous game of royal politics there is no evidence she was simple minded like her sister. Her family thrust her into the political and religious storm which followed the death of Edward VI, and then deserted her when the plot unravelled. And on balance she seems to have understood the risk she was taking.

Estranged from her mother, she was brought up in the household of former Queen Catherine Parr and her new husband, Sir Thomas Seymour. As a childhood companion of Princess Mary, Princess Elizabeth, and Prince Edward she was taught for a time by the royal tutors John Alymer and Roger Ascham. But there are no records of her grasp of school subjects and the rest of her childhood was spent in isolation at Bradgate Park. As a result, she grew up to be straight laced, untravelled, and narrow minded, and she was never close to her mother. When she was nine Edward Seymour, the Duke of Somerset, attempted to marry her to his son, the Earl of Hertford. And she was caught up in the power play between Somerset and his brother Thomas whose own plan was to marry Jane to the young Edward VI. With the downfall of both Seymours, however, Jane was left in peace for a period.

In 1551 her cousins, Henry and Charles Brandon, died of the Sweating Sickness, and Jane's father became Duke of Suffolk. With this she became extremely wealthy and the most eligible heiress in England. In 1553 when she was 16 she married Lord Guildford Dudley, the son of the Duke of Northumberland. As Head of the Privy Council and chief advisor to the young king, Northumberland's powerful position combined with Jane's royal lineage now made her a serious Protestant contender for the throne. Henry VIII and Edward VI had decreed the Brandons should succeed to the throne if Edward, Mary, and Elizabeth died without issue. But when Edward VI became seriously ill Northumberland persuaded him to name Jane's children as his successors. And when it became clear he was likely to die, a simple alteration to the will named Jane as his successor.

With powerful families jockeying for position, Jane's marriage revealed Northumberland as a dangerous power seeker. Peers were summoned to London to approve the king's new will but Northumberland was deceiving himself if he thought their signatures were to be trusted.

Jane was not told of the king's death until the earls filed into her presence and knelt to swear their allegiance. In the midst of this Jane was sometimes portrayed as an innocent victim, but she must have understood some of the risks because she fainted when told of the king had died.

Next day the letters patent were drawn up by Northumberland's supporters and Jane was proclaimed Queen. But the assent of Parliament had not been obtained and Mary had escaped to Norfolk where her Catholic support was strong. In the days which followed London proclaimed for Queen Jane and the counties proclaimed for Mary. Some cities proclaimed for both of them, others were too wary to proclaim for either, and those like Cambridge proclaimed for one and then switched sides. At the critical point Mary's support was bolder and more ruthless. Her religious bigotry had been a kept secret from many of the powerful players, and as Henry VIII's daughter she enjoyed wide support. In addition her supporters conducted a brilliant campaign of misinformation and when Northumberland's forces pursued her across East Anglia his support drained away and Mary's support grew. And by the time Northumberland reached Kings Lynn he threw his cap in the ring and cried, "God save Queen Mary."

Jane, her father, and her husband, were imprisoned in the Tower of London and she spent her time inspecting the royal jewels and ordering cloth for new robes. But she played no real role in proceedings and when she was tried for high treason she pleaded guilty and was sentenced to death. This was suspended through the winter of 1553 whilst she was kept in political limbo. But many friends deserted her and the relationship with her imprisoned husband turned sour.

When Mary repealed Edward VI's Articles of Religion and announced her marriage to Philip of Spain, a Protestant rebellion lead by Sir Thomas Wyatt broke out. This was crushed and as its figurehead Jane's fate was sealed. She and her husband were executed on February 12th 1554 and the night before her death she practiced with an execution block. On the scaffold she was accompanied by Nurse Ellen and Mrs Tilney, but blindfolded, she cried out, "What am I to do? Where is it?"

After her head was struck off with a single blow the crowd left, and her body was buried between Anne Boleyn and Catherine Howard in the church St. Peter ad Vincula. There was a legend that

Jane's remains were secretly reburied at Bradgate but in 1909 a small, broken coffin was discovered in a vault in St Peter ad Vincula, containing the remains of a female of diminutive stature, with the head severed from the body. Her skeleton crumbled when it was exposed to the atmosphere and was enclosed in an urn and placed under an inscription in the chancel.

# Mary I

Mary was the daughter of Henry VIII and Catherine of Aragon and was born at Greenwich in 1515. She was 38 when she became queen and she ruled for five years before dying of ovarian cancer at the age of 43.

As a young girl she grew up under Catherine Parr's guardianship and had a kind and gentle personality. She loved music and dancing and played the virginal. Later, however, she became serious, stubborn, and strong willed and regarded any compromise as weakness. In her 20s she was always ill and instead of cool sense, she developed religious fervour and her voice grew masculine and harsh.

She was a powerful pawn in the game of dynastic diplomacy and her first betrothal was proposed to the Dauphin of France. In her 20s she feared being left on the shelf and longed for a husband and children. Once Ann Boleyn had given birth to Elizabeth, Mary pleaded with her father to give her own future children precedence as heirs. But she never recognised Henry as head of the church, and she attended Mass and practiced the Catholic Royal Touch to cure Scrofula. She was devoted to her mother but was never allowed to see Catherine of Aragon at Kimbolt Castle. She became reconciled to her half-sister, Elizabeth, but her half-brother Edward did not know how to deal with her.

She succeeded to the throne in 1553 when Edward VI died and she decisively suppressed the claims of Lady Jane Grey who she eventually executed. She ruthlessly put down the Protestant rebellion of Thomas Wyatt but never realised that her popularity was because she was Henry VIII's daughter and not because she was a Catholic.

She never understood the emerging Protestant character of the English, and when she married Philip of Spain in 1554 she turned England into a Spanish colony and the majority of her people felt threatened. Two thousand clergy lost their benefices and 300 were burned at the stake, including Cranmer, the Archbishop of Canterbury, and Latymer and Ridley, two priests in the court of Edward VI. With these barbaric public executions she became known as Bloody Mary, and only her death avoided a national crisis. It was said her only lasting achievements were road improvements.

She married Philip of Spain in Winchester Cathedral in 1554 and to observe precedence at the wedding feast she dined on gold plate and Philip dined on silver. It was said she loved Philip but he merely tolerated her and used her to widen the designs of Spain.

*Philip of Spain*

In the years that followed, her Catholic supporters were disappointed when she failed to become pregnant and it is unclear if she could still have children for she was 43 years old. She had painful, irregular menstrual periods and it is thought she wanted a child so badly she was misled into thinking the symptoms of her menopause were those of pregnancy. These would have included missed periods, abdominal distension, and altered mood swings. In addition, she had dropsy and there may even have been a Catholic plot to pass off a surrogate infant as heir to the throne. Some of her suspected pregnancies were no more than hysterical pseudocyeses[29] or false pregnancies. And fearing her sterility was a punishment for the heresies practiced in England, she had fires lit in Smithfield to atone for this.

Philip deserted her for long periods but anticipating a birth in 1555, cradles were placed in the palace nursery and it was rumoured that a male child had been delivered. In 1558 she developed abdominal swelling which became painful and she lost weight. It was realised she was seriously ill and as she lay dying courtiers were leaving the palace in London for a court deep in the countryside where the Princess Elizabeth was waiting for news. Mary deteriorated and the likeliest cause of her death was ovarian cancer. She received

---

[29] See Medical Appendix – 15. Pseudocyesis, page 338.

the last rites of the Church and died in St James Palace. But except in her inner circle, there was no outpouring of grief and her husband was unmoved. She was buried in Westminster Abbey and 40 years later Elizabeth I was buried beside her.

# Elizabeth I

Elizabeth I was the daughter of Henry VIII and Ann Boleyn and was born at Greenwich Palace in 1533. She was 25 when she became queen, and she ruled for 45 years. She died at Richmond of pneumonia at the age of 69.

Many Catholics falsely accused her of being conceived out of wedlock and when the Anglican Archbishops refused to conduct her coronation she was crowned by the Bishop of Carlisle.

Her father's will provided for the succession of Edward, then Mary and then Elizabeth, and in the event of them being childless, the succession of the Brandon family of Henry's sister Mary. But Elizabeth later overruled this and willed the throne to the Stuart descendants of Henry's other sister, Margaret.

Until she was four her governess was Lady Bryan and her education was in the hands of Catherine Champerdowne. She learned Greek from John Cheke and Italian from Battisti Castiglione, and eventually she spoke nine languages including Cornish, Irish, and Welsh. She lived her youth at Catherine Parr's home at Sudely Castle where at the age of 14 she had to be rescued from the sexual advances of Thomas Seymour. She then went to live at Cheshunt with Kate Astley where Roger Ascham became her tutor. He said she spoke French, Italian, and Latin as well as she spoke English.

When Mary summoned her to London after the Protestant rebellion of Thomas Wyatt, her life was under threat and she fell ill with migraine headaches and had to be brought to Whitehall on a litter. It was never decided if her migraines were genuine or if she feigned them as an excuse, but she suffered from them all her life and took Fever Few to relieve them.

She was highly intelligent and incisive, dilatory, reflective, ruthless, manipulative, or devious whenever the situation demanded. She used female charm to win arguments and her subjects usually became devoted to her. She wooed parliaments and armies with spectacular speeches comparable to Shakespeare. And she ruled as a man, not a woman. She understood men's characters, and was at ease in the Privy Council with men like William Cecil who she called "the greatest counsellor in Christendom".

But the Middle Ages were only just ending and despite her sharp mind she still employed an astrologer called John Dee who selected the most propitious date of her coronation, and for the ailing Cecil advised a potion which contained an "English hedgehog, quartered in peeces in red wine, a pint of rose water, a quart of sugar, with Cinnamone and great Raisines".

But she had deep insight into the questions of the day, and would take time, some said too much time, to make her decisions. She also had a character of steel as was shown when she executed 200 Catholics who posed a threat to the realm. "I know," she once said, "that I have the body of a weak and feeble woman, but I have the heart and stomach of a king." So enemies like Mary Queen of Scots were sent to the scaffold, and even friends like Devereaux and Campion were sacrificed when the need arose. And when in 1586 she grappled with the consequences of executing Mary, she even considered having her privately murdered. In the end she was deceived by Burleigh into signing the death warrant, and facing her wrath, he seriously feared being sent to the Tower.

Under Sir Francis Walsingham, her spy network was like a modern secret service, and there was little which escaped her notice, as Mary found to her cost.

Elizabeth was just three years old when her mother Ann Boleyn was proclaimed a whore and executed, and Elizabeth was wrongly branded a Royal bastard. In her dangerous youth she kept a low profile and used the time to study. Just four years into her reign at Hampton Court she developed a high fever and a physician called Burcot attended her. But when he told her she had Smallpox, she shrieked, "Get the knave out of my sight." But within hours she became unconscious and the offended Burcot was dragged back to her by force. He ordered for her bed to be put by the fire and wrapped her in a great length of scarlet cloth. In an age when the mortality from Smallpox[30] was 60%, she and her carer, Lady Sidney, were both fortunate to survive. But her face was scarred and for the rest of her life she wore excessive facial make-up and banned mirrors from the palace.

She created an Established Church which satisfied the needs of different religious persuasions and the secular purpose of the state. As she put it, she "didn't care to make windows into men's minds and souls". She dealt with the plots of Mary Queen of Scots and the Spanish Armada. And playing the European nations against each other, she turned England into the greatest power of the age. Her poets wrote the finest English and her circumnavigators laid the foundations of the greatest empire the world had seen. She had a hard head for business and the return on her private investment in Sir Francis Drake's adventures was said to be 5,000%. She exacted Ship Money from inland towns and demanded voluntary donations from wealthier citizens. And as her personal wealth grew, she was said to own 3,000 gowns and 628 pieces of jewellery.

When the Spanish Armada threatened in 1588 the Pope renewed the excommunication she had received in 1570 and this led to

---

[30] See Medical Appendix – 4. Smallpox, page 307.

Catholic rebellions in Ireland and the north of England.

She ran a national lottery to fund the building of warships and new ports, and sold 400,000 tickets each costing 10 shillings for a first prize of £5,000 plus freedom from arrest for many crimes. The Armada was a close-run thing but she was lucky and "God's winds blew, and they were scattered". Forty-four of the 130 Spanish galleons never returned to Spain and Elizabeth emerged as the mistress of the seven seas and was painted as Gloriana, with her hand upon the globe.

The Spanish lost their Armada but England lost no ships and only a handful of men. But after the war at sea, the men were starving and were it not for the Spanish prize money the 15,000 English sailors who subsequently died from Typhus could have been far more. Typhus is caused by a virulent bacterium called *Rickettsia prowazekii* and is spread from rodents by lice and ticks. Epidemics were often seen in medieval warships and before modern treatment with antibiotics the mortality rate was 40%.

She had political and personal reasons for not marrying and she used her potential marriage as a powerful instrument of foreign policy. She realised at an early age that when men looked upon her, it was the throne they eyed. She resented women who had the freedom to do otherwise and sometimes she withheld permission for her ladies to marry. At the age of 14, she was pursued by the ambitious Sir Thomas Seymour, and since she was accused of being with child, at least some sexual dalliance took place in her private chambers. Seymour even broke into her apartments and shot her little terrier, and this dangerous dalliance continued until Lady Catherine Parr intervened. But Elizabeth was dangerously compromised and when Seymour was executed, it changed her attitude towards marriage and men.

When Queen Mary died, Philip of Spain offered to marry Elizabeth but she turned him down, and she did the same to other European monarchs. She used their interest to her advantage but it was not practical for her to be subservient to a man and she was rightly terrified of childbirth. And she realised that to rule as a man she would have to rule better than men, and to do this, she needed her good health and all her energy. To the French ambassador she once said, "Although I may not be a lion, I am a lion's cub, and I have a lion's heart."

Sir Christopher Hatton professed love for her and Sir Thomas Heneage was a suitor, and Walter Raleigh too. In the case of Robert Dudley Earl of Leicester, however, she found a kindred spirit and they showered each other with gifts. She made him her Master of Horse and many historians believe he was more than just her admirer. He gave magnificent banquets for her at his house in Kew but the relationship soured when his wife Amy Robsart died in a suspicious fall in 1560. The court rumoured that Dudley had murdered Amy in order to marry the queen, and at Kennilworth he did propose marriage to her but she replied that she would rather be a single beggar woman than a married queen. At the age of 48 she toyed with marriage to Alencon, the brother of the King of France, and they even exchanged wedding rings. He was half her age, and when Leicester secretly married Lettice Knollys it was kept from the queen in order to prevent her falling for Alencon's flattery. Leicester died in 1588 and when Elizabeth died 15 years later a private letter from him was discovered on which she had written "his last letter".

In old age her contemporaries began to die and she took the death of Lord Burleigh very badly and nursed him on his deathbed. "You are," she told him, "all things to me, my Alpha and my Omega."

In the case of Robert Devereux, Earl of Essex, she was flattered by his youth and energy and saw in him the son she never had. She once even gave him a love token, which promised a pardon should he ever anger her, but he took this too literally and when he plotted against her government she sent him to the scaffold.

Inevitably in old age she began to lose her grip, and in the Privy Council great men were replaced by lesser sons. Corruption grew, and the Fleet Street riots were over her award of lucrative monopolies. At the age of 69 she enjoyed a brief Indian Summer and took to riding and dancing galliards once more. She had always loved dancing and in her youth and could step La Volta and the Entre Chattio. But now increasingly she watched others dance, and particularly the young men.

But her grey hair thinned beneath a red wig, her teeth fell out and she wore wooden dentures. She had a weakness for sweet foods and her teeth were black and carious. On one occasion she had toothache and a barber surgeon recommended an extraction. But before she would submit, a bishop had to volunteer to demonstrate that dental extraction was bearable. Numerous portraits of her were painted but these were for propaganda and were of a resplendent young queen.

Her advancing years caused consternation because she refused to name a successor. Spain was interfering with the Protestant succession in France and Protestants in England feared a similar Catholic intervention. Her Smallpox scars ruined her image and she used pomegranate juice and some said too much facial make up. Only one portrait survives of an old queen in failing health and that was painted from her death mask. She was troubled with nightmares and when the Bishop of St David's predicted the year of her death she told him to keep his arithmetic to himself. On one occasion when her demise was falsely rumoured she said, "Dead but not buried, dead but not buried." And on another occasion when someone tried to be light hearted she said, "When thou dost feel Time at thy gate these fooleries will please thee less."

But harvests were failing, taxes were rising, and the talk at court was of the succession. She wooed Parliament with a last Golden Speech, and over Christmas 1602 she became ill with throat ulcers, fever, and she could not eat. A tonsillar quinsy developed and until this burst in her throat it caused agony. She lost interest in the government and for comfort she lay on her cushions and read Chaucer. Contemplating death and the succession she sat alone for weeks, and once locked herself in her room and stood continuously for 15 hours.

"You must go to bed," urged Robert Cecil.

To which she replied, "the word 'must' should not be used to Princes, little man. You know that I must die and that makes you presumptuous. If only you saw what I see when I go to bed."

She died in 1603 and on her deathbed a list of possible successors was read aloud to her. And when it reached "the Kyng of Scottes", she raised her hand in assent. John Whitgift, the Archbishop of Canterbury, was summoned, and she died quietly in her bed from pneumonia. Secret negotiations had taken place between Robert Cecil and James VI of Scotland and when the end came, fresh horses had been posted at 20-mile intervals on the route north. And the messenger, John Carey, reached Holyrood in just three days with the news of her death.

She had left instructions that her body should not be touched by the embalmers whose custom was to remove the heart and bowels for burial in separate urns, sometimes at different burial sites. There was a scurrilous rumour that her naked body was concealed because she was not a true woman, but there is no evidence to support this. In a break with tradition, the corpse was not dressed in Coronation robes, but in a simple cerecloth. Her wax effigy was placed on top of the coffin, and she was rowed down the river to Whitehall to lie in state for five days, watched over by her ladies. At Greenwich where she was born, and at Richmond where she died, monies were distributed to the poor. But here, the lack of embalming caused her sealed coffin to burst apart with a loud crack. She was originally buried in her grandfather's vault in the Lady Chapel of Westminster Abbey but she was moved three years later to a large white marble tomb which she shared with her stepsister, Mary.

*The tomb of Elizabeth I and Mary*

# STUARTS & CROMWELLS

## 1603-1714

*Mary Queen of Scots*

*James I    Charles I   Oliver Cromwell*

*Richard Cromwell    Charles II*

*James II    William II and Mary II    Anne I*

# Mary Queen of Scots

Mary was the daughter of the James V of Scotland and Mary of Guise. She was born in 1542 and was six days old when she became Queen of Scots. From 1567 she was a political prisoner of Elizabeth I and in 1586 she was executed at Fotheringay Castle at the age of 45.

She was Queen of Scotland, Queen of France, and through her descent from Queen Margaret of Scotland and her marriage to Lord Darnley she had a strong claim to the English throne. She was never Queen of England but she founded the Stuart dynasty from which every modern English monarch is descended. She also suffered from the hereditary Porphyria which affected English monarchs for 400 years.

Mary was born at Linlithgow and six days later her father died of Porphyria at the age of only 30. James V of Scotland treated women badly and Mary's mother led an unhappy married life. He was prone to hysteria and physical collapse during moments of stress and it is now known this was caused by Acute Intermittent Porphyria[31]. He is the first British monarch identified with the disease and he died during an acute attack.

There had been no adult successors to the Scottish throne for seven generations and young Scottish monarchs were merely crown stewards answerable to powerful nobles. In Mary's case the new Scottish Regent, the Earl of Arran, was singularly unsuited for this role.

Negotiations were opened to wed the infant princess to Edward VI of England, but these broke down and Mary was removed to France. She learned to speak French and her school books reveal an earnest but unaccomplished scholar. She inherited blue eyes, sandy hair, and a weak chin from her mother, and the cyclical spirits of manic depression from her father. At the age of eight she had her first unexplained attacks of diarrhoea, and these were followed by episodes of nervous anxiety accompanied by indigestion and vomiting. At the age of 14 she began to suffer from the fevers which bedevilled her for the rest of her life and which were symptoms of hereditary Porphyria.

Accounts of her great beauty are over flattering but she was six feet in height, red headed, and had beautiful skin which survived disfigurement from Smallpox. At the age of 15 she married the wizened Francis of France who eventually died of Syphilis[32].

The secret marriage contract ceded Scotland to France in the event of Mary dying childless, but this soon became known in England and gave rise to the serious mistrust which the English always felt towards her. Any lingering doubts were swept away when Elizabeth succeeded to the English throne in 1558 and Henry I of France proclaimed she was a bastard and Mary was the rightful Queen of England.

---

[31] See Medical Appendix – 2. Porphyria, page 296.
[32] See Medical Appendix – 10. Syphilis, page 325.

*King Francis of France*

In 1559 Mary fell seriously ill and the court physicians said she had an incurable malady and feared for her life.

She was pale, dizzy, and short of breath, and had fainting spells, which can all be attributed to acute Porphyria.

In 1560, King Henry of France was killed jousting, and Francis and Mary became King and Queen of France. Her fainting became a regular feature of court life, and pregnancy was frequently suspected, despite the likelihood that her marriage was never consummated. In 1559, she had a complete collapse when she heard her mother had died in Scotland.

Then Francis I developed red patches on his cheeks due to secondary Syphilis, and his physical appearance was so alarming that peasants fled when he passed by. In 1560 at the age of 16 he became ill with headaches, fever, vomiting, and loss of speech. An Orleans's barber was accused of the unlikely crime of poisoning his ear and when he developed photophobia, Mary helped nurse him in a darkened room. But he deteriorated rapidly and died from Syphilitic meningitis, leaving Mary a widow at 18 years of age.

In 1561 the return of fevers prevented her travelling to Rheims for the coronation of Charles IX. A list of kings and noble lords were suggested for her to choose a new husband, but her position in France had become superfluous and she returned instead to Scotland.

When she landed at Leith it was said she spoke the Scots language with a French accent. Scotland was in the grip of freezing weather, her home country was fiercely Protestant and the violent nobles were lawless.

Mary had a reckless personality, and until she had a serious riding accident, she hunted recklessly on horseback. But her spells of merriment were interspersed with bouts of weeping and depression. She found it difficult to cope with the affairs of state and for weeks on end she took to her bed with pains in her side. These were to recur for the rest of her life and were another symptom of Porphyria.

Any judgement she had left deserted her when she married Henry Lord Darnley who was in line for the English throne. They were cousins and needed papal dispensation to marry, but she fell for his handsome looks and William Cecil described the marriage as carnal and predicted it would end in strife. Darnley was a vain, sadistic, bisexual brute, and when Mary's health failed again, he left her to suffer and took himself off hunting.

*Henry Lord Darnley*

When she was two months pregnant with the future James I she moved to Linlithgow. Pregnancy is now a well-known aggravating factor of Porphyria and the pains in her abdomen returned. The court at Holyrood was rife with rumours that the child was fathered by her favourite courtesan, the Italian David Riccio, and a group of courtiers set upon him and killed him. In Mary's presence he was stabbed 56 times whilst Mary had a pistol held against her pregnant belly.

Mary's life and the life of her child were now in grave danger and she fled to Dunbar Castle. There she had abdominal pains for a month before she went into a long and difficult labour. Witchcraft was said to have been used to transfer her labour pains to Lady Reves who lay alongside her in the labour bed. She delivered a fine healthy boy but this joyous event served to displace Darnley further down the line of succession and his behaviour became even worse. It was at this stage that Mary began to regret the marriage.

Four months later she suffered a prolonged attack of abdominal pain and many thought she could not survive. She was ill with vomiting for eight months and developed limb paralysis, blindness, epileptiform seizures and episodes of coma. These new symptoms of Porphyria worsened and her face became distorted, her limbs contracted, and when wine was forced into her mouth (the worst thing for Porphyria), she vomited "corrupt blood". Prayers were said in churches and mourning clothes were ordered for the court. Her pulse weakened due to low blood pressure and this was treated by her physician Dr Arnault, by bandaging her legs. This approach proved effective and she slowly recovered.

Darnley spent the whole of this time debauching himself on the west coast of Scotland until he was struck down with a fever. The Diurnal of Occurents says that this was due to the Great Pox, and a modern examination of his skull in the Royal College of Surgeons of London, confirms the characteristic bony pit marks of Syphilis. It is therefore likely that his behaviour was due to neurosyphilis and had he survived longer he would have died a natural death from this. But convalescing in Kirk O Fields in Edinburgh, he was blown up with gunpowder by his enemies and dragged outside the demolished building and strangled. He was 21 years of age.

The shock robbed Mary of every shred of judgement and she

entered a state of deep melancholy. Darnley's probable murderer, James Hepburn, 4th Earl of Bothwell, became de facto King of Scotland and he abducted Mary and her son to Dunbar where it was said he raped her.

*James Hepburn, Earl of Bothwell*

Taken back to Edinburgh, she married him, and unhappy to the point of suicide she discovered she was pregnant. Bothwell's rivals fell into a regicidal frame of mind and Mary feared being poisoned. And when Bothwell fled to Denmark, she had another nervous collapse and was separated from her son. Imprisoned on the Isle of Lochleven, she never saw him again.

It was reported by her secretary Claude Nau that she miscarried a twin pregnancy on July 24th 1567 at Loch Levan Castle in Kinross. Modern paediatricians say that a 12-week twin pregnancy would have required careful inspection, and discernible stillborn twins would have needed to be at least 16 weeks' gestation. Their conception was therefore at or before the 24th March which is two months before she married Bothwell and a month before he abducted her to Dunbar and allegedly raped her. Darnley was sick with Syphilis and living apart from Mary at that time and was murdered in February, so he could not have been the father, and it is likely that the twins were conceived in a relationship Mary had with Bothwell before they were married.

She fell seriously ill again, this time with limb swelling, jaundice, and skin blisters which indicate she suffered from a variegate form of Porphyria. In this state of health she was forced to abdicate and her 13-month-old son was crowned James VI of Scotland, with Lord Moray as Regent.

She then recovered and escaped from the Isle of Lochleven in a rowing boat to the mainland. But her tiny army of supporters was rounded up at Langside and she fled on horseback. But instead of heading for the safety of France, she crossed into England and entered a lifetime of captivity, religious intrigue, and eventual execution. The famous casket letters which are now believed to be forged, incriminated her in the murder of Darnley, but Queen Elizabeth believed the evidence and never trusted her cousin again. Mary now discovered that Elizabeth was no longer her friend, and marzipan and sweet nuts to satisfy Elizabeth's sweet taste buds made no difference. Elizabeth wanted Mary back in Scotland but as the years passed the Scots refused to allow her son James to share the throne.

Kept outside the political mainstream, she was spied upon and moved from place to place, and much of the time she spent at her embroidery. The further attacks of pain she experienced were diagnosed as "Grief of the spleen" and when the pains made her faint, it was said the "windy matter had ascended to her brain." She endured frequent painful episodes, and her face swelled and she wept in anguish. She declined safe marriages which the English Privy Council attempted to force upon her, but she could not resist the dangerous plots in which her Catholic supporters proposed to murder Elizabeth and put Mary on the English throne.

In 1573 she had symptoms of "flying gout" which were due to Porphyria. She was allowed to take the mineral waters at Buxton, which were owned by Bess of Hardwick and were reputed to be efficacious for gout. But if there were any benefits, they were short lived. Worse still, she abused her new freedom and was moved to Tutbury which she was far less comfortable and where it was said the middens stank beneath her window. She had more attacks which left her unable to write letters, and in 1581, she nearly died of "gastric influenza" and became lame. Her constant pains, vomiting, and seizures gradually convinced Elizabeth that Mary was seriously ill, though some cynics continued to say her symptoms were fabricated.

Contemporary medical theories dictated that her four body humours were imbalanced, but this came nowhere near explaining her disease or providing an effective treatment. She pined for her son in Scotland and put on weight and lost her good looks. She escaped execution by a hair's breadth when the Throgmorton plot to depose Elizabeth failed in 1583. In 1586 she had to be carried in her chair to watch the duck hunting, and by this time she was being hunted by Walsingham's spy network. The discovery of the Babbington plot and the execution of the 10 conspirators was the final straw for Elizabeth. Mary had been foolishly attracted into this with secret cyphers that Walsingham had decoded, and by Babbington's fantasies of an armed uprising. Imprisoned and awaiting trial, Mary could not walk without assistance or use her hands to write. Her memory was failing and English was only a second language to her. Furthermore, she did not understand English law and she was denied a secretary, witnesses, or a lawyer.

Her conviction was a forgone conclusion and following this, she became serene at last. She declared no fear of death and requested her body be buried in France. Elizabeth wrestled with the dreadful prospect of executing an anointed queen and the execution warrant remained unsigned for weeks. A secret murder by poison or by smothering was considered, and eventually Elizabeth was tricked by Burghley into signing an execution warrant. He may even have falsified reports of a Spanish invasion of Wales to support her execution.

The council then went ahead without Elizabeth's knowledge and an executioner called Ball was hired for a fee of £10. The day before the execution, Mary had no idea of what was going on behind the scenes and her ladies were searching in the villages near Fotheringay for herbal remedies for her pains.

On receiving the news of her execution next day, she told her staff that "they should not weep, for the end of Mary Stuart's troubles is now done". One cannot doubt she meant it and she was bowed by a lifetime of suffering when she made her way on to the scaffold. There was an argument when she was denied a servant to accompany her to the block, and she was only allowed a rosary and a Latin prayer book but was not permitted to distribute jewellery. She had walked to her death dressed in a black cloak but on reaching the block she removed this and revealed beneath the blood red petticoat of a Catholic martyr. Her head was struck off with three blows of the axe and when it was raised aloft, a red wig came loose and revealed thin grey hair beneath it. Her lips were seen to move for 15 minutes, and it was then her terrified lap dog, a Sky terrier, was discovered beneath her red petticoat. Apparently the animal later pined away. She was 45 years old.

Elizabeth now had the blood of an anointed queen on her hands and she angrily blamed her councillors for deceiving her. No relics were allowed to be distributed and only Mary's rosary and prayer book survive today. Dr Stanford performed the autopsy and declared her heart was sound and apart from a slight excess of fluid, the other organs were healthy too. Bearing in mind that George III had Porphyria but lived until he was 82, it seems that Mary might have lived on for years.

Her body was embalmed in a wax winding sheet and buried in a wall tomb at Fotheringay. In the summer it was reburied in Peterborough Cathedral and in the years that followed Fotheringay fell into ruins.

After the death of Elizabeth I, however, James I constructed a tomb for Mary in Westminster Abbey, with a marble effigy modelled on a death mask. Her body was removed from Peterborough where there is no tombstone, and reburied in Westminster Abbey. In subsequent years Catholic miracles were ascribed to the shrine and when a search of the tomb was made by Dean Stanley in 1867, the body of the Queen of Scots was discovered lying amid the coffins of the dead children of the dynasty she had founded – 10 of James II's children and 15 of Queen Anne's. Mary's coffin was huge and no attempt was made to disturb it.

# James VI & I

James VI of Scotland and I of England was born in Edinburgh in 1566. He was the only son of Mary Queen of Scots and Henry Lord Darnley and was one year old when his mother was deposed and he became King of Scotland. He was 37 when he became King of England and he ruled England and Scotland for 22 years, until he died of a stroke at the age of 59.

On his mother's side he was descended from Margaret Tudor, and on his father's side from Mary Tudor, both daughters of Henry VII. Mary Queen of Scots had a difficult labour with James and during the puerperium it was feared they both might die. He was born with a spastic paralysis of the legs which prevented him from walking until he was seven. He inherited Porphyria[33] from his mother and this can cause paralysis, but not in the newborn. As a result his spasticity was more likely due to a brain injury during his difficult birth. In boyhood he needed to be tied to the saddle when riding on horseback, and he had a strange shambling limp and a tendency to slobber saliva.

Held captive by violent Scottish nobles in his early years, James was born a Catholic but raised a Protestant. In Elizabeth I's court it was not allowed to mention his name above a whisper but Elizabeth recognised he was a man who could rule two kingdoms, and crucially he had sons. He was brought the news of Queen Elizabeth's death by Robert Carey and when he made his way to London he was entertained in country houses along the way. But reaching the private chambers of the late queen, Sir Robert Cecil remarked that her sweet scent of orange blossom was fading and James stank of horses and stale sweat.

His enduring achievement was to commission the Authorised Bible and in 1604 he wrote and published *Basilkon Doron* which was a treatise on good government. Even so, he overestimated his own abilities and he was arrogant and disliked. He prided himself on his kingcraft, but behind his back he was called the wisest fool in Christendom. As King of England he was earnest, intellectual and tactless, and Macaulay wrote that he was a witty, well read, drivelling idiot. He failed to control religious factions and when he reneged on his promises to Catholics, Guy Fawkes and the Gunpowder Plotters attempted to assassinate him during the 1605 opening of Parliament.

He was King of Scotland and England but when he tried to achieve a political union he lost the support of both people. His belief in the Divine Right of Kings led to endless quarrels with Parliament and when Sir Walter Raleigh's Guiana venture threatened relationships with Spain, James ordered Raleigh's execution but failed to salvage the Spanish alliance. He spent a fortune on his daughter's wedding but failed to raise the money from Parliament. As a result he had to sell monopolies to favourites and corruption flourished.

He travelled to Christiana (Oslo) in 1589 and married Ann of Denmark who was 15. But he was contemptuous of women and after

---

[33] See Medical Appendix – 2. Porphyria, page 296.

he became bored with her, she led a miserable life. Four of their seven children died in infancy and their daughter Elizabeth had Porphyria. And at the age of 16 Elizabeth married Frederick the Elector of Palatine and passed the disease to her daughter Sophia and thence to George I of England.

Openly bisexual, James seduced his young gentlemen of the bedchamber, and had a notorious affair with the handsome Duke of Buckingham who was murdered. James was also attracted to Robert Carr, Lord D'Aubigny Lennox, and to James Villiers who was also murdered. And after his enemies attempted to kill James himself he wore bulky doublets and breeches to protect himself.

*Anne of Denmark*         *Henry, Prince of Wales*

James I's eldest son Henry, Prince of Wales, was born in 1594 and was a handsome, athletic extrovert who was adored by everyone. He attracted merriment, and marriage feelers were put out for him in all the courts of Europe. He played tennis, hunted, swam in the River Thames, and enjoyed long riverside walks.

But in 1612 at the age of 18, he suddenly became unwell with a fever and giddiness, violent headaches, diarrhoea, rigors, and delirium. His eyes became sunken, and when he took to his bed the court physicians reported that his pulse was rapid and that with the "alienation of his braine, his ravynge and idle speeches were out of purpose". They then prescribed every remedy known to man. He was administered a clyster (enema), sharpe tarte cordials, cooling juleps, repeated purges and frequent bleedings. He had freshly killed pigeons applied to his shaven head, and a "cocke cloven by the back" applied to the soles of his feet. But his pulse quickened, his face reddened and his belly swelled.

Eventually the queen sent for Sir Walter Raleigh's secret cordial, which was made up by the Tower of London's famous prisoner in a specially equipped laboratory. This consisted of an extraordinary collection of ingredients from Raleigh's travels around the world, and the fragments of the formula which have survived included 40 roots and spices distilled in wine, red coral and pearls dissolved in oil of vitriol, and sulphur, terra sigillata, hartshorn, ambergris, tinctures of bezoar stone (a hairball retrieved from the gut of a cat), along with musk and cane sugar. This caused Henry to sweat a great deal but it was not the cure Sir Walter might have hoped for. Henry's sister, the Princess Elizabeth, was refused permission to see Henry in case his appearance frightened her, and when she disguised herself as a coachman, she was discovered and ejected from the sick room. The squeamish King and Queen distanced themselves from their dying son and sent instead the Archbishop of Canterbury. A naked commoner attempted to gain entry to the court saying he was a ghost come down from heaven with a message for the king, but he was declared mad and thrashed and thrown out.

A series of violent convulsions "caused Prince Henry's backbone, shoulders, arms and tongue to divide" and he lapsed into a coma and died. The doctors all blamed each other and inevitably there were rumours of poison. An autopsy suggested an infection and the presence of an enlarged spleen raised the possibility of Typhoid. Later observers noted the Prince's habit of swimming in the River Thames, which was little more than an open sewer, and they too suggested the possibility of Typhoid. Others thought the Prince's death was caused by an ague which was affecting much of England at that time, perhaps Influenza. But modern opinion is the Prince's symptoms were due to an acute attack of the Porphyria[34] which he inherited from his father. Prince Henry died of his first attack of Porphyria and his death allowed the succession of his younger brother Charles and may have brought about the English Civil War.

---

[34] See Medical Appendix – 2. Porphyria, page 296.

Because of his own Porphyria, James' arms were sometimes covered in wheals due to skin photosensitivity. When he had fevers and lay crying out with abdominal pains, the court went about on tiptoe. And during one attack he was only able to assent to the prayers for his recovery by raising his eyebrow.

James and Anne of Denmark drifted apart in later years and she died in 1619. James was so ill at the time it was feared he might die too, and the embalmed Queen lay in state for eight weeks to see if the king would recover. Ann had privately converted to Catholicism, and when the Archbishop of Canterbury insisted on a Protestant funeral in Westminster Abbey the court argued bitterly. The King's illness also resulted in Anne dying intestate, and her jewellery was stolen by the servants.

James grew to look older than his 58 years and towards the end of his life he lost his mental sharpness and handed many duties to his son, Charles. It is debated whether he was burned out with overwork or senile dementia, and he developed a weakness on one side which was probably due to a stroke. He also suffered shaking hand movements which raised the possibility of Parkinson's Disease.

His Porphyria symptoms of gout, fevers, abdominal pains, and vomiting continued. And his legs became atrophied and he was carried around in a litter and bathed with cold water. He was also given cold beer to drink which was the worst thing possible for Porphyria. When he died in 1625 he had moved to Theobalds in Hertfordshire to escape an outbreak of Plague[35]. At one stage he was administered a tonic prescribed by an Essex physician called Dr Remington. But the court physicians refused to endorse its safety and when his fingers went black and his hair fell out they diagnosed Arsenic poisoning[36]. On his deathbed James had a long discussion with his son Charles from which courtiers were ordered several rooms distant. He was administered Communion by the Bishop of Lincoln, and then had a convulsion which left him speechless. He died of another stroke, and an autopsy was carried out by William Watton but all it showed was damaged kidneys and kidney stones. His embalmed body lay in state for five weeks at Denmark House in the Strand and his funeral hearse was designed by Inigo Jones. And

[35] See Medical Appendix – 6. Plague, page 314.
[36] See Medical Appendix – 23. Poison, page 359.

when the eulogy in Westminster Abbey lasted two hours, many drifted away before the ceremony finished.

# Charles I

Charles I was the son of James VI of Scotland (James I England) and Anne of Denmark and he was born in Dunfermline in 1600. He became king in 1625 and was executed in London at the age of 49.

Like his father he suffered a birth injury and was baptised immediately for fear he would not survive. He was unable to speak until the age of five and then only with a stammer. As a result there was a discussion if he should have the frenulum of his tongue divided by a surgeon[37]. He was unable to walk until he was seven and he wore special iron boots to correct a shambling gait. He may have suffered from the green sickness due to the iron deficiency anaemia, and he

---

[37] See Medical Appendix – 22. Speech Impediments, page 356.

was only 5' 4" tall. As a result he was considered too delicate to travel to his father's new court in London and followed later in a litter. Having fallen for Princess Henrietta Maria of France, he was forbidden by his father to marry her. But the wedding took place as soon as James I died, and it nearly caused war with Spain. Of their nine children three died in infancy and an older daughter and son died from Tuberculosis and Smallpox.

Their daughter Mary married William, Prince of Orange, and gave birth to the future William III. And their second daughter, Henrietta Anne (Minette), became the mistress of King Louis XIV. She was frequently ill with abdominal pain and died of what now seems certain to have been Porphyria[38]. In contrast, her brothers, Charles and James, were obligate carriers of the disease but were asymptomatic.

Charles I was a sophisticated man who flooded his court with art and patronised Rubens, van Dyke, Ben Johnson, and Inigo Jones. But he was lazy and humourless and was unable to shore up his absolute authority with any trust. As a result he was a political disaster. When the Commons refused to grant him taxes for the war with Spain, he tried to dissolve Parliament which responded with a Petition of Rights. Even when his friend Buckingham was assassinated in 1628, Charles failed to heed the warning and clung firmly to the Divine Right of Kings. Rubens' ceiling in the Banqueting Hall depicts a world of chaos in which only a divinely appointed monarch brought law and order, and this was the last thing he saw as he stepped out to the scaffold to be executed.

He alienated Puritans and Bishops, and imprisoned Dissenters and cut off their ears. Scotland was full of fervent Presbyterians and Charles had been an absent king for years when in 1637 he tried to impose a new Prayer Book. Calvinists threw footstools and thousands signed the National Covenant. In 1640 Parliament declined more taxes and he sent for his Catholic army in Ireland to intimidate them with disastrous consequences. Men attacked their own officers and Speaker Pymm demanded yet more parliamentary powers. The Scots remained in control in Northumberland and Durham, and when Stafford was scapegoated Charles signed his friend's execution warrant and Catholics were appalled. In Ireland the

---

[38] See Medical Appendix – 2. Porphyria, page 296.

Catholics feared the Protestants and began pre-emptive mass slaughters, and Protestants in England were aghast and thought it would be their turn next.

Parliament controlled 2/3 of the nation's population and 3/4 of its wealth. But Charles ruled for 11 years without its support and when he failed to arrest Speaker Pymm, he looked like a blundering despot. Men were forced to choose sides and the dispute parted every corner of the kingdom and every family. Civil War followed and whilst Charles was a good field commander he was no military strategist and he was incapable of compromise. At Edgehill, he and his brother James and their cousin Rupert raised the Royal Standard and the first battle of the English Civil War left 3,000 men dead on the battlefield. Terrible but indecisive battles wearied both sides until Oliver Cromwell and the New Model Army destroyed the Royal Army at Naseby. There were some in Parliament prepared to forgive and forget, but Charles refused to share power and continued plotting. When more fighting broke out in 1648, Parliamentarians called him a man of blood, and the vengefulness of the New Model Army at the Battle of Preston was extreme. Charles was eventually arrested at Newark and Cromwell realised that a kingless state was the only solution.

In captivity Charles was sworn at and spat upon, and his guards blew tobacco smoke in his face. His show trial was chaired by John Bradshaw a Cheshire lawyer, and it found him guilty of high treason by a majority of 68 to 67. After the sentence of death was passed he declined his right to speak. It was said the Short Parliament had taken away his money and the Long Parliament took away his life. He was taken in a closed sedan chair to St James Palace where he could hear to his scaffold being constructed outside the Banqueting House. Only his little son Henry and 13-year-old daughter Elizabeth were allowed to see him, and he told her she was not to grieve, and that his love for her mother was the same until the last. He said he intended to make a glorious death and the family should forgive their enemies but never trust them. Then taking Henry on his knee, he told him he was not to allow Parliament to make him king because that way they would all lose their heads. To which the little boy replied he would rather be torn to pieces. Both children then cried and Elizabeth promised to write down what he had told them so they would not forget.

His children, servants, and his dogs were then taken from him and on 30th January after what was apparently a good night's sleep, he was awakened two hours before dawn. His companion Thomas Herbert, distributed presents for the servants, and he said his last prayers with Bishop Juxon. He famously selected two warm shirts to protect him from the bitter January cold, so he would not shake and give a false impression he was fearful.

*The Banqueting House*

At 10 o'clock they knocked on his door and in the company of his gaoler Colonel Thomlinson, and Bishop Juxton, they set out across the park with the king walking fast, between two rows of soldiers and talking cheerfully. The scaffold outside the Banqueting House in Whitehall was draped in black and the crowds were quiet and murmured prayers. Charles then took Communion and bade "the rogues come for him as he most heartily forgave them all". At this stage there was a terrible delay of four hours for a legally signed death warrant to appear, and during this long wait Charles was reluctant to eat to ward off any faintness, as he had just received Communion. At this stage Herbert's nerve failed him and he fled with the promise that he would return later.

At 2 o'clock the warrant arrived and hiding their true identities with false wigs and beards, the executioners, Richard Brandon and Ralph Jones, joined the king on the scaffold. Staples had been driven into the scaffold to fasten the king if he resisted but they had misjudged their man. He made a short speech which was not heard by many of those assembled but was recorded in shorthand by secretaries standing by. The gist was he would never agree to be a Parliamentary monarch, and a subject and a sovereign are "clean different things". He then tucked his long hair under his white shirt collar and declared his willingness to go from a corruptible to an incorruptible crown. The block was only ten inches high so as to expose his neck and he was forced to lie down on the scaffold. He then told the axeman to wait for his order, said a short prayer, held out his arms and called, "Strike." The axe thudded, the severed head was held aloft and the assembled thousands moaned loudly.

The reunited body was taken in a coffin up the back stairs of St James's Palace and was visited that night by a solitary hooded figure who the guards recognised was Cromwell. The King's remains were placed on limited display but without any trappings of state. Permission for burial in Westminster Abbey was refused lest it became a shrine for Royalist supporters, and Charles was buried in a private ceremony at Windsor where the spot selected turned out to be the vault of Henry VIII and Jane Seymour. And when Bishop Juxon was refused permission to read the burial service from the Book of Common Prayer, he wept over the coffin. Charles's wife and sons in Paris and his daughters in Holland plunged their courts into mourning, but in England no grieving was permitted.

After the execution a story circulated that refusing to bow his head to any subject, he was executed face upwards, and the anxious axeman botched the first stroke and cut off his chin. This was said to have been picked up by a pikeman and handed down through the man's family until it was returned in 1939 to King George VI. In addition, Charles's coffin was opened in 1813 and a vertebra was removed for examination and was returned to the Prince of Wales in 1888.

# Oliver Cromwell

Oliver Cromwell was the son of Robert Cromwell and Elizabeth Steward and he was born in Huntingdon High Street in 1599. He was Lord Protector of England from 1653 to 1658 and he died aged 59 in Whitehall from convulsions caused by Laudanum which he took for renal colic.

His father was descended from Thomas Cromwell Chief Minister to Henry VIII and his mother Elizabeth Steward was a remote relative of the Scottish royal house of Stuart. At the time of Oliver's birth however, they were minor country landowners in Ely and Oliver was one of ten children.

*The Cromwell home in Ely*

He attended the local grammar school, and spent a year at Sidney Sussex College Cambridge before finally studying law at Lincolns Inn. He was 5 feet 10 inches tall, powerfully built, with long hair, a massive leonine head, and a large wart on his chin. He was restlessly energetic with what was almost certainly Bipolar Disorder[39] and he was easily moved to tears and had a fearful temper. Inwardly, however, he was unpretentious and he famously told his portraitist to paint him warts and all.

In 1620 he married Elizabeth Bouchier, the daughter of Sir James Bouchier, an Essex landowner and London leather merchant. Their older sons, Robert and Oliver, died from Smallpox as teenagers and it was Oliver's third and least able son, Richard, who eventually succeeded him.

---

[39] See Medical Appendix – 21. Mental Illness, page 350.

*Elizabeth Bouchier*

He believed individuals should establish their own contact with God and the purpose of the clergy was to inspire this through preaching. His upbringing nurtured a profound distaste of Popery but he also disliked extreme Puritanism, smoked tobacco, drank wine, hunted, hawked, played bowls, and was fond of music. In later life he caused a scandal when he allowed mixed dancing at his daughter's wedding.

In 1628 he became a Member of Parliament and made fiery speeches against the Bishop of Ely. Some said his oratory was clumsy but he made up for this with passion. He considered emigrating to the New World but in 1636 he inherited some land and remained in England.

His family fell out with Charles I when anti-Royalist pamphleteers were sentenced to have their ears cut off in marketplaces and men from inland towns were imprisoned for refusing to pay the Ship tax. Scottish Covenanters refused to accept a new liturgy for the Church of Scotland and there were massacres of Protestants in Ireland.

When the king's request for Parliamentary funds were refused, Charles marched his guards into the Commons to arrest Speaker Pymm. But this failed and it was an unknown Cromwell who formed a troop and rode into Cambridge with flags flying and drums beating, to prevent the colleges melting down their silver plate for the Royal cause. In 1642 the king raised his standard at Edgehill and 3,000 men were killed in the first battle of the English Civil War.

Cromwell was impressed by the tactics of Prince Rupert but vowed the Royalists would not prevail. Promoted to Colonel at the Battle of Winceby, he narrowly escaped death and leading the charge his horse was killed beneath him. His military discipline impressed Parliament, and in 1643 they asked him to form a model army. This distinguished itself at the Battle of Marston Moor in 1644, when the largest ever forces on English soil confronted each other. Cromwell's command saved the day against Prince Rupert of the Rhine, but the carnage was fearful and included Boy, Prince Rupert's spaniel.

His superior, Sir Thomas Fairfax, promoted him second in overall command but as a Lieutenant General, Cromwell fell out with his commander the Earl of Manchester. When the armies met again in 1645 at Naseby, Cromwell's cavalry fought impressively and from that day the Royalist army ceased to be an organised military force. And Charles's treasure chest of jewels, his military intelligence, and great quantities of artillery fell into Parliament's hands.

In pursuit of the king at Bristol, a bullet grazed Cromwell's head and this escape convinced him he had a divine purpose in life. Further west, the war deteriorated and the custom grew to give no quarter to the enemy. In 1646 with the king out of the country, Cromwell moved his family from Ely to London. But with no pomp to entertain the masses and the Christmas festivities cancelled, unrest grew and Cromwell descended into a black depression. He had previously sought treatment for this from a London doctor called Theodore de Mayerne but there were also episodes of hyperactivity which were the other aspect of his Bipolar Disorder.

In 1647 on campaign in Ireland he fell ill with boils on his head and Mayerne told him he had a kidney stone[40]. He was also depressed and told a friend he would rather be dead. But he slowly recovered and it was during the next period of Parliamentary intrigue that he rose to power as a politician. Parliament wished to disband the army but the officers threatened rebellion if they did not receive their pay arrears. Cromwell negotiated with great skill and developed a tendency to break into tears if he wanted to gain sympathy.

---

[40] See Medical Appendix – 17. Urinary Tract Stones, page 340.

With Levellers baying for royal blood Cromwell spoke initially in support of the king and tried to persuade Charles to become a constitutional monarch. But the king was obstinate and his collusion with the Scots turned Cromwell against him. In response the Royalists depicted Cromwell in cartoons and alleged he was a copper-nosed drunk from a family of brewers.

He suppressed uprisings in Wales, and when the Scots invaded Berwick-on-Tweed, he marched north and defeated them at Preston. There were 2,000 killed and another 2,000 taken prisoner, and when the English marched into Scotland the Scots capitulated and stood down their army. Charles was handed over to Parliament for a bribe of £100,000, and interned on the Isle of Wight he tried to escape to France but was betrayed and transferred to London.

Spying, bribery, and coercion were used to construct a case against the king, and when a special court of the House of Commons convicted him, the witnesses had all been coached. Charles' only argument was that the trial was illegal, and the 135 judges supported his death sentence by a majority of one. Louis XIV's pleas for clemency were ignored, an Act of Parliament forbad him naming a successor, and on 30th January 1649, he strode out of the Banqueting House to execution.

A new Great Seal of England was commissioned, the Royal arms were taken down from public buildings, a new coinage was struck, and the Royal collections of art and jewels were sold to private collections. High ranking Royalists were executed, the House of Lords was abolished, and all the offices of government were replaced by a Council of State consisting of 41 nominated members.

Pockets of Royalist rebellion persisted in the West, but these were put down and the leaders dragged from churches and shot without trial. When the Army then sailed for Dublin with Cromwell at the head of 100 ships, the weather was bad and he was seasick. His health deteriorated again and in great pain from kidney stones he lost control of his troops. At the siege of Drogheda the city walls were breached by cannon and a massacre of the inhabitants followed. Four thousand were slaughtered in the streets and women and children were burned alive in churches. At Wexford Cromwell had more attacks of fever and his dark depression returned.

His fever could have been due to Benign Tertian Malaria[41] but he refused treatment with the Quinine in Peruvian Bark because of its association with the Jesuits. His fevers were just as likely caused by kidney stones and whatever the explanation Parliament was alarmed and ordered him home. By April he was fit again and at the head of an army in Scotland where Charles Stuart had landed from France. Here Cromwell outmanoeuvred him, and in a military masterpiece of the Civil War, killed 3,000 Royalists and took 10,000 prisoners. The weather was appalling and he once more fell ill. He would only be nursed by his French valet, Jean Duret, who himself sickened and died. And at one point Cromwell was in so much pain he threatened to shoot two officers who tried to insist on seeing him. Only kidney stones could explain pain of this severity and in Glasgow he relapsed, and this time two London physicians were dispatched to attend him.

He was only 52 and after he returned from Scotland he was never fit again. His latest bout of renal colic allowed Charles Stuart to march over the Scottish border into Carlisle and be crowned King of England. Charles' army then marched south to Worcester but was surrounded by 28,000 of Cromwell's forces and the bridges over the River Severn were blown up. As the siege progressed the streets were piled with dead bodies, and the king only escaped after a series of adventures and found his way to Paris where his ragged appearance shocked the French court.

In 1651 Cromwell became Captain General of the Army and had the first and last word in everything. He used captured prisoners of war to drain his family properties on the Fens and on an enormous personal salary he lived the life of a Puritan prince. But others started to fear his power and in Ireland his best friend and son in law Henry Ireton died of the Plague and set in train a series of family quarrels. Parliament became more Puritanical, and its popularity plummeted when it enacted the execution of adulterers, banned the use of facial make up and abolished Christmas. And when the 1652 Dutch trade war broke out and the navy needed new frigates the nation's finances came under intolerable strain.

At Carisbrooke Castle on the Isle of Wight the king's daughter Elizabeth died of Tuberculosis and the rumour was circulated that Cromwell had ordered her to be poisoned. In 1653 the Rump

---

[41] See Medical Appendix – 9. Malaria, page 322.

Parliament tried to prolong its own life and Cromwell marched musketeers into the chamber and evicted the Speaker. His fury at what he called an assembly of rogues was spectacular, and whilst the Speaker escaped with his life, the House was replaced by a chamber of 145 nominated members of a Council of State.

London traders complained of a fall in business and talk spread of what a return of the king might bring. In the midst of the intrigue, Cromwell was heard to compare himself to Moses, but others were sceptical and some likened him to Machiavelli. As Lord Protector he now resided in Hampton Court and was addressed as Your Highness and signed his signature Oliver P.

He liked music and promoted the first opera to be performed on the English stage. He loved dancing and watched sport, but he disapproved of gambling and banned pagan festivals like May Day. He continued to rebuild London and set in train far-reaching reforms of the law. But he was reducing the aristocracy to the status of beggars and Royalist intrigue was spreading. In a coaching accident in Hyde Park in 1653 he was dragged by the horses and a companion's pistol was accidentally discharged and the bullet narrowly missed him. He was still lame from this when his mother died and he fell into another black depression.

In 1654 expeditions were sent to capture Hispaniola and Jamaica from the Spanish, and though thousands of troops died from tropical fevers, the islands were eventually colonised by English Protestants. Cromwell's friends in England were given large swathes of the country and accusations of corruption became widespread. He had long admired Dutch Jews for their merchandising and banking skills and in 1655 a contingent was allowed to set up in London.

That year he was ill again with kidney stones, and in agony he sent for a renowned French surgeon to perform a lithotomy operation to remove them. This involved cutting through the perineum into the bladder, and in the era before anaesthetics few men would agree to this. When the surgeon demanded a huge fee in advance this led Cromwell to refuse the operation. Instead, Sir James Moleyns, the Surgeon for the Stone at St Thomas's Hospital, attended him, and Cromwell recovered without surgery. Moleyns was a Royalist sympathiser and declined to submit a fee, but Cromwell sent him £1,000 and insisted he accept it "in the name of King Charles".

By 1656 his health was disintegrating under the strain and he suffered from gout and more boils. For his kidney stones he tried endless concoctions and he was even reduced to riding in a bumpy coach in extraordinary attempts to dislodge the stones. And in the end he became addicted to Laudanum. The following spring he had another coach accident on the Westminster ferry when all six horses were drowned. There were plots to assassinate him but despite a near successful attempt at Shepherds Bush he still took walks in public places without a guard. It was said these murder attempts would cease if he were king because then they would constitute treason and few men would risk the penalty for that. But when Parliament voted by 123 to 62 votes to offer him the throne he hesitated and accepted instead the title of Lord Protector.

Educational reform became his chief objective and there followed the introduction of grammar schools, literary workhouses, and new universities. But the expense of the Army and Navy remained a blind spot and he was never able to set the nation's finances on a sound footing. At Hampton Court that winter his handwriting became shaky, and there was much talk about his failing health. His boils recurred and at times he fainted and looked half dead from taking too much Laudanum. In August he was stricken with abdominal pains and convulsions. Some said this was a recurrence of his Malaria but English Malaria does not cause fits and the convulsions were more likely from taking overdoses of Laudanum.

He sensed he was beyond recovery and in September he named his son Richard as successor. He could as easily have named Fleetwood or Lambert but this final act proved to be a great error. He completed his will and on 3rd September on the anniversary of the Battle of Worcester he cried out in pain and died. The effort of ruling the country had taken a huge toll on his health and he was only 59 years old.

The autopsy was conducted by a Dr Bate who reported that the spleen was enlarged and septic due to Malaria or infected kidney stones. But apart from some congestion of the lungs and the brain, there were no other abnormal findings. The body was embalmed for lying in state, but the procedure was bungled and the corpse had to be buried quickly. This was undertaken at a private funeral in the Henry VII Chapel in Westminster Abbey, and the lying in state at

Somerset House continued with a life size waxen effigy made from a death mask.

At the grand military funeral, the streets of London were cleared of traffic and lined by the New Model Army, their buttons blacked and their ensigns draped with cypress. The procession took seven hours to pass and was brought up at the rear by Cromwell's favourite musicians. When they arrived at the Abbey, however, darkness was falling and the all ticket congregation was told it was too late for prayers or eulogies. Instead the hearse was installed in the Chapel where it remained for the public to pay to view it. Both this spectacle and the £100,000 cost of the funeral appalled the Quakers.

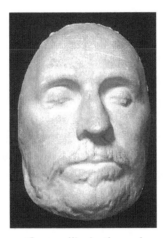

*Cromwell's death mask*

When the monarchy was restored Charles II declared an amnesty for Commonwealth officials, but the Restoration Parliament reversed this and ordered the waxen effigy of Cromwell to be hanged from a window in Whitehall and the hearse removed from Westminster Abbey. His body was exhumed, and after resting overnight in the Red Lion Inn in Holburn, it was dragged on a hurdle to Tyburn where it was symbolically hanged. His head was then struck off with eight blows of an axe, and the ears and fingers severed. The bodies of the Lord Protector and two other regicides were then thrown into a common pit at Tyburn, probably on the corner of what is now Connaught Street. The head was stuck on a pole outside Westminster

Hall where it remained for 18 years until it was blown down in a storm during the reign of James II. A passing soldier recovered the skull and it eventually found its way to Cromwell's daughter who later sold it to Sidney Sussex College where it was buried in the 1960s at a secret location within the Chapel.

*Sidney Sussex College and Chiswick Church*

In later years legends circulated about the corpse. One was that it was substituted in the Red Lion Inn and the real body was buried on the battlefield at Naseby, which was Cromwell's wish. Another was that it was retrieved from the pit at Tyburn and buried by his daughter Mary in her own eventual grave in the churchyard of St Nicholas in Chiswick. And when her vault was examined in 1882 it was found to contain an extra unmarked coffin.

# *Richard Cromwell*

Richard Cromwell was the son of Oliver Cromwell and Elizabeth Bouchier and was born in 1626. He became Lord Protector in 1658 and he ruled for just 264 days. He abdicated and lived in exile for many years and died at the age of 86.

He was his father's third son but an older brother, Robert, died at school and a younger brother, Oliver, died in the Army from Smallpox. His remaining brother, Henry, served with their father in Ireland and became Chancellor of Trinity College Dublin.

Richard was educated at Felsted Grammar School and Lincoln's Inn, but nothing is known of his youth. There were unsubstantiated Royalist allegations that he was bisexual, and in 1649 he married Dorothy Major with whom he had six children.

Whilst his father struggled with the problems of ruling Britain after the civil war, Richard lived the life of a country squire and annoyed his father with his easy-going ways and recurrent debts. He was given a regiment to command in the Army and was created Chancellor of Oxford University. He also became a Justice of the Peace for Hampshire, a Member of Parliament, and a member of the Council of State. But he disliked the Army and had no enthusiasm for his other duties. And when the constitution was changed in 1657 to allow his father to name a successor, it surprised everyone when Cromwell named Richard.

Throughout history the successors of great men have borne a heavy burden and Richard was quite unequal to the tasks his father set him. The Lord Protector would have been better advised to nominate his younger son, Henry, or someone on the Council who was not a relative. As it was, Richard had none of his father's qualities and he soon disappointed or offended everyone. Most critically, he had none of his father's iron will and he was naively unprepared to spill blood in order to protect his position.

He almost immediately lost control in the disputes between the Army and Parliament and was unable to prevent them withdrawing his powers. He was forbidden to call meetings of the Council of State without Parliament's permission, and a new Committee of Safety was set up to appoint judges and foreign ambassadors. Richard then blundered into a series of errors, the most serious of which was to usurp personal command of the army over vastly more experienced and capable men. As pay arrears in the Army and Navy mounted, he was forced to sell the Palace of Whitehall and Somerset House, along with the silver plate and furniture from Hampton Court. But his own debts grew and became mixed up with the Protectorate's growing insolvency. Movements like the Sealed Knot Society increased their secret plans to restore the monarchy and in propaganda leaflets Richard was nicknamed Tumbledown and Queen Dick. In 1559 Parliament resolved to cancel his debts and grant him immunity from arrest if he agreed to abdicate. And when they finalised terms for the restoration of Charles II, the administration of the country was handed to a Council of State.

He had ruled for just eight months and in return he was granted safe passage to France. His family remained at Hursley in Hampshire and he never saw them again. His exile was destined to last 20 years during which time he lived in Paris and Geneva, and under the pseudonym of John Clarke he read books and sketched landscapes. By 1680 when he was 54, he was declared harmless and allowed to return to England. He lived as a private citizen at Cheshunt in Buckinghamshire where he was fearful of politics and haunted by the prospect of assassination. Living in seclusion, he passed into old age in the company of Rachel Pengelly, the daughter of one of his old student friends. Few local people knew who he was and those that did described him as a little, neat old gentleman with a placid countenance. Enjoying rude health into old age, he could gallop a horse when he was 80, and it was said he grew to look like his father.

He survived Charles II, James II, and William and Mary, and dying at the age of 86 during the reign of Queen Anne, he was buried in Hursley Church in Hampshire.

*Hursley Church*

# Charles II

Charles II was the second son of Charles I and Henrietta Maria of France. He was born in London in 1630 and ruled from 1660 to 1685. He married Catherine of Braganza but had no legitimate children and he died in London of a stroke at the age of 55.

*Catherine of Braganza*

He was born a big baby but so ugly his mother was ashamed of him. But he grew to be six feet two inches tall and his Portuguese looks were enormously attractive to women.

He was tutored by the Earl of Newcastle who taught him he would learn more from people than from books. By the time he was eight his father was ruling without Parliament and civil war broke out. Aged 12 at the Battle of Edgehill Charles found himself in the thick of the fighting and he and his physician Dr William Harvey were dangerously cut off by Parliamentary cavalry and nearly killed by artillery fire.

As the royal physician to Charles I, Harvey attended the king on stag hunts and had access to carcasses for anatomical studies. As a result in 1628 he published *De Motu Cordis* in which the correct circulation of the blood was described for the first time. On business for the king, Harvey travelled widely in Europe and met Galileo. But after he became physician to James II his medical practice declined and he died in obscurity.

Charles spent much of the civil war in Oxford but in 1644 he was at his father's side at the Battle of Croperdy Bridge. In 1645 they fought together in the West Country but were then parted and never saw each other again. Aged 15, serving with Prince Rupert of the Rhine, he escaped an outbreak of Bubonic Plague[42] in Bridport, and when military defeats followed he retreated from Cornwall to the Scilly Isles and then to Jersey before joining his mother in France.

Present when the Scots were crushed by the new Model Army at Preston, Charles and his brother James fled to Holland to join their sister, Mary, in the court of William of Orange. Charles then sailed to Scotland and was crowned king, but when his army moved south they were defeated at the siege of Worcester. Charles fled dressed as a woodman and with a hefty ransom on his head he famously hid in an oak tree to escape capture. But eventually he made his way to the coast and sailed from Shoreham for France again.

When Richard Cromwell succeeded his father in 1658, Royalists were quietly taking over the country, and in 1660 Charles reached favourable terms with Parliament and sailed with his brother, James, from Holland. Charles's mother and his sister, Minette, then followed from France, and his sister, Mary, from Holland.

They rode into London to scenes of jubilation and a promise of amnesty for the Protectorate. But the Restoration Parliament arrested the regicides, 12 were hanged, 19 were condemned but later spared, and the gory fate of Cromwell's exhumed body served to remind everyone that the Stuarts would re-impose the Divine Right of Kings by whatever means necessary.

But the royal family celebrations were short lived and they started to succumb to the unhealthy conditions in London. First, Charles's youngest brother Henry, Duke of Gloucester, contracted Typhoid[43] and died. Then during the Christmas celebrations, his sister, Mary, became ill with Smallpox[44] and the court panicked. Cold beer was prescribed and her rash disappeared, but having bled Prince Henry too little, they bled Mary too much, and she fainted, had fits, and died. It was Christmas Eve and she was 29. Her husband, William of Orange, had died of Smallpox at the age of 24, and now their son, the future William III, was orphaned in Holland under the care of his grandmother.

---

[42] See Medical Appendix – 6. Plague, page 314.
[43] See Medical Appendix – 12. Typhoid, page 331.
[44] See Medical Appendix – 4. Smallpox, page 307.

In 1662 Charles' sister, Elizabeth of Bohemia, visited London and died of pneumonia. And in 1667 James's only son, the Duke of Cambridge, died of Smallpox. With the London streets squalid and the River Thames an open sewer, this was an unhealthy environment and with the court in constant mourning Queen Catherine returned to France with her sister-in-law, Minette.

In 1665 the Great Plague[45] struck London and Charles and his court fled to the safety of Oxford. Londoners were quarantined behind closed doors, magistrates lost control of the streets, and the death toll was probably double the official figure of 68,000. In 1666, the Plague was followed by an epidemic of Typhus, and then by the Great Fire. This began in Thomas Farriner's bakery in Pudding Lane and was driven by an easterly wind. Dorset House and St Paul's Cathedral were burned down and a square mile of the city was destroyed. It continued for three days as the king's guards fought the blaze, and Royal Navy victuallers fed the survivors.

Charles was personally charming and politically adept, and he trod a fine line between being a public Protestant and a private Catholic. He reformed his Court, the Army, and the Church, and he founded the Royal Society, the Society of Adventurers, and the Royal Observatory. He amassed the finest private art collection including works by Rembrandt, Titian, and Van Dyke, and he rebuffed two Parliamentary Exclusion Bills and the Popish Plots of Titus Oates, to ensure his more openly Catholic brother succeeded him.

But his spending was always out of control and he borrowed heavily from the Jews who Cromwell had allowed into England. The Navy was owed £1 million and after its defeat in the Thames estuary by the Dutch, Charles scapegoated Clarendon the Chancellor who he sacked. By 1670, Charles owed the Prince of Orange so much money he spent most of his time in London trying to reclaim it. Charles also borrowed huge sums from Louis XIV and much of his foreign policy was based on balancing these foreign debts. Even when he had no money he continued spending, and his extravaganzas included 60-foot fountains in Windsor Park which pumped a mixture of water and red wine. And he endlessly expanded his household with the appointment of Royal stablers, gardeners, falconers, cormorant keepers, and many more.

---

45 See Medical Appendix – 6. Plague, page 314.

He played tennis at 6am every morning, swam in the River Thames, enjoyed long walks, and hunted and hawked. He built a Royal Yacht Squadron and loved sailing off the Isle of Wight. And with his brother James he enjoyed horse racing at Newmarket. He enjoyed constructing public gardens, patronised the London theatre, and loved Restoration Comedy. He sometimes stayed late in Parliament to listen to debates and he loved masked balls and the music of Henry Purcell. People loved his grand style but he was also famous for his romantic life. His first experience was aged 15 with a local adventuress called Mrs Wyndham when he was fighting with Prince Rupert in the West Country. In exile during the rule of Cromwell, he lived in various European courts where he had love affairs and fathered illegitimate children. These included Charlotte FitzRoy born to Elizabeth Pettigrew, Charles FitzCharles to Catherine Pegge, and the Duke of Monmouth, born to Lucy Walters. Lucy later procured abortions for two more illegitimate pregnancies and died of venereal disease[46].

Once crowned, the pressure grew for him to marry, and in 1662 he chose Catherine of Braganza. Her dowry was £360,000 plus the Portuguese colonies of Tangiers and Bombay and full trading rights in India. She spoke only enough English to ask for a cup of tea and Charles mischievously taught her swear words. They had a private Catholic marriage followed by a public Protestant ceremony. But on her wedding night Catherine discovered Charles' mistress Barbara Palmer was still at court, and she told him she was too unwell to consummate the marriage. What followed became known as the Bedchamber Crisis, with Catherine screaming tears of rage and collapsing hysterically on the floor.

Within a year she became seriously ill with signs of peritonitis. This could have been due to acute appendicitis or an ectopic pregnancy but a more likely diagnosis was gonorrhoeal salpingitis. Charles's promiscuity involved women from all levels of society including bar maids, actresses, and common prostitutes, and venereal disease was common at court and even caused the death of one of his mistresses.

Queen Catherine miscarried her first pregnancy and was never pregnant again. As a result the king and queen drifted apart and when

---

[46] See Medical Appendix – 10. Syphilis, page 325.

the need for a Protestant heir became serious, his remarriage was considered. An infertile Queen was grounds for divorce, but when Lord Roos applied to Parliament to divorce his barren wife, he was refused and Charles took note and lost interest in pursuing a similar course. Next it was suggested Charles should claim he had married Lucy Walters who was now dead. His marriage to Catherine would therefore have been illegal and he could declare legitimate Lucy's son, James Duke of Monmouth. The Baton Sinister was the symbol of illegitimacy on Monmouth's coat of arms, but when Charles removed it Queen Catherine was beside herself with fury and the idea was dropped.

Another mistress, Barbara Palmer went on to have six children by Charles, and this growing brood were a constant reminder to Catherine that the infertility was hers and not the king's.

He was highly attractive to women, and regarding his mistresses as a recreation he once admitted to 39 extramarital affairs, the same number, he said, as the Articles of the Church of England. In an age when Lord Egremont fathered 43 illegitimate children, endless actresses and barmaids were escorted up the back stairs to Charles' palace by the Keeper of the Privy Closet and were rewarded so long as they remained discreet. Those who mothered his illegitimate children received wealth and titles, and Charles' favourites included Barbara Palmer, Nell Gwynn, Hortense Mancini, Lucy Walters, Elizabeth Killegrew, Catherine Pegge, Barbara Villiers, Moll Davies, and in his declining years, Louise de Keroualle. At least 16 illegitimate children were born to his mistresses and Charles remained a loyal father to them all. Six were given Dukedoms and all except Monmouth turned out to be agreeable.

In 1670 his 26-year-old sister Henrietta Anne (Minette) died. As a mistress of Louis XIV, she had played a crucial role in securing French money for Charles, and he collapsed on hearing the news of her death. Henrietta began complaining of pains in her side in 1667. By 1670, she had severe digestive problems and at Saint Cloud after drinking cold chicory water she felt a pain and cried out, "I must be poisoned." She begged for an antidote and for someone to examine the chicory water but to no avail. The family arrived at Saint Cloud and Bishop Bossuet administered Extreme Unction. She died on 30 June 1670, and 19 physicians and 100 onlookers observed the autopsy. The official report stated "death from cholera morbus caused by heated bile" But many were mystified and modern opinion is that she died of Porphyria[47].

As he grew older, Charles took less exercise, slept after meals, became grey haired and went bald. He suffered bouts of fever and was bled by his physicians. Further bouts were cured with Jesuit's Powder and whilst thought to be Malaria they could have been due to the Porphyria from which his sister died.

Charles had been famous for his robust health but now his mortality was recognised and a Protestant succession became the focus.

In 1683, the Rye House plotters conspired to kill Charles and James on their way to the Newmarket races, and though Monmouth was among the ringleaders he was reprieved. In contrast, Essex committed suicide and Sidney was executed.

Charles's death in 1685 was a notable event and his last days were recorded by John Evelyn. He spent the evening at Louise de Kerroualle's apartments, where courtiers at the gaming table were losing 20,000 gold coins at a single sitting. A French boy sang love songs and Charles ate goose eggs and retired early to bed. With him tossing and turning all night, the spaniels padding in and out of his room and the clocks chiming in the corridors, Thomas Bruce the Gentleman in Waiting, and Harry Killegrew the Groom of the Bedchamber, had little sleep.

The king woke feeling unwell and looked pale when his sore leg was dressed by the physician. He then went to his closet to take King's Drops, which were a quack potion of bone extract prescribed by Dr Jonathon Goddard. But he lingered longer than usual and when the staff went to find him, he could not speak properly. Then, seated in the window whilst being shaved he had a violent convulsion, let out a cry and fell unconscious to the floor. Dr Edmund King immediately bled him, but this normally required the consent of the Chief Minister and would have had serious consequences had the king died at that point. But fortunately for the doctor Charles felt better and his speech returned.

[47] See Medical Appendix – 2. Porphyria, page 296.

The Privy Council was summoned and when his brother, James, was informed, he attended the palace so fast he lost a shoe. Sir Edmund King then bled the king again and shaved his head and applied Cantharides as a blistering agent. With his eyeballs turned to the ceiling, he was a frightening sight, and when they crowded into the bedchamber, his mistresses swooned and Queen Catherine became hysterical. The Duchess of Portsmouth removed two gold rings from his fingers and despite the Duke of York reprimanding her, she never returned them. The Whitehall guards were reinforced, and all the country's ports were closed to block communications with Monmouth and the Prince of Orange.

Over the next five days 58 different potions were administered to the king. Most were useless and some were harmful, and Macaulay later described him as being tortured like an Indian at the stake. Hellebore root was stuffed up his nose, burgundy pitch was applied to his feet, plasters were placed on his head, rock salt and buckthorn enemas up his rectum, and meat infusions down his throat, along with Peony water, Cowslip distillations, antispasmodic juleps, and extracts of goat bezoars and human skulls. Red hot irons were applied to his feet, and he was purged, bled, cupped, cauterised, and blistered. When he had more convulsions, his mouth was forced apart with irons to force feed him with broths and liquid possets. Then a naval surgeon botched a bloodletting from the jugular neck vein and fainted in a pool of the king's blood. Charles suffered with surprising good humour and apologised to the court for taking so long to die. He made a brief recovery but his fever returned and at times as many as 75 lords, counsellors, surgeons, servants and bishops, were crowded into his bedchamber.

After two days, the last medicine to be tried was Raleigh's Cordial which was a mixture of every exotic potion known to man. When this failed, the 14 doctors were dismissed and Queen Catherine was brought in to see him for the last time and fainted. All his natural children except Monmouth came to bid their farewells and then the bishops moved in. At this stage his close family revealed he had always been a secret Catholic, and when James asked him in a whisper if he wanted a priest, Charles answered, "Yes, with all my heart."

But Catherine's priests spoke only Portuguese and were known to the court which was hostile towards them. Eventually they traced

Father John Huddlestone who had helped Charles escape from the siege of Worcester. They disguised him in a wig and cassock to get him in to see the king, and after James cleared the bedroom Charles embraced his old friend and told him he wished to die in the Catholic faith. He confessed his sins, received absolution and was anointed, but when he received the host it stuck in his throat and he had to be helped to prevent him choking. Huddlestone left him grasping a crucifix, and Charles handed his keys to James and wished him a long and prosperous reign.

When he died next day he was 55, and amid an outpouring of national grief Queen Catherine took to her mourning bed. His convulsions have been widely debated and in 1861 Sir Norman Chevers suggested the king's final illness was due to Malaria. But the autopsy was attended by 20 observers including Dr Richard Lower, and though the original report was lost in the Whitehall fire of 1697 a copy was later published in the British Medical Journal. This suggested that Charles had Bright's Disease of the kidneys, and his fits were due to renal failure, hypertension, and a cerebral haemorrhage.

But the new King James was convinced that accidental Mercury poisoning[48] was the cause of the fits, as Charles had been preoccupied with refining Mercury for medicinal purposes, and he and his chemical physician operated a basement laboratory in Whitehall where they distilled Mercury from Cinnabar without any safety precautions. The alchemists Blaise Pascal and Michael Faraday had died this way and the novelist Barbara Cartland suggested in 1959 that Charles had suffered from an acute Mercury encephalopathy called Erethrism and which caused Mad Hatters Disease. In 1967, however, his hair was analysed by nuclear mission spectroscopy and showed high levels of Lead but no Mercury.

After the embalming, he lay in state for eight days in a coffin designed by Christopher Wren and he was buried at night in the Henry VII Chapel in Westminster Abbey. No public concessions were made to his Catholicism and the Archbishop read the Anglican burial service. His grave is marked by a simple stone inscription in the floor of Westminster Abbey and was inspected in 1867.

---

[48] See Medical Appendix – 23. Poison, page 359.

# *James II*

James II was the third son of James I and Anne of Denmark. He was born in 1633 and became king when he was 52 years old. He abdicated three years later and died of a stroke in France at the age of 68.

He was three years younger than Charles II and was raised at Hampton Court to escape the outbreaks of Plague in London. And as a gesture to both religious persuasions he had a Catholic wet nurse and a Protestant governess. He grew up to be good looking, with a high forehead and fair hair, but he had a stammer which became more pronounced in old age, and a stubborn character which made him less suited to rule than his brother.

With his father and brother at the Battle of Edgehill he was only nine and in the first of many adventures he hid behind a hedge to avoid capture by Parliamentary troops. After this his father and brother were always away from home without him, and when his sister Mary married the Prince of Orange and left for Holland, James was alone at court in Oxford. When his father was arrested the rest of the family fled abroad, and James was taken into the care of Sir George Radcliffe, and met Cromwell who knelt and kissed his hand. In London he briefly met his captured father who gave him whispered advice about coded ciphers for future correspondence. James eventually escaped house arrest in St James's Palace during a game of hide and seek, when he slipped out of London dressed as a girl and made his way by ship to Flushing. In Holland he was no longer close to his brother Charles or his cousin Rupert, and in 1649 he joined his mother and sister in Paris. But the French court was ravaged by Smallpox and with the women overprotective towards him, he ran away and became a soldier.

Joining the French army of Louis XIV, his reputation grew and he went on to become its youngest general. On several occasions he narrowly escaped death and these experiences hardened him to the suffering of others and he developed a cruel streak. When Cromwell died in 1659 James joined Charles in Brussels, and there he met Ann Hyde. When the Commonwealth collapsed in 1660, he was declared Lord Admiral of England and sailed with Charles to Dover. When he entered London with the new King the streets were strewn with flowers, church bells pealed, and the fountains ran with wine. But he made few friends and his lack of astuteness served to isolate him.

He did not relate easily to women and his brother said he chose ugly lovers out of a Catholic sense of guilt. Ann Hyde was a maid of honour in the French court of his sister Minette. She followed him to London and became pregnant, and when she went to a Dr Rumph for "a strong physic to carry all away", the abortion failed and she gave birth to a son. Everyone including Ann's father, Sir Edward Hyde, was against the marriage, but Ann was a formidable woman and James was very fond of her. So he ignored advice, dismissed his other mistress, Lady Southesk, and married Ann in secret.

The government and the church were furious and wanted to annul the marriage, but James stood fast and ever the pragmatic monarch Charles intervened and declared the business was now done and everyone must live with it. They had eight children of whom six died and when Ann Hyde lost her good looks, James became a philanderer and was rumoured to have contracted venereal disease. He had nine illegitimate children and one of his mistresses, Margaret Denham, was poisoned by her jealous husband. Despite these scandals Ann remained the major influence over him and eventually she was recognised as his legal wife. When Mary the Princess Royal died of Smallpox[49], Ann became the first lady in the land and she died of breast cancer in 1671. She had converted to Catholicism and her body was interred in the vault of Mary Queen of Scots in Westminster Abbey.

*Ann Hyde*

Commercial rivalry drove England and Holland to war again, and James set about rectifying the Navy's lack of men and resources. Samuel Pepys recorded how he stamped out corruption, introduced pressgangs, and was in command of the fleet in 1665 at the English victory at the Battle of Lowestoft. His personal courage was again

---

[49] See Medical Appendix – 4. Smallpox, page 307.

evident when three of his friends were shot dead beside him and he was covered in blood. But the king had no legitimate children and as heir to the throne James was never allowed to risk his life again. When the king started to pursue a divorce from Queen Catherine, this threatened James's position and the brothers' relationship became strained. Both had been tempted into Catholicism by one of Charles's illegitimate sons, Father Pierre la Cloche, and James liked Catholicism and had fought alongside Catholics on the continent. He also depended on the support of the Catholic King Louis of France and had access to the French treasury via his sister Minette who was Louis' mistress.

In 1665 the Great Plague[50] hit London and with 7,000 dying in just the first month, James took to sterilising his correspondence with vinegar. There was no treatment for the infection and the only prevention was quarantine. Entire families were left to their fate in padlocked houses, whole areas of cities were turned into no go areas, and traders were paid for supplies with coins sterilised in vinegar.

The Plague struck down rich and poor alike, and the court joined in the panic and fled to safe havens in the country. When the Great Plague of 1665 was followed by the Great Fire in 1666, James was put in charge of the capital. He posted sentries to prevent looting, demolished damaged houses, and used explosives to clear buildings from the path of the fire. The official death toll was just eight but the unofficial figure was 2,000. Hooke and Wren were put in charge of rebuilding a stone city and much of the grandeur of modern London is due to them.

In 1667 James survived an attack of Smallpox[51] but his face was badly pock marked. Within three months of Ann Hyde dying in 1671, he married the 15-year-old Catholic Princess Mary Beatrice d'Este of Modena.

---

[50] See Medical Appendix – 6. Plague, page 314.
[51] See Medical Appendix – 4. Smallpox, page 307.

*Mary of Modena*

The teenager was shocked by his pock marked face, and was horrified to be confronted openly at court by his mistresses. But she grew fond of her stepdaughters, Mary and Ann, and in 1675 a first child, Catherine, was born but soon died. Next year another daughter, Isabel, was born, but she was always ill and died at the age of four. Altogether, nine of Mary's infants died so that from James's two marriages, 11 of his 15 children died in infancy and their little coffins filled the vault of Mary Queen of Scots in Westminster Abbey.

Mary d'Este visited the spa waters at Bath which were reputed to be good for unsuccessful mothers, and a miracle was accomplished when she became pregnant again. In 1688 she produced a healthy son and there were 67 Catholics and Protestants in the labour room to witness the birth of this important little Catholic child. The doctor who conducted the birth was knighted on the spot and the Catholic kitchen cabinet were cock a hoop. But the Protestants countered with a masterpiece of propaganda in which they alleged the baby was stillborn and a substitute had been smuggled into the bedroom in a warming pan.

As a result the Bishop of London and six Protestant nobles who travelled to Holland to invite William of Orange to seize the throne of England, told William that not one in a thousand men believed the baby was James's child. James Francis Edward, the future Old Pretender, was a resilient little baby who on his first day on Earth survived a near fatal dose of laxatives which his doctors prescribed to relieve colic. Within days, he was nearly starved to death when he was taken from the breast and fed a diet of currants and barley water which he vomited. But the birth of a Catholic heir now guaranteed a Protestant backlash, and from then on it was said an invasion by William of Orange was only delayed by the wind.

In 1677 James's daughter Mary was married to William of Orange, and in 1683 his other daughter, Anne, was married to George of Denmark. James described Ann as "a plain dumpling" and George "a dull Prince if ever there was one". In 1678 with pressure on Catholics mounting, a Popish Plot by the daring liar, Titus Oates, forced James to resign from public office and his Catholic wife to move abroad. When this nightmare had run its course, men had been murdered, others exiled or executed and countless careers had been ruined. Had it not been for the loyalty of King Charles, James would have fallen, but the experience did not prevent him making further serious errors of judgement. He put down minor revolts with extreme savagery and executed Scottish Covenanters for their religious beliefs. Some were tortured in James's presence, and following the foundering of his warship off Yarmouth, James ordered navy ratings off the lifeboats to make room for the royal dogs. He proceeded to watch 160 men drown and the opposition saw to it that this story was spread widely.

His unpopularity grew and there was an attempt to assassinate him and the king on their way to the Newmarket races. But this was foiled and more executions followed. James was in Brussels when the king had the first of his seizures. He raced back to London with John Churchill but such was his unpopularity he was forced to disguise himself as a French officer and Churchill as a servant. With Monmouth also in London, the court was dismayed at the acrimony surrounding the dying king and ordered both James and Monmouth to leave the country. But James reneged and returned in secret, and this cost Monmouth the throne.

Essex, Halifax, and Sunderland failed to block James' succession but his coronation went on for nine hours and his succession speech set completely the wrong tone. The Queen was recovering from pneumonia and barely survived the ceremony, and the crown did not fit James's high forehead and kept threatening to topple off.

His reign started with a trade boom but he inherited huge debts from his brother. In June 1685 Monmouth landed an invasion at Lyme Regis. He was a hot-tempered young man and the darling of the West Country who denied his illegitimacy, called James a usurper and accused him of starting the Great Fire of London and poisoning the king. Monmouth felt the English would never support a Catholic king but he was wrong. The English gentry were unsure what to make of this and were not keen to support him. And when he was defeated by James at the Battle of Sedgemoor, the supporters who died for Monmouth were mostly peasants. He was discovered in the New Forest dressed as a rustic, and his cowardice hardened James's heart further. He was tried and sentenced, and at his execution on Tower Hill the executioner missed with all three blows and threw down the axe. With Monmouth writhing in agony an assistant stepped forward and finished the job with a knife. Many of the captured peasants at Sedgemoor had been summarily executed, and those who survived were brought before the Bloody Assizes of Judge Jeffries. Daughters and wives sacrificed their honour to save their menfolk, and parents paid swingeing fines to release little children whose only crime had been to sew banners and flags. Men betrayed each other out of terror, and lenient juries were ordered to change their verdicts to guilty. Three thousand hanged bodies were left to rot on gibbets along West Country highways, and many went to gaol where they died of Smallpox or were deported to sugar plantations in the Caribbean.

James was now at the height of his powers and he misused them spectacularly. With an income from France and a standing Catholic army stationed at Hounslow Heath, he sent bishops to the Tower, persecuted French Huegenots, packed his court with Jesuits, and publicly entertained the Papal Nuncio at Windsor. He issued writs of libel against Titus Oates, appointed a commission to prevent anti-Catholic preaching, and passed laws to permit Catholic Privy Councillors. In 1688 he even tried the Archbishop of Canterbury and six Anglican bishops for seditious libel and tried to pack Parliament so as to overturn the anti-Catholic Test Acts. But when he threw Parliamentarians into prison and described Parliament as a gigantic confidence trick, the merchant classes glowered and the economy collapsed.

The Immortal Seven who rode to petition William of Orange to save England for the Protestant religion were the Lords Compton, Devonshire, Danby, Lumley, Russell, Shrewsbury, and Sidney. On 19th October 1688, a fleet of Dutch, Germans, and Huegenots set sail for England, but was scattered by gales. It managed to regain port without great loss of life and on November 1st it sailed again down the English Channel and let fly its famous banner "Je maintainderai". But they miscalculated their landing in Plymouth and the army of 35,000 troops came ashore at Brixham. As it marched towards London most of the gentry joined them, and then James's supporters led by Colonel Churchill defected and an uprising in the North took place.

His daughters Mary and Ann fled from London, and with James living in isolation the morale of the court plummeted. The best he could look forward to was a civil war with huge loss of life, and on 10th December he left London and abdicated by throwing the Great Seal into the River Thames. Briefly captured he ordered his remaining troops to lay down their arms and was then allowed to sail for France where he set up court at St Germain. In contrast William entered London in triumph with his troops singing "Lillibulero".

Louis XIV offered to have James elected King of Poland but James feared his acceptance might prevent him from ever becoming King of England and he declined. But exile did not sit easy and he soon left for Ireland. He was welcomed in the Catholic south but in the north the inhabitants of Londonderry posted No Surrender, and held out against him until the blockade was lifted by English warships. When the food ran out they ate rats, and when the munitions were all gone, they fired bricks as cannonballs. James won a minor victory in Bantry Bay but when the decisive battle was fought at the River Boyne in 1690, his regiments fled the field and he returned to France.

James was served by a small court of Scottish defectors and when his daughter Mary died of Smallpox in England in 1694, he refused to put his French court into mourning. In 1696 his Jacobite rebellion at Berwick was defeated and from then on his French support waned. With advancing years his stutter became worse and he wrote a series of religious meditations which were at first vigorous and clear but later became incoherent and confused. James recognised late in life, the limitations of the power of kings, and he wrote a memorandum to his son advising him how to govern England and expressing regret for the debauchery of his youth. And he took to saying his prayers three times every day. In 1700 he fainted in chapel but recovered, and a week later he had a stroke. He tried to recuperate in the spa waters of Bourbon but in 1701 he was forced to take to his bed again. King Louis visited him and told him he would always recognise his son as the heir to the English throne, and this set the scene for another 40 years of conflict. On his deathbed in Saint Germain in 1701, James forgave his enemies, comforted his wife, saw his children one last time and quietly died of a brain haemorrhage.

His body was autopsied and his brain preserved in a silver case in the Scots College in Paris. His heart went to the Convent of the Visitandine Nuns at Chaillot and his intestines were divided between the English Church of St Omer and the parish church of St Germain-en-Laye. The rest of his body was buried in the English Benedictine Church of St Edmund in Rue St Jacques in Paris, and in 1734 the Archbishop of Paris heard evidence to support his canonisation. Candles were kept burning around the tomb until the French Revolution in 1789 when a mob attacked the church and his lead coffin was sold for scrap.

*James II memorial in Rue St Jacques in Paris*

Mary of Modena lived on in Paris where she died in 1718. Their son, James Francis Stuart, was born in 1688 but his Catholic claims to the English throne were overruled in 1701 by the Act of Succession. Called the Old Pretender, he led the unsuccessful Jacobite rebellion of 1715 and he lived in Italy where he drank heavily and abused his wives and mistresses. He died of a stroke aged 67 and was buried in St Peter's basilica in Rome.

*James Francis Stuart*

*The Old Pretender*

*Charles Edward Stuart*

*The Young Pretender*

His son, Charles Edward Stuart, was born to Maria Clementina Sobieski in a papal palace in Rome. As Bonny Prince Charlie he led the Jacobite rebellion of 1745 which was crushed at the Battle of Culloden and was followed by the highland clearances of his Scottish clan supporters. From France, he visited England incognito and announced his conversion to the Protestant faith. But this came to no avail and when he married in Rome his wife deserted him. He failed to legitimise a daughter born to a Scottish mistress called Clementina Walkenshaw and he died of a stroke aged 67. His brother Henry died in Padua in 1807 and with this the Stuart claim to the English throne ended.

# William III and Mary II

Mary was born in St James palace in 1662, the daughter of James II and Ann Hyde. She married her cousin, William of Orange, in 1677 and died of Smallpox in London in 1694. William was ten years older and was born in the Hague to Prince William of Orange and Princess Mary, the sister of Charles II. He became joint monarch with Mary in 1688 and after her death he ruled alone for eight years. He died in 1702 aged 50 after falling from a horse and fracturing his collarbone.

When he invaded England in 1688, William was the champion of European Protestantism and a bulwark to the Catholic ambitions of Louis XIV. His marriage to Mary was a diplomatic triumph for the Dutch and when he entered London at the head of an army he made it clear that he would rule as king, not as regent. In her turn, Mary, who was just 15, was happy to obey her husband and to preside in England during his absences abroad.

She was a pretty child, with brown eyes, auburn curls, and a delicate pink complexion. She was intelligent, sensitive, and light-hearted, and had a talent for friendship. She was nine years old when her mother died of cancer and her father married Princess Mary of Modena. The two Marys were the same age and became good friends.

William III had a cold, melancholic personality and by the time he married Mary he had sewn all his wild oats and was only interested in politics and war. He was short in stature, had a rather comic long nose, and he resembled a hunchback. He was probably bisexual, suffered badly with asthma, and did not appeal to the emotional teenager who cried bitterly when she was told of the betrothal. But William had made a favourable impression on James II, and the youngsters were promptly married at St James's Palace. With Smallpox[52] rife in London, however, they left immediately for Holland where Mary soon became depressed. Her sister, Ann, was sent as a companion but Smallpox struck the Dutch court and Ann fell ill with it and nearly died. William's mistress, Betty Villiers, did not survive it, however.

William was an able man who spoke English, Dutch, French, German, Spanish, Italian, and Latin. He was a workaholic and often slept at work and ordered he should be woken to receive dispatches. He understood the English, and when a deputation of seven English noblemen invited him to save England for the Protestant faith, he knew he had enough support in England to depose James. They encountered foul weather during the crossing to England and when William came ashore at Brixham in 1688, he was so seasick he had to be carried. John Churchill deserted King James, and then Princess Ann and her husband the Prince of Denmark did too. As the Protestant army neared the capital, William suffered five days of torrential nosebleeds, and had a physical collapse. But in London James was isolated and had sufficient military experience to know he faced a bloody struggle with no hope of success. He ordered his troops to lay down their arms and when William entered London with his troops singing Lillibullero, William gave his father-in-law safe passage to France.

William and Mary were crowned jointly in Westminster Abbey the following year. They were an odd couple who made the best of a difficult relationship and came to love each other. Mary became pregnant within a year but miscarried at three months. She then had a second miscarriage accompanied by a prolonged fever and the

---

[52] See Medical Appendix – 4. Smallpox, page 307.

physicians feared for her life. This may have been due to Porphyria[53] and it occurred again in 1680.

The miscarriages left Mary infertile and with William spending more time abroad there were no more pregnancies.

The revolution in England was bloodless but in Scotland there were violent Jacobite insurrections. When James II landed in Ireland in 1689, William directed the relief of Londonderry and led the army which defeated James at the Battle of the Boyne. In 1692 the infamous massacre at Glencoe took place and it was William who exonerated the guilty troops. From then on he spent much time on the continent, fighting the war of the Spanish succession and restraining the ambitions of Louis XIV. And in 1697 he succeeded by concluding the Treaty of Rijswijk.

In the little time he spent with Mary they enjoyed entertaining and laying out new homes and gardens. But in 1694 Smallpox broke out again in London, and when Mary felt unwell she had a premonition and locked herself in her private room. She burned her diaries and correspondence and wrote her will. She then took a dose of Quinine for the fever and went to bed. But next day a rash appeared and haemorrhagic Smallpox was diagnosed. Her life soon hung by a thread and William, who had seen his mother die of the disease, went to pieces. The sick room was crowded with courtiers and physicians, and the air was foul. A team of nine doctors led by Dr John Radcliffe could do little to help her, and Archbishop Tenison was sent for. He told Mary she might die and gave her Communion, and when she did die William was beside her and broke down in grief.

Her body was embalmed and lay in state at Kensington Palace where her ladies were given her furnishings, and Purcell was commissioned to write a funeral anthem. Catholic France rejoiced at a new opportunity to reinstate James II and the Dutch realised William would need their support to rule without her. William had not liked Princess Ann, his sister-in-law, but now he reconciled his differences with her and became governor to her only surviving son, the 9-year-old William Duke of Gloucester. This little boy was the last Protestant Stuart and suffered with hydrocephalic swelling of the brain probably caused by a birth injury. This can progress to

---

[53] See Medical Appendix – 2. Porphyria, page 296.

blindness, seizures, and coma, and it is unlikely the little Duke could have survived into adult life.

But in 1700 like so many in his family, he contracted Smallpox and died. Princess Ann was now the childless heir to the throne and William's court became a gloomy place.

In 1701 William was exhausted after a hunting trip in Holland. His lifelong asthma had become worse and he developed leg swelling. In 1703 his horse, Sorrel, stumbled on a molehill at Hampton Court and he was thrown and fractured his collar bone. In later years this gave rise to the Jacobite toast "to the wee gentleman in black velvet". His arm was immobilised in a sling, but the fracture would not reunite and the arm became swollen. Infective and thrombotic complications of a fractured clavicle are unusual and death from them is rare, but William refused all medical advice as he had seen what the medical profession had done to others, and this probably contributed to his demise. A high fever caused him to vomit, and then his breathing became laboured and he developed pneumonia.

He said goodbye to his Dutch courtiers, and when he died he was wearing a ribbon around his neck with a gold ring and a lock of Mary's hair. But in London he had always been regarded as a foreigner and there was little grieving at the funeral in Westminster Abbey. It was held at midnight with Queen Anne as the chief mourner and he was buried with Mary.

# Queen Anne

Queen Anne was the second daughter of James II and Ann Hyde and was born in St James' Palace in 1665. She became queen in 1702 and died of a Porphyria-related stroke at the age of 49.

She was plump, with reddish hair, pretty hands, and a musical voice which was the result of elocution lessons from an actress called Mrs Betterton. She was neither beautiful nor clever and had none of the easy style of some of the Stuarts. Remote from the succession, she was not educated as a future monarch and some said the only more stupid person in the kingdom was her husband. Remarkably she had a passion for hunting, and her huge frame was often seen pursuing stags across the countryside in a specially reinforced chariot.

She was a devout Protestant and believed her Catholic stepbrother was an imposter smuggled into the labour room in a warming pan. She was terrified during her father's abdication crisis in 1688 and fled from London rather than confront him. With the succession of William and Mary, Anne moved into what became known as the cockpit, at 10 Downing Street, and then to Berkeley House in Piccadilly where she was joined by Sarah Churchill as a companion. William II and John Churchill were frequently away at the wars together and Anne became close to the ambitious Sarah, who encouraged her to mock William as an uncouth Caliban. But then a quarrel took place between the friends over the rewards which Sarah felt were owing to her husband for securing British dominance of Europe and the Treaty of Utrecht. And the estrangement between the two women sent shock waves through society.

When Anne succeeded William II in 1702, she was middle aged and overweight. She had suffered for years with Flying Gout which caused recurrent pain and paralysis of her limbs and was due to hereditary Porphyria[54]. Her legs were always bound and bandaged but it is not known if she had discoloured urine.

She was aged 12 on a visit to her sister in Holland, when she contracted Smallpox[55]. Others at court died including one of William's mistresses but Anne survived though with scarred eyelids and chronic watering eyes. At the age of 15, it was proposed she should marry George of Hanover, the future George I of England. But when they met in London, he was horrified and fled. At the age of 17 she was amorously pursued by the Earl of Musgrave, but he was considered unsuitable and was dispatched to a foreign posting in Tangiers in a royal naval frigate.

---

[54] See Medical Appendix – 2. Porphyria, page 296.
[55] See Medical Appendix – 4. Smallpox, page 307.

*Prince George of Denmark*

Aged 18 she was married to Prince George of Denmark who was an unambitious man who stayed in the background and was so dull King William said he "had tried him drunk and tried him sober but found nothing in the man". But the couple were devoted to each other and throughout their 17-year marriage Anne was constantly pregnant. But all 17 of her babies died except William of Gloucester who was disabled with hydrocephalus and died of Smallpox aged nine.

Pregnancy is now known to exacerbate the symptoms of Porphyria, and Porphyria in turn causes pre-eclampsia, foetal growth retardation, low birth weight, premature delivery, spontaneous abortion, and perinatal death. In 1688 she spent time at Tunbridge Wells in the hope that rest and the spa waters would stop her miscarrying. But the next child lived only a few months. She was seriously ill during all her pregnancies and became pregnant for the last time in 1700 when she was 35 years old. Her babies were all buried in the Mary Queen of Scots vault in Westminster Abbey, and when the Act of Settlement stipulated a Protestant successor, it was Sophie of Hanover who inherited the throne.

When Anne's stolid husband died of heart failure in 1708 she nursed him in his sickbed, but afterwards she retreated into seclusion surrounded by his books and carpentry tools, and she cut a lonely figure in a court which Jonathan Swift said lacked all conversation. Despite her sad private life, Anne's reign was marked by important events such as the British victory at Blenheim which ended French ambitions in Europe, and the Act of Union which formalised the union of England and Scotland. It was also the era of Swift, Pope, Wren, Locke, and Newton. She presided over weekly meetings of her quarrelsome Cabinet but her Lord Treasurer never came at the appointed time, was often drunk and behaved towards her with indecency. He was seldom understood and when he tried to explain himself, she could not depend upon the truth of what he said. Eventually she dismissed him.

But her pregnancies exhausted her health and her "huge body crushed the feeble life within it". In 1713 she was unable to walk for six months and that Christmas, she was feverish, unconscious, and rumoured to be dying. She recovered, but was seriously ill again in 1714. Her doctors blamed this on the strain of government and advised her to stop her late-night meetings of the cabinet. But exhausted after a two-day meeting of her council, she became confused. She was cupped and recovered for 24 hours but was then was seized by fits, lost her speech, and fell unconscious. Her physicians Sir John Arbuthnot and Sir Hans Sloane said her constitutional gout had flown to her head and that she had suffered a stroke. She endured their attentions for only three days, and when she died Arbuthnot told Jonathan Swift that sleep was never more welcome to a weary traveller. Her body lay in state for three weeks in Kensington Palace and at her private funeral it took 14 carpenters to lower her coffin into her husband's grave in Westminster Abbey. The Stuart dynasty and the Divine Right of Kings died with her and from then on her successors wielded political influence but not political power.

The heir to the throne, Sophia of Hanover had died two months earlier, and under the Act of Settlement, her son George inherited the British Crown and the Catholic Stuarts were excluded.

# THE HANOVERIANS

## 1714-1901

George I      George II      George III

George IV      William IV      Victoria

# George I

George I was the son of Ernst of Hanover and Sophia, the granddaughter of James I. He was born at Osnabrück in Lower Saxony in 1660, became King of England in 1714, and died of a stroke at the age of 67.

*Sophia of the Palatinate*

George was an obligate carrier of Porphyria[56] which he inherited from his grandmother, Elizabeth of Bohemia. But apart from his sadistic personality he had no recorded symptoms of the disease which he passed to his son George II and then famously to George III.

In 1698 George inherited the dukedom of Hanover and during the War of the Spanish Succession he became Imperial Field Marshal of the army on the Rhine.

His mother described him as a conscientious child who set a good example to his brothers and sisters. He was a blue-eyed, soldierly man and at the Battle of Vienna he was the last English monarch to fight on the battlefield. And it was from his army days that he was attended by Mustapha and Mahomet, two favourite servants who were captured on campaign in Turkey. He was shy, suspicious and unimaginative, and he spoke German, French, and broken English. He loved the music of George Frederic Handel who he invited to London. But at times he lacked judgment and he was frankly stupid in affairs of the heart. He had a coarse appetite for sex, preferred fat, complacent mistresses and he returned often to Germany to enjoy Hanoverian paramours.

In 1682 he married his empty-headed cousin, Sophia Dorothea of Celle. She was rich but George's mother was against the match as Sophia was not royal and had been conceived out of wedlock. After she bore him two children the couple became estranged, and George preferred the company of his mistress, Melusine von der Schulenburg, by whom he had two illegitimate daughters. Sophia had her own romance with a Swedish count called Philip Christoph von Königsmarck, and threatened with scandal the Hanoverian court urged her to desist but to no avail. According to diplomatic sources the count was murdered in 1694 and his body was weighted with stones and thrown into the River Leine. The marriage was then dissolved and she was imprisoned in Castle Ahlden in Celle where she died 32 years later. She never visited England and was denied access to her children, forbidden to remarry, and was only allowed to walk unchaperoned within the castle courtyard. When she died in

---

[56] See Medical Appendix – 2. Porphyria, page 296.

1726 George forbad all mourning and this brutal behaviour soured George's relationship with his son, and they grew to loathe each other.

*Sophia Dorothea of Celle*

Following the death in 1701 of Queen Anne's only son the Duke of Gloucester, the English Parliament passed the Act of Settlement in which George's mother Sophia was designated heir to the throne. And there were further Acts of Parliament to naturalise her and arrange the eventual transfer of power. The Stuarts had a far stronger claim to the throne but 56 of them were overlooked because of their Catholicism. Sophia was the closest Protestant relative of Queen Anne, and when William and Mary died it was Sophia who became heir to the throne. She was older than Ann by 35 years, but she was remarkably fit and healthy and she invested much time and energy to secure the succession for herself and her son. And from 1710 she had her agent, Baron von Bothmar representing her in London. Scotland refused to recognise her but the English made threats to cripple the Scottish economy and in 1707 they passed the Act of Union which created the largest free trade area in Europe.

Sophia showed no signs of the Porphyria gene which she carried and she died in 1714 at the age of 83 after rushing to shelter from a shower of rain in the Herrenhausen gardens. Had she survived another two months she would have outlived Queen Anne and become Queen of England, but with her death it was George who became heir to the throne. As Ann's health failed, British politicians began jostling for power and George had to revise the membership of the Regency Council. And when Ann died, the list of councillors was opened and George was proclaimed King of Great Britain, Ireland, and Hanover. But contrary winds kept him in the Hague waiting for a sea passage, and he did not arrive in Britain for several months to crowned in Westminster Abbey.

Queen Anne's court had been intensely conservative and her lack of intelligence frustrated the leaders of the day. But now George brought to England his highly intelligent daughter-in-law, Caroline of Anspach and she opened England's doors to the finest minds in Europe. As a result George's court was a sophisticated society graced by the likes of Leibniz and Handel. George himself was considerably more modern than the Stuarts, and he had a pathological eye for detail. But he could not speak good English and this led to the appointment of Walpole, the country's first Prime Minister. On arriving in London George sided with the Whigs and his first act was to reinstate Marlborough. The Jacobite rebellion kept him in England from 1715 but he returned to Germany in 1719 where he ruled England from his summer palace at Herrenhausen and was visited regularly by English politicians.

But he became estranged from his son and they argued so badly that he once placed him under house arrest. Numerous attempts at reconciliation failed and the relationship between father and son remained bad. This pattern was perpetuated throughout the Hanoverian dynasty so that none of the Georges liked their sons and none of the sons liked their fathers. And since they all carried the genes for Porphyria[57] this probably contributed. The Prince of Wales sat in the cabinet alongside his father and because of the king's supposed lack of English, the cabinet papers were recorded in French. Eventually George gave up the cabinet meetings and ceased to attend them. In contrast the Prince of Wales understood English very well and when the king was in Hanover the prince presided over

[57] See Medical Appendix – 2. Porphyria, page 296.

the cabinet in England. In actual fact George was able to speak English, and documents show that he understood and wrote it too. He also understood and spoke German, French, Latin, Italian, and Dutch, and whilst the British perceived him as unintelligent, he was regarded in Hanover as a leading figure of the Enlightenment. But he was reserved, and disliked social events, avoided the royal box at the opera and liked to travel incognito. And despite anti-German sentiments in England he was regarded by most Englishmen as a better alternative than the Roman Catholic Stuarts.

Within a year of George's accession the Whigs won the General Election of 1715 and angry Jacobites sought to place Ann's Catholic half-brother, James Francis Stuart, on the throne.

In 1719 the South Sea Company took over three fifths of the British national debt by exchanging government securities for company stock.

The directors bribed ministers and enticed bondholders to convert high-interest, irredeemable bonds to low-interest, more easily traded stocks. Company prices soared until the Government passed the Bubble Act and the stock plummeted. Many including the king lost vast fortunes and it was only Walpole's skilful management that achieved financial stability.

On the road from Delden to Nordhorn during his sixth trip to Hanover in 1727, he suffered a stroke and was taken by carriage to his birth place at the bishop's palace at Osnabrück. He thus he died in the same room as he was born and he was buried in the Chapel of Leine Castle. After World War II, however, his remains were moved to a new mausoleum in the gardens at Herrenhausen.

*George I's tomb at Herrenhausen*

# George II

George II was born in 1683 at Herrenhausen and was the son of George of Hanover (later George I) and Sophia Dorothea of Celle. He became king of England aged 44 and died of a heart attack in London at the age of 77. His father always disliked him and George responded by being obnoxious. In addition, his father's brutal treatment of George's mother led to George loathing him even more and eventually they became totally estranged.

In his youth George regarded men and women as creatures he might kick or kiss for his amusement. But at the age of 23 he married Princess Caroline of Anspach and she changed him a little. They had nine children and the oldest was Frederick Prince of Wales, who some described as the greatest villain ever born, and George hated.

Caroline was an outstanding Queen Consort who helped guide England into the age of reason. She was interested in all the latest ideas and surrounded herself with the most modern minds. Just one example was when she popularised the Turkish practice of inoculating children against Smallpox[58]. George also had an outstanding Prime Minister in Robert Walpole and whilst George had many shortcomings, he had the sense to be guided by these two. As Prince and Princess of Wales, George and Caroline set up a rival court at St James' Palace which was happier and more intellectual than the king's court.

Here they strove to accommodate Englishmen and English ways, and through Caroline's friendship with Walpole they exerted influence over the king.

*Caroline of Anspach*

George II was a complicated and somewhat stupid man and it was said that he was a bad son, a worse father, an unfaithful husband, and an ungraceful lover. And since he was an obligate carrier of Acute Intermittent Porphyria[59] his personality may have been due to this. But he spoke several European languages and with a good memory he applied himself seriously to the business of state. He also had a formidable knowledge of genealogy and an eye for the minute details of national uniforms and flags.

He had regular mistresses but loved his wife, even when she grew

---

[58] See Medical Appendix – 4. Smallpox, page 307.
[59] See Medical Appendix – 2. Porphyria, page 296.

fat in middle age. He also loved the company of intelligent people who in turn found him tedious. His wife was interested in philosophy and theology and was a friend of Liebnitz. George in turn loved music and encouraged Handel to settle in England. He also promoted and came to depend on Robert Walpole, who packed the offices of state with family members.

George hated criticism and in an age of sycophancy he became a lonely figure. His father died in 1727 and when George ascended the throne he was pilloried in the newspapers which accused him of snubbing England in favour of Hanover. William Pitt emerged to lead the wars which Wolfe and Clive waged against France, and England started to become an industrialised society.

And with Hanoverian England under threat from Jacobites, a National Anthem was composed in 1745 and was played for the first at the Theatre Royal in Drury Lane.

In 1737 at the age of 54, Queen Caroline was suddenly taken ill with colic in the library of St James's Palace. She returned home and dosed herself with Daffy's Elixir but the pain and vomiting increased. The king was quite intolerant to the discomfort of others, but a doctor was summoned and prescribed Snake Root which made her worse. Lord Harvey joined the king in admonishing Caroline and when the Prince of Wales asked to see his mother, the king refused. Ranby, the king's surgeon, was then called and discovered a strangulated umbilical hernia which she had developed after the birth of her daughter. He carried out a series of operations without anaesthetic and then battled to control the postoperative infections. Quite extraordinarily Caroline was moved to laughter when his wig caught fire in a candle in the middle of a surgical procedure. She pretended the rupture was not serious and kept it from the king. But she knew she was dying, returned her jewels to George, thanked him for everything she had received from him and urged him to re-marry. The archbishop failed to persuade her to take the sacraments and after 12 days of painful illness she died. She was widely mourned and a desolate George said he had never known another woman who was fit to buckle her shoe. Her body lay in state for a month and was frequently visited by the king. And at the funeral service the choir sang an anthem which was composed by Handel and was sung again at Queen Victoria's funeral 164 years later.

The king eventually picked up his life again but was subject to morbid thoughts and nightmares. Lord Wentworth reported that one night the king awoke from a dream, drove to Westminster Abbey in a carriage and ordered the queen's vault and her coffin to be opened. Eventually he went back to Hanover and enjoyed quiet evenings playing cards with his married daughters. But he didn't take up again with his mistresses and he never remarried. At one stage a marriage to the 17-year-old Princess Augusta of Saxe Coburg was proposed but she arrived carrying a doll and was turned away.

The Prince of Wales eventually demanded his own household and set up an establishment in Leicester House which became the focus of political opposition to George. This rival court expanded and the English aristocracy split into two factions. But the Prince of Wales was licentious, unpredictable, and indifferent to the truth. And he ran up huge debts and left his wife, Princess Augusta of Saxe-Gotha, an impoverished widow with nine children. George II and Queen Caroline both loathed him and on her deathbed she declared she was glad she would never set eyes on him again.

*Frederic Louis, Prince of Wales*

In 1751 the Prince of Wales was in Carlton House playing cards when he had a coughing fit and chest pain. He cried out, fell back, and died immediately. A post-mortem examination revealed a rupture between the pericardium and the diaphragm which was fobbed off as an old tennis ball injury but must have been an aortic aneurysm. His widow, Princess Augusta, was pregnant with their ninth child and the press had a field day. He was buried alongside his mother with whom he had quarrelled so bitterly, and this funeral was the first one at which the Royal Family engaged the services of an undertaker.

George II remained calm whilst others panicked during the 1745 Jacobite rebellion. But from then on the Wars in India, Canada, and the Caribbean took their toll on him and in 1760 he died at Kensington Palace. After his morning chocolate he went to the loo and his German valet heard a groan and found him lying speechless on the floor. He died even before his daughter could reach him from an adjacent room, and Walpole described it as an enviable death. He was thus spared the attentions of the court doctors, and a post-mortem examination found the left ventricle of the heart had ruptured as a result of a heart attack.

He was buried at night by torchlight in Westminster Abbey and in a touching afterthought, he left instructions that he should lie alongside Queen Caroline with the sides of each coffin removed so they might lie together. And when the vault was opened in 1837 the two planks of their caskets were still lying propped against the wall.

# George III

George III was born in London in 1738 but his birthday was changed from 4th June to the 24th May when Britain adopted the Gregorian calendar. He was the son of Frederick Lewis, the Prince of Wales, and Princess Augusta of Saxe Coburg, and he inherited the throne from his grandfather in 1760. He died of the complications of Porphyria[60] in 1820.

His father died when George was 13 and he succeeded his grandfather as king when he was 22. In 1811 his famous illness brought about the Regency crisis but he survived another nine years, and at 82 he was the oldest man to rule the country. His family's medical history of Porphyria is the most intensively researched in history. His grandfather and father argued about everything including

---

[60] See Medical Appendix – 2. Porphyria, page 296.

whether George should be born in Hampton Court or St James's Palace. In the end his parents were evicted by the king and George was born in lodgings in St James' Square. Born prematurely, he was not expected to survive but he was successfully suckled by a wet nurse called Mary Smith.

He was brought up in an adult world which made him shy and he was not clever but worked hard. He also spent hours at prayer and was able to remain calm when others panicked. He was raised as a strict Protestant and was never allowed to forget the reasons why his family had inherited the throne. There were anti-German rumours that he could not read and write, but these were untrue. His education in fact was gruelling and from the age of 11 his lessons lasted from 7:30 in the morning until 8:00 at night. He spoke English without a German accent but he always spoke very fast and filled in gaps in the conversation with meaningless patter. Under a succession of tutors he learned Latin, Greek, history and mathematics, and he gained an excellent understanding of the British constitution.

He was blue eyed, tall and handsome, and his grandfather and his widowed mother quarrelled constantly over which German princess he should marry. Princess Charlotte of Mecklenburg was eventually chosen and despite being dull and some said formidably ugly, the marriage was happy and they had 15 children, most of whom survived despite carrying the gene for Porphyria. But his sons, Alfred and Octavius, died in infancy of Tuberculosis and his daughter, Amelia, died aged 27 from Erysipelas.

*Charlotte of Mecklenburg*

He was a devoted father but as adults his children resented the Royal Marriages Act which compelled their father's permission for them to marry legally.

As young men the Prince of Wales and Duke of York enjoyed the company of society prostitutes and were derided in the newspapers about their affairs with married women. When George's eldest son reached 21 he demanded his own household and aligned himself with the king's political adversary, James Fox. And when he secretly married a widowed Catholic commoner called Mrs Fitzherbert, the king's loathing for him became extreme.

His brother, the Duke of York, was a heartless dandy who drifted into political opposition to the king and died in Monaco in 1767 aged only 38. And a third son, Edward Duke of Kent, went into the Army and was the father of Queen Victoria. Kent was a difficult character who suffered clinically from Porphyria and died before he could succeed George IV. The fourth son, William Duke of Clarence, the future William IV, went into the Navy, where it was said he had a girl in every port and contracted Syphilis. But eventually he settled down with an actress called Mrs Jordan who went on to bear him 10 children. The next son, the Duke of Gloucester, grew up in poor

214

health and spent most of his life abroad. He married a commoner without informing the king and he died in Italy in 1771. The last son, the Duke of Cumberland, was a society rake who was named by Lord Grosvenor in an action for "criminal conversation" (adultery). Against the king's wishes he married a widow called Ann Horton and he rarely saw the king. George's other three sons were educated at Gottingen University and three of his six daughters were unmarried.

George lived mainly at Windsor where he regarded St George's Chapel as his parish church. After finishing his business in London, he rode home 20 miles on horseback to have dinner with the queen. He was a fine horseman, preferring to remain on horseback whatever the weather and he rarely travelled by coach. He rose at 6:00 am, dealt with the overnight correspondence, and then rode before a breakfast of tea and coffee with the queen. In the evenings they played cards together and were joined by the children. When he hunted or went horse racing at Epsom he only drank barley water, and his dislike of alcohol may have delayed the onset of his Porphyria. He also disliked gambling and his companions found him boring.

But he was curious about all manner of things, enjoyed funny stories, was comfortable in the company of great men and tenant farmers, and was generous to the poor. He wrote pamphlets about agricultural improvement under the pen-name of Ralph Robinson, and entertained Handle and Mozart during their time in England. He founded the Royal Academy and the British Library, was intrigued by Herschel's discovery of the planet Uranus, and he supported the Botanic Gardens at Kew. On his accession, the Crown lands were producing little income and he surrendered the Crown Estate to Parliament in return for a £3m civil list annuity.

From the age 18 he came under the influence of the Earl of Bute, the handsome lover of his mother, the Dowager Princess of Wales. Bute was incompetent but influential in the House of Lords and the friendship made George unpopular. As a result he became ill-tempered and he could become enraged if criticised.

His reign was marked by military conflicts in Europe, Africa, America, and Asia. Great Britain defeated France in the Seven Years' War, and became the dominant European power, but after the peace Pitt resigned and four other PMs followed in rapid succession. Then Lord North was appointed and was the man who lost America.

North was a sycophant and he and the king ran the government between them with disastrous results. They failed to manage the political problems of the new age and many of their decisions had to be reversed. Neither of them understood nationalism as a new force and they still viewed the colonies as a source of raw materials, a market for trade and a place to deport undesirables. American taxes were needed to govern the territories but less than a tenth were collected. When the Stamp Act was passed in 1765 it could only be imposed by military force, and in the crisis which followed Pitt was summoned from retirement.

But he was only a shadow of his former self and his gout was so severe he could not attend the king in London. Front-line politicians resigned their office and John Wilkes, the MP for Aylesbury, attacked the king in the columns of the newspapers. When the Stamp Act was repealed in 1766 new taxes were soon necessary but these also had to be imposed by military force.

The Tea Act of 1773 caused riots in Boston and when war came in 1775 George sought only the unconditional surrender of the colonists. Burgoyne was sent to conduct the war but was outmanoeuvred by George Washington, and when the war ended in 1783 Britain was drawn into further conflicts against France, Spain, and the Netherlands. These were followed by the rise of Napoleon and it wasn't until after the Battle of Waterloo in 1815 that Britain was at peace again.

George was allegedly healthy until January 1765 when he became ill with a heavy cold and was bled by his physician. This was followed by episodes of psychotic delusions in February and March, after which he officially recovered and was well until 1788. Unofficially, however, George had showed worrying behaviour since his marriage in 1761. A royal hairdresser called Mrs Papendeik testified that the king had lost his sanity several times during her employment but this was never made public on the orders of the Prime Minister. There were also unexplained absences from the Cabinet and Privy Council, and with George having the final say in all things, his health had a bearing on everything important, including the American colonies.

In 1788 at the age of 50 his mental health collapsed spectacularly when after a day's riding he had a convulsion and wouldn't stop talking. He was struck down with what his physicians called the flying gout and after dinner he attacked the Prince of Wales and tried to strangle him. In addition, he had a skin rash, developed jaundice, bloodshot eyes, swollen ankles, and red-coloured urine. A Dr Warren blistered him with Spanish poultices and the Reverend Francis Willis was consulted. At the time nothing was really known about the problem but it is now clear from modern DNA analysis that he had begun to suffer from Acute Intermittent Porphyria.

He next experienced what he called a pretty smart bilious attack and Sir George Baker, the President of the Royal College of Surgeons, advised him to rest. But he remained ill and was advised to take the waters at Cheltenham. There he remained at Lord Fauconberg's residence for five weeks, which was the longest he had ever been away from London. He attended a performance of Handel's Messiah at the Three Choirs Festival and went amongst the local people, which he enjoyed greatly. But after a month he developed severe facial pains, further biliousness, and leg cramps which made him lame. Baker told him it was rheumatism and the cause was his failure to remove his wet stockings. But his arms were covered in wheals and were similar to the skin photosensitivity which led James I to have special protective garments fitted.

He was mistakenly prescribed an overdose of purgatives, and announced he intended ban all further use of Senna. When he was given Laudanum to counteract this, he became delirious and he and the anxious Queen returned to Windsor. At a concert in October he started to talk incessantly again, and then he said there was a mist before his eyes. He talked so incoherently and persistently that he foamed at the mouth and his voice became hoarse. During one period he talked for 19 hours without a break and when he was disinhibited, some of his talk was indecent and out of character.

The Queen was terrified and her physician William Heberden agreed the king's mind was seriously disturbed and informed Pitt. It was said George's eyes were like blackcurrant jelly and the veins of his face were swollen. His nights became so disturbed the queen began to sleep apart from him, and when George began to visit her by candlelight she took to locking her bedroom door and he accused her of infidelity. His physicians would not allow him near a barber's razor and he went about unshaven. By November he was experiencing episodes of coma and it was announced he was close to death. The Prince of Wales took charge but when he tried to install a Regency council it disintegrated into chaos. Seven doctors were consulted and the illness was documented daily by George's equerry, Robert Grenville, including the purple-coloured urine which is the pathognomonic sign of Porphyria. The urine only darkens after standing in the gossunder overnight and from then on it was regularly monitored by physicians who made a living out of studying urine and who he called his piss prophets.

Stories abounded, like one occasion when he descended from his coach and tried to shake hands with an oak tree which he addressed as Frederick the Great. The embarrassment was considerable and great efforts were made to conceal such stories from the public. Eventually he was moved to Kew where he refused to eat or take his medications. His symptoms continued and he was visited by the Reverend Francis Willis, who was a quack Lincolnshire vicar with an interest in mental illness. He claimed some success in treating insane members of wealthy families but the court physicians regarded him as a charlatan and protested to the queen. The shame of insanity now became too much and George begged to retire to Hanover. But this was not allowed and he was bound in a strait jacket, tied to his bed, blistered with hot cups and made to vomit with emetics. If he used foul language he was gagged, and when he declared a sexual interest in Lady Pembroke he was tied into a chair with a strait waistcoat.

From January 1789, he slowly improved. The Queen began to visit him, he was shaved and ate normal meals, and the Gazette announced that health bulletins were no longer necessary. He returned to Windsor and began to sleep with the queen again, and Dr Willis left the court. A service of Thanksgiving was held in St Paul's Cathedral and George went to Weymouth to convalesce at the Duke of Gloucester's residence. When he felt well he went for excursions on a Royal Naval frigate anchored in the bay, and from then on he went every year on holiday in Weymouth.

The next 20 years were taken up with the war with France. This was conducted badly and the king's reputation suffered and mobs threw stones at his coach. The Bank of England was forced off the gold standard, there were mutinies in the Royal Navy, and when the Irish threatened rebellion they had to be granted a legislative assembly. In 1786 a mad woman called Margaret Nicholson tried to stab George and she was committed to Bedlam. In 1792 a soldier called Edward Despard was convicted of conspiring with Irish revolutionaries to kill him, and was the last person in Britain to be hanged drawn and quartered. In 1800 a James Hadfield tried to shoot him during a performance of Le Nozze di Figaro in Drury Lane Theatre, but the bullet missed and embedded itself in a pillar in the king's box, and the king remained calm and slept during the interval.

But just when the Porphyria seemed to have disappeared there were relapses which left him permanently disabled. From then on he could only mount a horse with difficulty and he was considered permanently insane. In 1801 he had a recurrence of all the symptoms and Willis virtually kidnapped him, and a Regency was again considered. When he was comatose for two days, Francis Willis and his son, Thomas, acted as intermediaries with Parliament, and in 1804 he had a recurrence and was attended by Dr Samuel Simmonds from St Luke's Hospital for Lunatics. A strait jacket was again used and he became emaciated and talked about himself as a dying man.

For most of his life he had no secretary and he wrote all his own letters. But after 1795 the Porphyria caused his eyesight to fail and he could no longer read. In 1805 an operation for cataracts was considered by John Taylor who was the most famous eye surgeon in Europe. But the composers Bach and Handel had both had cataracts removed by him without an anaesthetic, and both were left completely blind. As a result it was decided the king should not have surgery carried out and eventually he became blind without it.

In 1805 George expressed the unrealistic wish to lead his troops against Napoleon. This was very popular with the public, and on visits to Weymouth, villagers turned out to cheer him. But in 1810 the illness returned and effectively marked the end of his reign. For a year, the symptoms waxed and waned, and during his lucid moments he asked about the war. But he walked in his sleep and prayed to die, and in 1811 all judgement deserted him and the Regency Bill was passed in Parliament without his Royal Assent. He became completely isolated and ceased to enquire about his family. He grew a long beard, and from his Privy Purse of £60,000 per annum, his medical bills rose to £34,000. His physicians Halford, Baillie, and Heberden visited every week and the Willises went every day. Others also attended him, and from 1812 until his death, £272,000 was spent on medical fees. Parliament complained about the incompetence of the physicians and their great expense, but to no avail.

He played no role in the defeat of Napoleon in 1815 and deserted by his family, he lived in a twilight world. He was a pathetic blind and deaf figure with a white beard who played to himself on the harpsichord and talked of men long dead. In 1818 Queen Charlotte died at Kew after a 57-year marriage to the king. As a plain German princess, she had crossed the English Channel in a storm at sea and played God Save the King on the harpsichord whilst everyone around her was seasick. She had shared George's sufferings with fortitude and when she died Londoners wore black, all public entertainment was cancelled, and the great bell at St Paul's was tolled. A selected public was allowed to see her lying in state at Kew and she was buried at Windsor.

The Duke of York took over responsibility for his father and in his final years George developed an abdominal rupture and could only take food in liquid form. He was confined to bed and fed by hand and when he died in 1820 he was buried in St George's Chapel in Windsor.

He was mourned by the nation which said he saved England from French republicanism by his personal integrity. His reign witnessed the works of Dr Johnson, Gibbon, Austen, Byron, Coleridge, Shelly, Gainsborough, and Keats. He signed Acts to grant Ireland a legislative assembly and a formal union with Scotland, and in 1807 to abolish the slave trade. According to Sir William Knollys, the north terrace at Windsor was haunted by his bearded ghost and one ensign at a changing of the guard ordered, "Eyes right," when the spectre raised its hand to salute them.

# George IV

George IV was the son of George III and Charlotte of Mecklengberg Strelitz, and he was born in 1762 at St James Palace. He was Prince Regent from 1811 to 1820 and King from 1820 to 1830. He died in 1830 at the age of 68 from oesophageal varices caused by alcoholic cirrhosis.

He was the oldest of 15 children and a shy child. The family were brought up in Leicester House where he and his brother, the Duke of York, were educated by private tutors. He studied French, Latin, history, music, geography, commerce, agriculture and constitutional law. In addition, he was the first British monarch to study the science subjects chemistry, physics, astronomy, and mathematics. And he learned dancing, fencing, and riding.

At the age of 18 he was given his own household at Carlton House and he threw himself into a life of dissipation and wild extravagance. He obtained a grant from Parliament equivalent today to £6m, and from his father an annual income equivalent to £5m. His life of heavy drinking and endless mistresses evoked the animosity of his father who desired more frugal behaviour by the heir apparent. The King was also alienated by the Prince's friendship with Charles James Fox and other radical politicians. As a young man he was very handsome, but by the age of thirty Gillray depicted him as a "voluptuary under the horrors if digestion" and by 50 as a "libertine head over heels in disgrace and debt".

As young men he and the Duke of York enjoyed the company of society prostitutes and were derided in the newspapers for their drunkenness and affairs with married women. The Examiner portrayed George as a gambler, debtor, liar, glutton, and a drunk, for which its editor Leigh Hunt was arrested and imprisoned. In 1788 his father fell ill and George went round the London clubs disclosing intimate details and mimicking his father's ravings. But when sober he was the most intelligent of the Hanoverians and a man of taste who built houses to rival the finest in Europe. He read Jane Austen and Walter Scott and his acquisition of the Angerstein art collection formed the basis of the National Gallery. But he preferred a girl and a bottle to politics and sermons and after betraying the Whigs he betrayed the Tories and was eventually trusted by no one.

*Maria Fitzherbert*

He had an affair with Lady Melbourne, the wife of the Prime Minister, but when he was 21, he became infatuated with Maria Fitzherbert who was a commoner, six years older, twice widowed, and a Roman Catholic. Despite this, the Prince ignored the Act of Settlement and the Royal Marriages Act and determined to marry her. In 1785 the couple went through a private ceremony at her house in Mayfair, but the king's consent was not granted and the marriage was illegal. The Rev Robert Butt who conducted the service had been released from debtors' prison and was promised a bishopric for marrying them. And Maria believed church law held precedence and her marriage was legal. George's father refused to assist him and forced him to quit Carlton House and live at the Fitzherbert residence. But in 1787 his friends came to his aid and Parliament granted him the equivalent of £18m to pay off his debts and £7m for improvements to Carlton House.

George and Maria were married for nine years but had no children, and in return for Parliament writing off some of his debts he left her in 1795 to marry the wealthy Princess Caroline of Brunswick. This was a disaster and according to the Earl of Malmesbury, Caroline was "to the last degree, a slattern to such a point as to excite disgust, and in her conversation vulgar and indelicate beyond all degree". She was coarse, fat, and unwashed, and when George saw her for the first time he said he needed a brandy. The newlyweds found each other physically repulsive and when George appointed his mistress, Lady Jersey, to the royal bed chamber, Caroline's disgust turned to hatred. A daughter, Princess Charlotte, was born in 1796 but after that George and Caroline lived apart.

*Caroline of Brunswick*

Caroline was Princess of Wales from 1795 to 1820 and Queen Consort from 1820 until her death in 1821. But within a year of her marriage she deserted George and took lovers including an Italian valet called Bartolomeo Pergami. She proved to have an insatiable appetite for pleasure and her dresses were bizarre and her behaviour astonishing. She moved around Europe, and visiting Jerusalem she entered the city on an ass. She grew fatter and wore a black wig and the Englishmen she met abroad were shocked and ashamed.

In 1817 she was devastated when her daughter, Charlotte, died in childbirth and George did not inform her. Charlotte had died after giving birth to a stillborn son, and suffering antepartum bleeding and abdominal pains, she had gone three weeks past her expected date of delivery. The labour went on for an astonishing 51 hours and her physician, Sir Richard Croft, consulted his brother-in-law Dr Christian Stockmar, to advise on the use of obstetric forceps or caesarean section.

*Princess Charlotte*

But Charlotte had to give birth unaided and afterwards she slept and then vomited and complained of ear tinnitus. Her pulse quickened, she became cold, and with severe abdominal pains she flung herself around the bed. In retrospect it seems certain that she suffered from Porphyria[61] and the brandy and hot wine she was given in large quantities were the worst thing possible. But her doctors knew nothing of Porphyria, let alone what made it worse, and all they could advise was hot water bottles to relieve her pains.

She eventually drew up her knees in agony and died and the post-mortem examination revealed a post-partum haemorrhage and an embolus which had travelled to the lungs. The reputation of Dr Croft her senior physician was in tatters and when a similar outcome happened to another of his patients three months later, he shot himself.

Just prior to George becoming king in 1819, his brother, Edward Duke of Kent, died in Devon and within days their father, George III, died at Windsor. As the new king, George was faced with organising two funerals and a coronation, when in 1820 Caroline returned to England as his Queen Consort. But George was now determined to divorce her, and set up an investigation into her

---

[61] See Medical Appendix – 2. Porphyria, page 296.

adulteries. In 1821 his plan was for the most elaborate coronation ever seen and Queen Caroline was determined to attend it even when she was excluded from the coronation prayers. Lord Liverpool informed her she should not attend, but she persisted and had to be turned away at the doors of Westminster Abbey. She next attempted to enter via Westminster Hall, where many guests were gathered, and she stood at the door fuming as bayonets were held under her chin and the Chamberlain slammed the doors in her face. This terrible exhibition lost her public support and that night, she fell ill and took a large dose of milk of magnesia and some drops of Laudanum.

After three weeks in pain she realised she was nearing death and put her will in order. She burned her papers, and settled the arrangements for her burial in Brunswick in a tomb bearing the inscription "Here lies Caroline, the Injured Queen of England". She died at Brandenburg House at the age of 53 and even until her last moments, she was spied upon by agents of the Prime Minister. Some physicians thought she had an intestinal obstruction perhaps due to cancer, but others said she had been poisoned.

Afraid that a funeral procession through London could spark public unrest, Lord Liverpool ordered the cortège should pass north of the capital to Harwich and then to Brunswick. But angry crowds blocked the route with barricades, and soldiers opened fire and rode through the crowd with drawn sabres. In return the crowd threw cobblestones and two were killed. Eventually, the Chief Magistrate allowed the cortège to pass through London and then to Harwich via Chelmsford, and Colchester. On one of the stops her double coffin was pilfered and the stolen coffin plate is now in the British Museum. But the casket eventually reached Brunswick and she was buried according to her wishes.

As king, George's extravagance continued and he commissioned John Nash to build the Royal Pavilion in Brighton and remodel Buckingham Palace. He founded King's College London and Sir Jeffrey Wyattville was engaged to upgrade Windsor Castle. But for most of the reign, Lord Liverpool ran the government and received little help from George whose ministers found him irresponsible. In addition, taxpayers were angry about his extravagance at a time when Britain was at war with Napoleon. George had little to do with the victory at Waterloo in 1815 and it was Liverpool who negotiated the peace settlement. But following the Peterloo massacre in Manchester in 1819, the country was on the verge of revolution and a plot to assassinate the cabinet led to the ringleaders being hanged.

With advancing years George dressed like a gorgeous bird of paradise but weighed 17 stone and developed a 50-inch waist. By 1829 Sir David Wilkie reported George weighed 20 stone and looked like a "great sausage stuffed into its covering". He suffered from gout, arteriosclerosis, and dropsy, and his abdominal pains from Porphyria caused him to become addicted to Laudanum. His physician, Dr William Knighton, was a sinister court figure and with George's fantasies extending to the Battlefield at Waterloo there was talk of him going mad like his father. He became blind with cataracts and his heavy drinking led to liver cirrhosis[62] with abdominal ascites which the doctors drained. Oesophageal varices are swellings in the gullet due to cirrhosis of the liver and it was a massive haemorrhage from these that eventually killed him. Wellington said that George had a lot of good in him but William IV left before the end of the funeral service and the burial at Windsor.

---

[62] See Medical Appendix – 16. Liver Cirrhosis, page 339.

# William IV

William IV was the third son of George III and Charlotte of Mecklenburg Strelitz and was born in 1765 at Buckingham Palace. He became king at the age of 65 and died of a heart attack aged 72.

He had eight children from his 20-year illegal marriage to the actress Dorothea Bland but no surviving children from his legal marriage to Princess Adelaide of Saxe Coburg. And without a legitimate heir he was succeeded by his niece, Victoria.

He spent his early life in Richmond and Kew Palaces where he was educated by private tutors. Aged 13 he joined the Royal Navy and was treated like other ratings. He did his share of the ship's cooking and was arrested in Gibraltar after a drunken brawl. And it was during this time he was reported to have been treated for Syphilis[63]. He was a severe officer who had forthright opinions, used strong language, and made tactless speeches. Some thought of him as a fool and he was known to many as Silly Billy.

---

[63] See Medical Appendix – 10. Syphilis, page 325.

He served in New York during the American War of Independence and was unguarded until George Washington hatched a plot to kidnap him. In 1780 he served at the Battle of Cape St Vincent and in 1786 he became Captain of HMS *Pegasus*. Stationed in the West Indies under Horatio Nelson, the two regularly dined together and it was William who gave away the bride at Nelson's wedding. He commanded the frigate HMS *Andromeda* in 1788, and next year he was promoted to Rear-Admiral in command of HMS *Valiant*. He rose briefly to the rank of High Admiral but was not allowed to command a ship during the wars against revolutionary France.

In 1789 he asked the king for a dukedom, so as to receive a parliamentary grant like his older brothers, but his father was reluctant. To press his case, he threatened to stand for the House of Commons in the constituency of Totnes in Devon and with this prospect George III relented and created him Duke of Clarence.

But the episode led William to ally himself with the Whigs and join his older brothers in political opposition to the king. Britain declared war on France in 1793 but he broke his arm falling down some stairs drunk, and made an ill-considered speech in the House of Lords. On another occasion he disappeared on a warship and no one knew where he had gone. As a result he was not given command of another warship though he was promoted to Admiral of the Fleet and spent his time in the House of Lords where he spoke against the abolition of slavery and castigated Wilberforce.

Under the Royal Marriages Act 1772, William was forbidden from marrying without the consent of the king, and several of his brothers had chosen to cohabit with the women they loved, rather than seek permission to marry them. As a result, from 1791 George lived with an Irish actress called Dorothea Bland who was better known by her stage name, Mrs. Jordan. The title "Mrs." was to airbrush an inconvenient pregnancy and "Jordan" was used because she had "crossed the water" from Ireland to Britain. William did not expect to figure in the succession so he enjoyed his life with Mrs. Jordan, and George III eventually accepted them. They had ten children who were given the surname "FitzClarence", and in 1797 the king gave them a large residence at Bushy House in which George and Dorothea spent happy years. But in 1817 the heir to the throne, his niece Princess Charlotte, died in childbirth, and since William's brothers were all childless, the pressure grew on him to remarry and have legitimate children. Princess Adelaide of SaxeMeiningen was eventually found and she was amiable, home-loving, and willing to accept his illegitimate children. This marriage was also happy and lasted 20 years, but it only produced two daughters and neither survived childhood. Adelaide then suffered three miscarriages and William remained without a legitimate heir.

*Dorothea Bland*
*(Mrs Jordan)*

*Princess Adelaide*

In 1811 Mrs Jordan resumed acting in an effort to repay her debts, but her career faltered and she moved to France where in 1816 she died impoverished. With the deaths of George III, Princess Charlotte, and the Duke of York, William became heir to the throne. He was 64 when George IV died and was the oldest person to become king. He gave up the pomp and ceremony of George IV, walked unaccompanied through London and Brighton and was popular among ordinary people who saw him as approachable and down-to-earth. He was a conscientious monarch and his Prime Minister, the Duke of Wellington, said he did more business with William in ten minutes than he had done with George IV in as many days.

His coronation cost one tenth of George IV's and he dismissed the French chefs and German band from Buckingham Palace. He also gave George IV's art collection to the nation, and halved the royal stud. He cancelled the renovation of Buckingham Palace, and in 1834 he tried to donate it as a new Parliament when the Palace of Westminster burned down. But his informality was startling and when in residence at the Royal Pavilion in Brighton, he would send to the local hotels to invite anyone to dinner, and urge guests not to "bother about which clothes they wore". He also rode around London in an open carriage asking pedestrians if they needed a lift anywhere.

In the General Election of 1830, the Whigs under Earl Grey pledged to reform the electoral system, and when the House of Commons defeated the First Reform Bill William dissolved Parliament and forced new elections. After the rejection of a second reform Bill by the upper house in 1831 he threatened to create new peers to pass the legislation. And in 1834, he became the last British sovereign to choose a Prime Minister contrary to the will of Parliament.

He supported Belgian independence and favoured Prince Leopold as the new Belgian king. He foresaw the construction of a Suez Canal would require good relations with Egypt and he exercised personal charm to repair the Anglo-American relations damaged by his father. William and Adelaide were both fond of their niece, Princess Victoria, but their attempts at a closer relationship were frustrated by Victoria's widowed mother. William hoped he would survive until Princess Victoria was 18 so her mother and the Earl of Bute would not become Regents. And though ill, William survived until a month after Victoria's coming of age. "Poor old man," Victoria wrote as he was dying. "I feel sorry for him; he was always kind to me."

In 1837 Queen Adelaide nursed him after a heart attack at Windsor Castle and when he died the crown passed to Princess Victoria. The beneficiaries of his will were his children by Mrs. Jordan, and Adelaide retired to Bushy House where she died 12 years later.

# Queen Victoria

    Victoria was the daughter of Edward Duke of Kent, and Princess Victoria of Leningren, and she was born in 1819. She became queen at the age of 18, and died of a stroke on the Isle of Wight aged 82. She ruled England until 1901 and was Empress of India from 1876.

*Duke of Kent*                          *Victoria of Leningren*

She was only five feet tall but had piercing blue eyes and her nine children, 41 grandchildren and 87 great-grandchildren were married into the royal families of Germany, Russia, Greece, Romania, Sweden, Denmark, Norway and Belgium.

Her predecessor, William IV, survived long enough by just 37 days for Victoria to reach her 18<sup>th</sup> birthday and avoid a Regency led by her mother.

Victoria's father died when she was eight months old and suffered from Porphyria. He was the military Commander of North America and until his debts overcame him, he lived with Julie de St Laurent the wife of a French Colonel. He returned to Britain with Victoria to settle the succession and to pay off his debts by marrying Princess Victoria of Leningen, who was a wealthy widow with two children.

As a child Victoria slept in her mother's bedroom, played with dolls and had a pet spaniel called Dash. She kept a daily journal from the age of 13 until her death and this survives in her own hand or transcribed by her daughter Princess Beatrice. She received drawing and painting lessons from Richard Westall and William Leighton Leitch, and she became a good watercolour artist. She had lessons in French, German, Italian, and Latin and was taken on royal visits to all the fashionable towns in England. As a teenager she was the subject of various matrimonial plans but she developed an independent spirit and eventually banned schemers from the court.

In 1835 she was seriously ill with Typhoid Fever[64] and threw the court into a panic. Typhoid was spread by poor sanitation and this was present in the royal palaces until after the water closets invented by Edward Crapper in 1851. These were exhibited at the Great Exhibition and were used by nearly a million visitors who paid one penny for a clean toilet seat, a hand wash and towel, a comb and a shoe shine. And it was then that "to spend a penny" became an everyday phrase.

In 1819 her father died in Devon where he had rented Woolbrook Cottage in Sidmouth to holiday with his wife and daughter. On a visit to Salisbury Cathedral he caught a chill and was bled and cupped but worsened and died of pneumonia.

His body lay in Woolbrook Cottage and his brother, George, was making arrangements for the funeral in London, when their father George III died at Windsor.

Kent's coffin was the biggest ever seen in Devon and the journey back to London started badly when tradesmen in Honiton held up the cortege to demand his debts were paid. But from then on church bells tolled in villages the cortège passed through and the coffin was guarded overnight in parish churches along the route.

When she became queen in 1837 Victoria inherited Britain and the colonies, but was excluded by Salic law from the Hanoverian duchies in Germany. When she was crowned power drained away from her widowed mother and a rift opened over whether the Whigs could exchange their own Ladies in Waiting for the incumbent Tories. This Bedchamber Crisis was mishandled by the Prime Minister, Lord Melbourne, and on her way to the Ascot races the new queen was jeered by the public as "Mrs Melbourne".

In 1839 Victoria experienced her first major scandal when she ordered one of her unmarried Ladies in Waiting, Lady Flora Hastings, to be examined for a suspected pregnancy. The controversy was made public in the newspapers and it was rumoured that the dowager queen's lover, John Conroy, was the father of the child. Hastings refused the examination, was later diagnosed with cancer, and died. But she was a Plantagenet by descent and with a strong historic claim to the throne, her family were eventually persuaded to

---

[64] See Medical Appendix – 12. Typhoid, page 331.

emigrate. That same year Victoria visited her Saxe Coburg relations in Germany and immediately fell in love with her cousin, Prince Albert. Victoria and Albert were soulmates and were determined to marry even if the English establishment was against the match. After the wedding, she was advised not to let Albert see the state papers and initially their desks were set apart and he was only allowed to blot her signatures. But later their desks were moved together and eventually it was Albert who read and responded to most official communiqués.

*Prince Albert of Saxe Coburg*

Victoria was a vivacious young woman but was prescribed Cannabis for period pains by her physician, Sir Joshua Reynolds. The *indicans* strains of Cannabis are effective for dysmenorrhoea and its use was supported by leaders of the medical profession such as Sir William Osler. But modern evidence suggests that Cannabis can cause or accentuate mental illness[65], and from that time Victoria developed a melancholic personality which may have resulted from Cannabis use. When Albert died unexpectedly she fell into a serious depression and her withdrawal from public life was so prolonged it threatened the monarchy. She also suffered from depression after the birth of her children and these episodes also may have been aggravated by Cannabis. In addition, during pregnancy Cannabis crosses the placenta into the baby's circulation where it can retard

---

[65] See Medical Appendix – 21. Mental Illness, page 350.

foetal brain development and cause anxiety, depression, and attention deficit disorder. All these were exhibited by her eldest son, Edward, and it is possible that these too were the result of her use of Cannabis.

Children were born in rapid succession – Victoria in 1841, Edward POW in 1842, Alice in 1843, Alfred in 1844, Helena in 1846, Louise in 1848, and Arthur in 1850. Anaesthesia was not available up until that time but in 1853 Leopold was born with the aid of Chloroform. This made obstetric anaesthesia extremely popular and many grateful women christened their daughters "Anaesthesia." The Queen's anaesthetic was administered by Dr John Snow who later rose to fame for discovering the waterborne transmission of Cholera in a Soho public water pump. And Victoria's son Leopold turned out to be a haemophiliac which was falsely blamed on Chloroform and led to a decline in its use.

The Haemophilia[66] suffered by Leopold was inherited from his mother who was a carrier of the disease but did not suffer from it herself. Until recently, haemophiliacs died before they had children themselves and its prevalence in the population was only maintained by fresh genetic mutations in previously unaffected families. And since there is no record of Haemophilia in the royal family before Queen Victoria's children, the mutation must have occurred in Queen Victoria herself.

The disease appeared in the family for generations thereafter and Victoria has haemophiliac descendants alive today, though not in the ruling royal family.

The pattern of inheritance is sex-linked recessive, and the cousin marriage between Victoria and Albert was irrelevant. Leopold was born in 1853 and was a brilliant son who excelled at public speaking. But the queen wrote to Disraeli that he never went for more than a few months without being laid up, and he had four or five times been at death's door. But he survived until adulthood and at the age of 29 he married Helen of Waldeck. They had a daughter, Alice, who passed Haemophilia to their son, Rupert. And he died at the age of 21 from a cerebral haemorrhage after he fell down some stairs and struck his head.

---

[66] See Medical Appendix – 3. Haemophilia, page 302.

Victoria had four daughters, three of whom were Haemophilia carriers. Her eldest, Victoria married the future German emperor Frederick III, and all of their eight children were unaffected by Haemophilia, including the future Emperor Wilhelm II. Her next daughter, Alice, was born in 1843 and married Louis IV, Grand Duke of Hesse. Their son, Frederick, died of bleeding aged three, and two of their daughters, Irene and Alix, had haemophiliac sons, one of whom, called Waldemar, died of bleeding in 1945. Alix married Tsar Nicholas II and their son, Alexis, was the most famous haemophiliac in history. His bleeding was treated homeopathically by the monk Rasputin, whose influence over the Tsarina destabilised the Russian court and led to Rasputin's murder.

During the Russian revolution the Tsarevich's bleeding episodes limited the mobility of the Romanov family and led to their arrest by the Bolsheviks and the execution of the whole family. In this way Haemophilia altered the history of Russia and the modern world.

Victoria's fourth daughter, Beatrice, married Henry of Battenburg and two of their three sons were haemophiliacs. In addition, her daughter Eugenie married Alphonso XIII of Spain, whose descendants are haemophilic males and female carriers and live in Canada. Victoria's sons, Edward, Arthur, and Alfred, were not affected by the disease and Edward VII did not transmit the disease to the present-day monarchy.

In 1847 Victoria took to bathing in the sea at Osborne on the Isle of Wight and in the happy months spent there each year she and Albert moved their court into a wing of Osborne House which was separate from their private rooms. Prince Albert became chairman of many committees including housing, industry, and the arts, and most importantly the committees to rebuild the Houses of Parliament and organise the Great Exhibition in London.

This was a stunning success which ran for six months and which the queen visited almost daily. And from the profits Albert built the Victoria and Albert Museum in Kensington. But the Crimea War broke out in 1854 and their relations with the Prime Minister, Palmerston, became strained. The royal family vetted Palmerstone's foreign correspondence and eventually forced his resignation. But with Albert introducing German customs in to Britain he was branded a foreigner and a spy. Eventually Palmerston was brought back to conduct the war and it was he who created Albert, Prince Consort.

In 1861 Albert was unable to eat for several months and with severe weight loss, he probably had cancer of the stomach. He had visited his son Edward in Cambridge to lecture him about his scandalous affair with a lady called Nellie Clifton, and they were walking in the lanes around Grantchester when they were drenched in a rain shower and Albert caught a chill. He died soon afterwards and Victoria irrationally blamed his death on her son's bad behaviour and never forgave him. At the time, Albert's doctors diagnosed Typhoid Fever but there was no epidemic at the time and cancer is now regarded as a more likely diagnosis. When he died at Windsor Victoria was inconsolable and collapsed. No post-mortem examination was allowed and a definitive cause of his death has never been clear.

Victoria kept his clothes and room as if he was still alive; his toiletries were changed daily and his bath was filled once a day with warm water. She sank into a long period of depression and fostered a cult of widowhood which other widows followed across the country. This prevented her public engagements and lost her public support. As a result, republicanism became a serious threat to the monarchy and it was only John Brown, her gillie at Balmoral, who could raise her spirits. Even so, Osborne and Balmoral became gloomy households which were freezing cold and the servants drank prodigious amounts of whisky to keep warm. And dressed in Indian uniforms, they communicated in silence by passing each other written notes.

In 1897 Victoria celebrated 60 years on the throne and after the international tensions of the Boer War, her Diamond Jubilee was turned into national rejoicing. But it was said Victoria was the most shot-at sovereign in British history and there were seven unsuccessful assassination attempts on her life. When a disturbed youth fired at her in the Mall, the law on treason had just been changed and the man escaped execution. In addition, in 1887 the government infiltrated an Irish-American Fenian plot with a double agent called Francis Millen, and this led to the arrest in London of a group of "dynamitards" in possession of high explosives.

Disraeli made her Empress of India in 1876 and she thought of herself as a liberal, although she opposed female suffrage and disliked modern music and art. She deserted Buckingham Palace and her son,

Edward, called it the Sepulcher. In old age, she became lame with rheumatism and her eyesight was clouded with cataracts. On 16th January 1901, the Royal physician Sir James Reid warned the Prince of Wales and his son George that the queen had suffered a slight stroke. She told Sir James that she would like to live a little longer as there were still a few things she wished to settle. Newspaper men crowded to Osborne for news and after each medical bulletin the post office in Cowes was besieged as the press tried to telephone London. On 20th the news became grave and on 22nd her huge family had assembled and went in to see her one by one. There was an unsuccessful attempt by Victoria's daughters to prevent her seeing Kaiser Wilhelm her grandson, and half an hour after Alexandra attended, Victoria died and the family broke down in tears. The body was covered in flowers and the family came back to the death bed and said prayers together.

Victoria had written instructions for a military funeral befitting her role as commander in chief of the armed forces. And as a soldier's daughter she ordered white was to be worn instead of black. On 25 January, the new King Edward VII, the German Kaiser and Arthur Duke of Connaught lifted her into the coffin dressed in her white dress and wedding veil. Albert's dressing gown was placed by her side with a plaster cast of Albert's hand, a lock of John Brown's hair and a picture of Brown in her hand but concealed from view by flowers. And her funereal jewellery included the wedding ring of John Brown's mother, which had been given to Victoria by Brown in 1883.

Her body was taken across the Solent to London in the royal yacht Albert, and with 38 Royal Navy warships off Spithead firing muffled guns, there were war ships gathered from Germany, Portugal, France, and Japan. After two days lying-in-state her funeral cortege to Windsor Castle was a huge international occasion, which included monarchs as far away Siam. And when the horses pulling the gun carriage kicked over their traces, it was pulled instead to the Frogmore Mausoleum at Windsor Great Park by a contingent of Royal Navy ratings.

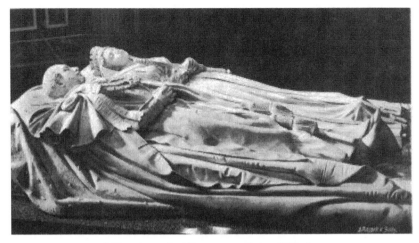

*Victoria and Albert memorial at Windsor*

Most people could not remember the time before she was queen or any of her Hanoverian predecessors. She had 10 Prime Ministers from Melbourne to Salisbury and her huge family established links throughout Europe. She reigned over an empire on which the sun never set and during her reign the Corn Laws were repealed, there was electoral reform and children were banned from working in the mines. An Education Act introduced universal education, flogging in the Army and the transportation of criminals were abolished, and she bequeathed a more modern country to the one she inherited.

# SAXE COBURG WINDSORS

## 1901-1952

*Edward VII*       *George V*

*Edward VIII*       *George VI*

# Edward VII

Edward VII was the oldest son of Queen Victoria and Prince Albert of Saxe Coburg. He was born in 1842, became king in 1901, and died of a heart attack at the age of 69.

He was a healthy baby and was inspected by the Duke of Wellington who liked his clear blue eyes. But from the age of five he developed a wilful lack of attention which caused concern. The Queen and Prince Albert had him examined by a phrenologist called Sir George Combe who said the boy's cranium was of a feeble-minded, obstinate, stray-willed individual and likened him to George III who had gone mad. Before long Queen Victoria came to feel that

Edward lived only for pleasure and he was unfit to succeed her.

For Victoria, the monarchy was the family business, and as a diversion from any dark habits he might have inherited from his Hanoverian ancestors, she inflicted a course of study on the little boy which gave him a perpetual sense of failure. He was slow to read and write and became a terrible scholar, and it now seems very likely that he had Attention Deficit Disorder and Victoria's use of Cannabis may have contributed to this. He hated being lectured about his royal duty and reacted against being taught gardening at Osborne House by throwing stones and breaking windows. Victoria once said she could not look at him without a shudder.

When he was handed into the care of an Eton schoolmaster called Henry Birch his temper tantrums became worse, and he sulked. He was isolated from other children and saw that his parents preferred his sisters to himself. When his behaviour worsened, Birch resigned and took Holy Orders, and Albert ordered a regimen of physical beating. For someone who could not spell let alone decline Latin nouns he was subjected to draconian schooling and developed a stammer and was teased by his sisters. He grew into an affectionate teenager but with no one on whom to lavish his affection, the visitors at Windsor were aghast at his tantrums and the endless sermons from his parents. There were outbursts of rage and he developed a tendency to be cruel to his friends and torment the servants. And when he became bored to tears more tutors came and left.

In 1855 at the age of 13 he accompanied Lord Clarendon to visit Napoleon III in Paris and he loved it. In 1857 he visited again and this time he got a little drunk and kissed a pretty girl. In 1859 he visited Rome and met the Pope, but he returned to England having failed to keep his promise to learn a little Italian. He next briefly attended Oxford University and stayed at Frewn Hall with six young friends. But he did no work, learned nothing, and was more interested in good food and expensive clothes than studying. He started to grow plump and a diet was prescribed but was unsuccessful. He also started smoking tobacco[67].

When he was 18 he went unaccompanied by his parents on the battleship *Hero* on a state visit to Canada and the USA. He met the

[67] See Medical Appendix – 18. Tobacco Diseases, page 342.

US President, watched Charles Blondin walk across the Niagara Falls on a tightrope, and went to balls. The visit was a great success and whilst some found him disappointing in conversation this first state trip taught him that charm was more important than knowledge, and this annoyed his parents who wanted to involve him in government. And from then on they regarded him unfit to wear the crown and he was given no more important duties.

He wanted to enlist in the Army but was sent instead to Cambridge University where his mentors kept him away from the decadent company of gentlemen students by housing him at Maddingly Hall four miles away.

But he absconded from lectures, fox hunted, went to the horse races and during a break which he spent with the Grenadier Guards near Dublin, he took up with a lady of easy virtue called Nellie Clifton. Following this it was decided he did not have the makings of a soldier and when he visited Napoleon III in Paris again he started to enjoy gambling.

In 1861, Prince Albert had been ill for three months but insisted on visiting Edward at Maddingly Hall where he lectured his errant son on the facts of life. He returned home but then died. Victoria blamed this on the stress of having a son like Edward and in a dark depression which lasted for years, she lost faith in him and excluded him from all affairs of state. He was not trusted to keep information confidential and was not allowed to meet foreign dignitaries or see cabinet papers. His mother warned him that his lifestyle would alienate the working classes and his response was to invite socialists to Sandringham and to serve meals in their rooms because they had no evening dress. Efforts were made to mend the rift between mother and son but to no avail, and with nothing to do he visited Venice, Egypt, Palestine, Constantinople, Greece, and Jordan.

When the news about Nellie Clifton became public, Victoria determined he should marry. Photographs were assembled of attractive Protestant European princesses and eventually Princess Alexandra of Denmark was selected. She was beautiful and unintellectual and they married in 1863 when he was 21, she dressed in Honiton lace and he in the uniform of a general.

*Princess Alexandra of Denmark*

Victoria turned the wedding into a second funeral for Albert and even took the married couple to visit Albert's mausoleum at Frogmore. With Victoria secluded at Osborne and Balmoral, the newlyweds achieved some marital independence by moving into Marlborough House in Pall Mall. Edward inherited the income from the Duchy of Cornwall with which he purchased a great shooting estate at Sandringham. But after his wedding he continued to visit London clubs and go horse racing, and associate with society women such as Lady Filmer, Lilly Langtry, Hortense Schneider, Lady Brook, and Alice Keppel.

An example of how he enriched these young ladies in return for sexual favours is shown by the case of Alice Keppel. Edward's friend, Sir Ernest Cassel, created a fund for her and instead of giving her money direct from the Privy Purse, gave her shares in a rubber company which gained, the modern equivalent of around £7.5 million. Edward's own bankers managed her financial affairs and to keep her husband content, Edward obtained him a good job working for Sir Thomas Lipton and appointed her brother to the royal household as a Groom in Waiting.

In 1863 Alexandra had her first child who was named after Prince Albert but was always called Edward or Eddie. A second son, George, was born, and then three daughters. But Alexandra then developed rheumatism which left her with a permanent limp which extraordinarily became fashionable and was imitated by women in society. She also inherited deafness from her mother and transmitted this to her son, George V. Alport's and Alstrom's Syndromes are hereditary forms of deafness which can be associated with kidney and eye disease. In Alexandra, however, this was not the case, though her deafness was a considerable disability and before modern deaf aids, she had to hide it by pretending to hear everyone. It was, however, the final straw and it effectively ended her marriage to Edward when she went to live with her mother.

Edward moved back to his former lifestyle and a public scandal soon followed. Sir Charles Mordaunt was a country gentleman who in 1868 invited Edward to Walton Hall on a fishing holiday, and there it was alleged Edward seduced Mordaunt's wife, Harriette, and she became pregnant. A divorce case followed in which Edward was cited for adultery, until his physician Sir William Gull testified that Harriette was insane. This was the first time in 500 years that an heir to the throne had been arraigned before the courts, and leading figures like Charles Bradlaugh pilloried him in the national newspapers and lost him huge public support. Harriette was certainly a strange person but it was harsh when she was consigned to a lunatic asylum for the rest of her life. Edward was acquitted but from then on he was not respected, and over 50 Republican clubs were formed.

Edward loved his visits to the hedonistic court of Napoleon III and he had a string of extramarital relationships with actresses like Sarah Bernhard, Cora Pearl, and Jenni Churchill, the future Prime minister's mother. In Paris he visited brothels which had special chairs and baths built for him to receive sexual gratification without effort on his part. Gossip was spread of his affairs with can-can dancers at the Moulin Rouge, and one of the gossipers, Lady Daisy Brook, became known as the Babbling Brook and Edward was called Edward the Caressor.

In 1891 he caught Typhoid Fever[68] after a visit to Lord Londsborough, and the bad drains in Scarborough were blamed for this. A fellow guest called the Earl of Chesterfield died from Typhoid and when Edward became seriously ill, national prayers were said. Queen Victoria nursed him through a delirium in which he berated a Dr Gull and knocked over Princess Alexandra with a pillow. At Sandringham he slowly recovered and he started drinking beer and

---

[68] See Medical Appendix – 12. Typhoid, page 331.

singing and whistling in bed. Then Disraeli agreed he could convalesce in the Mediterranean where there were fewer distractions and less risk of assassination.

When Napoleon III died in exile at Chislehurst in Kent, Edward unwisely expressed anti-German sentiments and created friction with the PM. Lavish parties and endless affairs followed, with married women and the involvement of the divorce courts. He was still blocked from seeing state papers by the queen and Disraeli, and when he spent more time abroad he was also criticised for this too. But in 1886 Lord Roseberry started to send him state papers and in 1892 he was given his father's golden key to the foreign office red boxes. He was then sent to India and after the enormous success of this trip Victoria was crowned Empress of India.

Back in England his life was an endless stream of parties and Lord Rothschild and Sir Christopher Sykes advised him about his finances and lent him money. Sometimes surviving on two hours' sleep a night, he rushed between his house to his club, to the theatre, the card tables, the spa, the yacht, and the grouse moor. He fenced and played billiards and at Sandringham as many as 3,000 birds and 6,000 rabbits were shot in a single day. He liked making his friends the butt of jokes and would eject them from his social circle if they complained.

He bullied his friends for money and sometimes he bankrupted them and refused them knighthoods. Since Victoria was absent from public life for many years after the death of Albert, the reputation of the monarchy plummeted, and sympathy for a French-style republic grew alarmingly.

After the Doncaster races at a party at Tranby Croft, Edward's indiscretion let him down in a very serious way when he participated in an illegal card game of Baccarat. This was judged a game of chance which required no skill and it was illegal if played for money. Worse still, a participant called Gordon Cumming was accused of cheating, and brought a case of libel against Edward. As a key witness Edward was seated next to the judge Lord Coleridge, and Gordon Cumming's case was rejected and Edward walked free. But he was booed by the crowds at Ascot, and Queen Victoria felt it was a terrible humiliation.

His gourmet dining led to him becoming extremely overweight and his Savile Row tailors, Henry Poole and Co., recorded that his waistline which had measured 29 ¼" when he was 19 years old, had expanded to 46 ½" when he was 51. He was threatened with murder but after the man was arrested Edward intervened to commute the man's prison sentence. In 1900 he survived a serious assassination attempt when a 16-year-old called Jean Baptiste Sipido fired a revolver but missed him at point-blank range. The attempt took place on the Royal train on a visit to Brussels just as Edward was taking a cup of tea. Sipido testified that he had attempted to kill Edward to protest the unnecessary sacrifice of human life in the Boer War, and he regretted not killing the prince. Following this Edward matured a little and took more care. But he still took endless mistresses and gave up trying to conceal this. Among these Alice Keppel was the most trustworthy, and being able to control Edward's short temper she remained a close companion until his death. His home at Marlborough House became the political epicentre of national politics and he developed a formidable information network at home and abroad and became known as Europe's uncle. He started to stand in for the aging Queen and persuaded her to celebrate her 1887 and 1897 jubilees.

When she died in 1901 he wept but couldn't get aboard the state coach fast enough. He ransacked Buckingham Palace for any remnants of John Brown, installed electric lights, modernised the household toilets and bathrooms, installed telephones, converted the coach houses to garages and swapped the horse carriages for motor cars. He had always enjoyed the rituals and regalia of Freemasonry and the whole monarchy was smartened up with new uniforms. He quickly restored the pageantry of the monarchy and resumed the practice of the monarch opening Parliament. He was against socialism, the welfare state, national insurance, and trades unions. And also female suffrage and devolving government to the colonies. In 1910, however, he accepted the removal of the veto of the House of Lords.

Aged 59, he was a stout 16 stone in weight and a grandfather with a grey beard and a bald head. But his personal income had risen spectacularly and he had boundless energy. He cycled on a specially reinforced tricycle, took up golf, enjoyed batting in cricket matches at Sandringham, drove huge German motor cars at high speed, and attended rowing and sailing regattas at Henley and Cowes. And among his stable of horses, Persimon won the Derby and Ambush won the Grand National in the same year, the only time this has ever happened.

In the years before the outbreak of WW1 he became the focus of international interest. But his involvement in politics became a serious problem for the Prime Minister, Arthur Balfour, especially when Edward had temper tantrums over policy. He travelled in France, Germany, and Russia, and with his cousin the Kaiser arming Germany against encirclement, Edward rejected the British policy of splendid isolation and saw France as a bulwark against Germany. The Kaiser regarded this as Machiavellian and accused Edward of building an anti-German alliance based on Royal Navy dreadnoughts and a Territorial Army. He visited France without the permission of the PM and was instrumental in promoting the Entente Cordiale. This cooled international tensions but eventually turned into a military alliance which embroiled Europe in WW1. As a result a monarch has never been allowed to delve into politics again.

In St Petersburg he attended the funeral of Czar Alexander and he took the French side in the Franco-Prussian war and alienated the German Kaiser. They vied with each other to build faster racing yachts and bigger battleships, and they avoided visiting the same cities at the same time so as not to meet each other inadvertently. On one occasion, he infuriated the Kaiser by giving ceremonial precedence over the Crown Prince of Germany to Kala Kua, the King of the Cannibal Islands. He opened hospitals, schools, libraries and art galleries, signed 6,000 commissions for the Army, and gave unscripted speeches to august bodies such as the Privy Council. He loved having his son's family at Sandringham and he adored his grandchildren.

But he ate vast 12-course meals of the richest foods at a rate which astonished his guests, and he even had cold chicken by his bedside in case he woke hungry in the night. He smoked 20 Egyptian cigarettes[69] and 10 Corona cigars a day, drank only champagne and brandy, preferred the conversation of women to men, had a memory for faces, and slept with a fox terrier called Caesar in his bedroom.

His travels continued and the list of his paramours spread across France and Germany and into Spain and Russia where he would sometimes give his police escort the slip. In 1871 he contracted Typhoid Fever again and in 1889 he suffered phlebitis. In 1898 he fell down the stairs at Ferdinand de Rothschild's home at Waddeston

---

[69] See Medical Appendix – 18. Tobacco Diseases, page 342.

Manor and fractured his kneecap. And in 1901, just before his coronation, he developed appendicitis. On 14th June he developed abdominal pains and cancelled attending Royal Ascot. The pains worsened and a diagnosis of an appendix abscess was made by the Royal Surgeon, Sir Frederick Treves, who later became famous for treating Joseph Merrick, the Elephant Man. Treves strongly advised Edward to undergo an appendicectomy. But the arrangements for the coronation had reached an advanced stage and Edward refused surgery until Treves told him the only way he was going to Westminster Abbey was in a coffin.

An operating theatre was set up in Buckingham Palace and during the anaesthetic Edward's breathing stopped and his face turned black. But Treves successfully drained the abscess and next day Edward was sitting up in bed smoking a cigar. His delayed coronation took place in 1902 and many of his mistresses were seated together in Westminster Abbey in what the aristocracy called his loose box. It was a much less grand occasion than originally planned and some said that his appendicitis saved the country a fortune. In addition, Edward's survival also avoided the succession of his profligate older son, Eddie, and the republic which many predicted if Eddie ever became king.

With his prodigious weight and worsening emphysema, Edward's hectic lifestyle slowed and he became sexually impotent, and received electrical therapy to improve his vital energy. Quack remedies and devices such as electropathic belts were popular at the time but they worked no better than whips or cold baths and there is no evidence they worked in the king's case.

By 1909 he could hardly climb stairs and Sir James Reid attended him for coughing seizures and fainting spells. He would not stop smoking and had one public fall at the theatre and another at a dinner party.

In 1910 at the age of 69 he returned from Biarritz to hear Madam Tetrazzini sing in Rigoletto at Covent Garden, and next day he attended a private viewing at the Royal Academy. He returned to Sandringham where his smoker's cough worsened and he became unable to breathe normally or speak above a whisper. He then suffered a series of heart attacks and Dr Reid attended him.

He was given oxygen and morphine, and the vasodilators,

strychnine, tyramine, and ether. His son was told his father was very ill and Queen Alexandra was called back from holiday in Corfu. He insisted on being dressed formally in his frock coat and was propped up in a chair to see her. And when the Archbishop of Canterbury was next to see him he asked him if his horse Witch of the Air had won at Kempton Park. The family were shocked when he worsened next day and he was transferred to Buckingham Palace. Alice Keppel was allowed to visit him but he then fell unconscious and on the night of 6th May he died in his bed. Asquith, the Prime Minister, was in Gibraltar and rushed home on HMS *Enchantress*.

Edward was laid in state for three days in Westminster Hall and big crowds filed past the coffin. The funeral was attended by the German and Japanese Emperors, eight kings and two presidents, and his funeral cortege was led by his son the new King George V. His horse, Kildare, and his pet dog, Caesar, were part of the funeral procession, and in later years Caesar "wrote" a book called *Where's Master?* which was very popular. At the wake, they all signed each other's invitation cards as souvenirs and Edward was buried in Windsor where his tomb includes a figure of the dog.

In retrospect and despite all his faults, Edward was responsible for laying the foundations of the modern constitutional monarchy, and Lord Fisher said that he wasn't clever but he did the right things. In addition, the newspaper eulogies did not mention his manifold sins. Queen Alexandra lived on quietly in Sandringham and having been a ravishing young beauty she greatly minded her vanishing good looks. She became completely deaf and almost without eyesight but demanded that her son, George, keep her informed about family affairs and ever the dutiful son, he obliged. She continued to live in the big house whilst King George and Queen May used Yorke Cottage, and they were all at Sandringham when she died after a heart attack in 1925 at the age of 81. She was laid in state for four days looked over by the men of the Sandringham estate, and was buried alongside Edward at Windsor.

# George V

George V was born in 1865 and was the son of Edward VII and Princess Alexandra of Denmark. He became Prince of Wales when his older brother died of Influenza[70] in 1892 and he became king when he was 45. He died of heart failure and a stroke at the age of 71.

He was brought up by Queen Alexandra who disliked and avoided her husband's licentious social life. As a result, George and his five siblings were raised in virtual isolation at Yorke Cottage on the Sandringham estate. She read the Bible to them every day and their relationship remained infantile into adult life when she still referred to him as "little Georgie". Queen Victoria ruled out schooling with other children and they were educated privately under the tutelage of a clergyman called John Dalton. George was a poor scholar but his older brother Eddie was even worse, and could not spell, or read or speak a foreign language.

---

[70] See Medical Appendix – 7. Influenza, page 317.

Dalton was a martinet who shared Queen Victoria's fear of Hanoverian moral impurity, and from 7am until 8pm he subjected the children to the quarter deck discipline of the Royal Navy. They had a drill sergeant and gymnastic, fencing, riding, and dancing instructors. They also learned tennis, croquet, and shooting, and whenever Dalton passed them presents from Queen Victoria it was always with a reminder to do their duty.

As the spare, not the heir, George was destined for a career at sea and at the age of 12 he became a naval cadet at Britannia Royal Naval College in Dartmouth. Eddie was already there under the supervision of Dalton and though the princes were abysmal scholars, George developed good common sense and excelled in practical subjects like sailing. He also acquired a bluff salty sense of humour which not everyone found funny, and in later life he said the tough training had done him no good at all.

After two years Eddie, George and Dalton were transferred to HMS *Bacchante* and it was in an atmosphere of orderliness and routine that George began writing a diary which ran from 1880 until he died in 1936. In clear handwriting he always recorded the wind direction, the barometric pressure, the places he had visited, the people he met and, if at Sandringham, how many pheasants he had shot. In one entry he also recorded he had read Oliver Twist and Nicholas Nickleby.

On HMS *Bacchante* they cruised the world and they were in South Africa at the outbreak of the Boer War. The two boys were treated as midshipmen without special privileges, and George was often seasick. In 1882 Eddie had failed to progress; he and Dalton were withdrawn to London, leaving George lonely and heartbroken. By the age of 21 he had grown a beard and his public image as a sailor was established. He learned to speak German and in the company of his father he visited the Kaiser in Berlin. Queen Alexandra repeatedly asked George to remain pure "for her sake" but unbeknown to her he fell under the influence of his brother and visited girlfriends in Southsea and in parts of London.

*Prince Albert, Duke of Clarence*

In 1891 George caught Typhoid Fever[71] and it took him seven weeks to recover. Eddie's behaviour went from bad to worse and he became embroiled in every sort of scandal. He came close to public humiliation for using a male brothel in Cleveland Street, and others like the Earl of Euston and Lord Somerset stood trial or fled abroad. Eddie was obliged to admit to less serious misdemeanours and when these were made public the London club circle called it an establishment cover-up and circulated ridiculous rumours including his alleged involvement in the Jack the Ripper murders.

The royal family became desperate and decided to marry Eddie to Princess Mary of Teck. She was a lively and enquiring young woman who was prepared to overlook Eddie's bisexuality because she believed it could be cured by marriage. But in January 1892 Eddie caught Influenza[72]. This virulent epidemic originated in Bukharan in Russia and eventually it swept around the world, killing over one million victims.

Within a week Eddie had died of pneumonia and George became heir to the throne. Many thought this saved the monarchy from a

---

[71] See Medical Appendix – 12. Typhoid, page 331.
[72] See Medical Appendix – 7. Influenza, page 317.

disastrous king and most people were secretly relieved. Princess Mary's bridal gown was laid on her fiancée's coffin and her wedding was turned into a funeral. George seemed not to have caught the disease and was devastated at Eddie's death. The spare was now the heir and he gave up his naval career and began to attend the House of Lords and travel abroad on official engagements. In 1893 Queen Victoria suggested he should marry his dead brother's fiancée and when they got to know one another they became enamoured.

*Princess Mary of Teck*

After the state wedding they went to live modestly in York Cottage on the Sandringham estate in Norfolk. It was an overflow bachelor's cottage for the Prince of Wales' shooting parties, and George and Mary lived there until he succeeded to the throne 17 years later. Here he led the life of a Norfolk country squire and it was entirely fitted out by a shop on Tottenham Court Road.

George was in awe of his father with whom he was allowed to work on state affairs, and they shared the same private secretary. But he avoided the social life of his father's circle when this moved periodically to the big house at Sandringham, and George devoted his life to his family. Yorke Cottage remained silent alongside the gaiety and late-night glamour in the big house, and with his father's parties in full swing, the lights in the cottage went out at precisely 11:10pm every night.

George and Mary had five sons, two of whom succeeded to the throne as Edward VIII and George VI, and they were all healthy except the youngest, Prince John, who was backward from birth and died at the age of 13. He was a severe epileptic[73] and in an age before effective treatment, the family was embarrassed by his seizures and did not want him exposed to public life. As a result, he was brought up in isolation by a nanny on Wood Farm on the Sandringham estate. Until one day when he had fallen asleep after a fit and a nurse found him dead in bed. It seems likely that his airway had become obstructed by his tongue or he inhaled vomit. And it occurred during the 1919 state visit of President Wilson of the USA, from which the king and queen absented themselves and returned to Sandringham. Their son, Henry, Duke of Gloucester, served in the Guards and his only ambition in life was to become their colonel. He married Alice Montague Douglas Scott from Boughton House in Northamptonshire and kept out of the intrigue which surrounded his brothers. But he inherited and passed on the family's Porphyria[74] to the next generation and confirmed that Queen Victoria and her father, the Duke of Kent, were obligate carriers of the disease.

*Prince John*

---

[73] See Medical Appendix – 20. Epilepsy, page 348.
[74] See Medical Appendix – 2. Porphyria, page 296.

George and Mary's other son, George, Duke of Kent, led an unconventional social life. For a period he frequented the London club circuit, acquired cocaine and opium addictions, and was subjected to blackmail attempts. He mixed in the celebrity social set and had sexual relationships with men and women including Barbara Cartland the novelist, Anthony Blunt the Soviet spy, and Noel Coward the playwright. One story from that time was how he and Coward dressed as women were arrested in London as suspected prostitutes. He fathered several illegitimate children and dated a black American revue artiste, but his marriage proposal to a debutante called Poppy Baring was judged a move too far and it was blocked by Buckingham Palace. He eventually married Princess Marina of Greece and his lifestyle changed. In the lead-up to WW2 he was trained in intelligence work and may have been involved in last-minute attempts to negotiate with German Nazis to avoid war. He gained his pilot's license and became the first member of the royal family to fly across the Atlantic. But in 1942 he joined the RAF and was killed in a Sunderland flying boat in Scotland. It crashed into a mountain and only the rear gunner survived. Much suspicion was aroused as he was carrying large sums of Swedish currency and one suggestion was he was en route to pick up the defecting Nazi leader, Rudolph Hesse.

George and Mary were loving parents but George subjected his sons to military discipline and terrified them with his temper. In addition, they were bullied by a sadistic nanny called Mary Edwards. As a result, David always looked at the ground when he spoke, Bertie had a stammer, and Henry had a nervous laugh. And whilst Bertie grew up to show kindness to others, David rebelled and caused trouble. As a result, a gap developed between him and his father and this was never resolved.

For recreation George sailed, played golf and tennis and shot pheasants, and the clocks in Yorke Cottage were advanced half an hour ahead of Greenwich Mean Time to maximise the day's pheasant shooting. He became one of the finest of marksmen, killed over one million pheasants, and it was said he kept a gun next to his bed for him to practice gun handling before going down to breakfast. Sandringham was turned into the finest game shoot in the country and the birds were fattened so much they could hardly fly.

Only occasionally did he go up to London to attend parties and play billiards, and instead he developed an interest in philately. His spectacular stamp collection included a unique 2p Mauritius Blue and nowadays it is still the most important private stamp collection in existence. He attended the funeral of the murdered Tsar Alexander in St Petersburg and was a pall bearer at Gladstone's funeral. He witnessed the first attempts at flying and visited the first cinemas. He also travelled widely throughout the Empire and in 1901 it was said that he shook hands with 24,855 people.

When his grandmother, Queen Victoria, died in 1901, he said she was the greatest woman who had ever lived. And when his father, King Edward VII, died in 1910, he said he had lost his best friend. These statements may not have been strictly true but this sort of good nature was largely responsible for his success as a monarch. His coronation was marred by the death of Queen Mary's brother, Prince Francis of Teck, who had bequeathed the family's Cambridge emeralds in his will to one of his mistresses. To minimise publicity the new Queen Mary was forced to buy these back for an enormous sum of money and since that time all Royal wills have been sealed by the Family Division of the High Court.

Immediately after George's coronation the Liberal government proposed a budget which the House of Lords blocked. Lloyd George demanded a Parliament Bill to squash the powers of the Lords and he pressurised the new king to create 500 new peers in order to pass the budget. George was in an untenable position until the Lords capitulated and passed the Parliament Bill to prevent it happening again. George viewed the whole episode with distaste as it permanently removed the Lords' prerogative and the last illusions of the monarch's power.

After the coronation George and Mary travelled to India and conducted a bizarre but successful Coronation Durbar at which he accepted the oath of loyalty of the Indian princes. There was a ceremony to found the nation's new capital, Delhi, and the king and queen presented themselves to the Indian people from the balcony of Shah Jahan's Palace. George then went off to Nepal to shoot tigers.

In 1890 came the only scandal of his reign when he successfully sued a newspaper which accused him of having secretly married an admiral's daughter in Malta. The journalist was convicted of sedition and imprisoned. George diligently attended to cabinet papers but his early reign was marked by the rise of trades unionism, Irish republicanism and women's suffrage, all of which he disliked.

The German Imperial Navy grew to threaten Britain's dominance at sea and both countries began constructing dreadnought battleships. In 1911 anarchists fought a pitched battle in Sidney Street, and troops were deployed in London. In England there were 800 industrial strikes and in Ireland there was civil unrest. In Parliament, the Minimum Wages Act and the Trades Dispute Act protected Trades Unions for the first time, and the National Insurance Act laid the foundation of the modern welfare state. That year too, the Imperial Conference set up a chain of wireless stations around the world and the empire shrank in size. Conflicts of interest between European nations threatened the peace and at the outbreak of WW1 in 1914, George tried to keep his Anglo-German family ties out of the conflict and even tried to retain the honorary appointments which he and his cousin, the Kaiser Wilhelm, held in opposing armies. He travelled widely throughout the war, made hundreds of regimental and hospital visits and presented thousands of medals. He also gave up alcohol as an example to munitions workers and to dispel the unwarranted myth that he was a clandestine alcoholic.

But during a visit to Labuissiere in France in 1915 he was thrown from his horse when three cheers went up at a parade of the Royal Flying Corps. Slipping on wet ground, the horse fell backwards on top of him and he was seriously injured. He was removed on a stretcher and an X-ray showed a fractured pelvis. In such pain he did not sleep for three days, he was transferred by hospital train and was seasick on the stormy crossing back to England. He needed strong painkillers for four weeks and most people said he was never the same again.

Whilst he seemed untouched by the suffering of the troops, his son David was more obviously moved and this widened the rift between them. Wartime atrocities gave rise to anti-German riots in Britain and when Gotha bombers raided London, the risk to the Sax Coburg Gotha dynasty became acute. As a result and acting on advice from Lord Stamfordham, it was decided in 1917 to change the royal family name to Windsor. In addition, the Tecks became Cambridges and the Battenburgs became Mountbattens. The German Kaiser referred to them all as the Merry Wives of Saxe Coburg but when HG Wells described them as alien and uninspiring, George retorted that he might be uninspiring but he was damned if he was alien.

This attention to image-making continued in 1918 when his Romanov cousins in Russia sought refuge in England during the Bolshevik revolution. Following the increasing unrest in Russia, communications between George and Nicholas became difficult, and when the Russian ambassador in London died in the Influenza[75] pandemic which was sweeping Europe, he was not replaced. The Tsar's family found it more difficult to travel because of the Haemophilia[76] of the young Tsarevich. Eventually the British cabinet decided it was unwise for Britain to ally itself to Russian autocrats, and George's cousins were left to fend for themselves and were shot by the Bolsheviks.

Over one million men died in the trenches in France and Belgium but on 11th November 1918, Marshal Foch signed the armistice in a train in the Forest of Compiègne. The war sanctions imposed upon the Germans at the Versailles Conference shocked the king and as social unrest grew in England, mass rallies were organised and radicals preached republicanism. Faced with the growth of socialism and interest in the Soviet system, George's response was unforeseen and inspired. He started visiting coal mines and football matches, took up the nation's interest in horse racing and in 1928 his filly, Scuttle, won the 1,000 Guineas at Newmarket. His perception of the changing working classes was astute and at one of the football matches he remarked that he could see no Bolsheviks in the huge crowd of spectators.

Lord Leopold Mountbatten was George's cousin, and in 1922 he died at the age of 32 when he bled to death after a minor operation. A further reminder of the family's Haemophilia[77] came in 1928 when Princess Alice's son, Rupert, died at the age of 21 in France. He was recovering from a minor road traffic accident when he disturbed his bandages and the bleeding restarted. There were other continental cousins affected with Haemophilia but George's immediate family

---

[75] See Medical Appendix – 7. Influenza, page 317.
[76] See Medical Appendix – 3. Haemophilia, page 302.
[77] See Medical Appendix – 3. Haemophilia, page 302.

and his subsequent heirs did not inherit the disease.

After the General Election in 1923 George exercised his only remaining prerogative when the government was split and he sent for Baldwin, not Curzon, as Prime Minister. But in 1925 his tobacco smoking[78] began to take its toll and he suffered heavy attacks of bronchitis. He was unable to write his diary for 13 days and when ordered to convalesce he went on the royal yacht for two weeks to Sicily. Though he returned refreshed, he next had to face the miners' and national strikes and in his diary he asked what Queen Victoria might have felt about a Labour government.

Through cinema news reports he became better known than any previous monarch, and through his BBC radio broadcasts at Christmas he inspired loyalty and affection from all sections of society. He and his son the future Edward VIII continued to travel widely and the royal tours were a great success.

But George had become an extremely conservative personality who loathed change and had bizarre attitudes to everyday frustrations. He inherited family deafness from his mother and came to dislike socialists, jazz, new dance steps, cocktails, and ladies with painted fingernails. A minor fashion change to his wife's skirt length could send him into a furore and he shouted in public at women who wore shorter skirts. He once attacked a painting by Cezanne with a cane and berated his son for not wearing gloves at a ball.

Queen Mary was deferential but the Prince of Wales found him intolerable. The Prince could communicate instinctively with all sections of society but this popularity annoyed the king who was aghast at the women who threw themselves at his son. In addition, David's affairs with married women created serious family quarrels. It was said that George had set out to raise his older son as a paragon of virtue and he ended up with a monster. When David eventually took up with Wallis Simpson, the twice-divorced American who was to become his wife and force his abdication, the king would not accept her and David told all sorts of lies in order to have her admitted to Buckingham Palace. When George's second son, Bertie, married the much more acceptable Elizabeth Bowes Lyon, unfavourable comparisons were drawn with Wallis Simpson, and

---

[78] See Medical Appendix – 18. Tobacco Diseases, page 342.

George said he prayed that Bertie, not David, would become his successor. But through all of these difficulties George got on extremely well with his grandchildren and he was remembered with great affection by the future Queen Elizabeth II.

He continued to suffer pain from his old horse-riding injury and at a time when the dangers of tobacco were unknown, he remained a lifelong chain smoker. Following a chest infection in 1928 a chest X-ray revealed a lung abscess. Lord Dawson supervised the medical management and senior sisters from London hospitals were brought in to nurse him. But it was Queen Mary who was credited for giving him the will to survive. Under general anaesthetic on 12th December a chest effusion was drained but the surgical wound burst open and a second operation was needed.

Deep X-ray therapy (radiotherapy) was administered because a cancer was suspected. But his condition weakened and when heart failure appeared he lost consciousness. Large crowds assembled to read the daily medical bulletins posted on the gates of Buckingham Palace and when a Royal warrant appointed a Council to rule in his stead, he was barely strong enough to sign it. But within a couple of months it was felt that he would survive and he was sent to convalesce in Bognor.

He made little of his suffering, constantly thanked his nurses, and in between periods of semi-consciousness his greatest concern was to keep his beard trimmed. Now and again his navy humour returned and when asked to bestow the title "Regis" on the town he told an aide to "bugger Bognor". He was allowed to smoke again and was taken back to London by the St John's Ambulance Corps. He had lost a lot of weight but enjoyed watching Elizabeth, his granddaughter, play, and was entertained by a military band and started writing his diary again.

There were two relapses for which he underwent a thoracoplasty under general anaesthetic to remove a rib and drain chest fluid. And after this he made a slow return to royal duties. This illness left him looking older than his 64 years and from then on Sister Catherine Black of the London Hospital was kept on the permanent staff of the palace.

This all took place against the background of the Great Depression, the General Strike, and republican threats to the monarchy. He gave up part of his Civil List income to set an example, but the Fascist Party of Oswald Moseley marched in London and the Red Flag was sung in Trafalgar Square. In 1931 Mahatma Gandhi started moves towards Indian independence and the Pound Sterling came under pressure.

Then his closest friend Lord Stamfordham died and King Alfonso of Spain was deposed. In 1932 from a tiny room under the stairs at Sandringham he broadcast a Christmas message written for him by Rudyard Kipling.

Germany began to resist the reparations imposed under the Versailles Treaty and during Hitler's rise to power it was said that George was shocked to hear that Hitler did not play cricket. From then on he had recurrent chest infections and became a lonely figure who gave up visiting Cowes and shooting pheasants at Sandringham. More and more his family life dominated, and this included a parrot called Charlotte and a pony called Jack.

In 1935 George and Mary celebrated their Silver Jubilee. They paraded through London's East End and when they presented themselves on the balcony at Buckingham Palace, the crowds loved it and he was deeply touched. But in December 1935 his bronchitis deteriorated and this time there was serious heart failure. In the newspapers the nation was made aware that his condition was grave and the radio light entertainment was replaced with solemn music. As the nation was re-arming, he lay dying, and it was Queen Mary who made the last entries in his diary.

His red dispatch boxes went unattended and in January the Privy Council attended for him to sign a proclamation handing over power to a Council of State. As he sat in a Tibetan dressing gown he apologised for keeping them waiting, and having lost the power of his right hand because of a minor stroke, he signed "xx" with his left hand. His son David returned from France and when Archbishop Cosmo Lang was asked to confer a blessing many of those present were in tears.

His senior physician Lord Dawson announced to the nation that the king's life was drawing peacefully to a close, and according to a witness report he orchestrated the king's death to time its announcement in the more respectable national newspapers. George slipped into a coma at five minutes to midnight, and as Dawson administered an injection of 60mg of cocaine and 40mg morphine into the king's jugular vein his last words were, "How is the Empire?" This was a lethal dose and is the only instance of medical euthanasia in the history of the British monarchy. It was also illegal and was only divulged years later after the death of the only witness, Sister Catherine Black.

The news was flashed around the world by telegraph and in India the bazaars were closed and the mosques were filled with worshippers. In Singapore an aeroplane flew overhead with a long black streamer and in Hong Kong the newspapers carried black edging. It was said that in some parts of Africa the news was spread by the beating of drums.

In a coffin built from an oak tree on the Sandringham estate, his body was removed to London on the Royal train. Over one million people filed past the coffin as he lay in state, and unknown to the public on the last night, the new king and his brothers, Bertie, Harry, and George stood guard over the catafalque in dress uniform. But his Maltese Cross fell from the coffin, and people took this to be a bad omen for the new king's reign.

*The catafalque of George V*

The funeral cortege included his pony, Jack, and a piper playing Flowers of the Forest, and it drew the largest crowds London had ever seen. And when one of the sailors drawing the coffin on its gun carriage fainted, his comrades closed ranks and carried him upright between them. Microphones had been erected along the route for a worldwide radio broadcast, but all that was heard was the tramp of marching feet and the roll of muffled drums. He was buried in St George's chapel at Windsor in a tomb designed by Sir Edwin Lutyens and it was said "there had sat on the throne of England more brilliant, more able monarchs, but no sovereign who had proved himself more honourable". He had helped steer the nation through scandal, war, and upheaval and the nation loved him. His only great fault was that he raised his oldest son badly, and depending on how well people knew the future king, they looked towards the reign of Edward VIII with a sense of eagerness or trepidation.

Queen Mary lived on until 1953 and died in London aged 86. She is buried alongside George at Windsor.

# Edward VIII

Edward VIII was the son of George V and Princess Mary of Teck and was born at White Lodge in Richmond Park in 1894. He became king at the age of 42 but abdicated after 11 months and died in France of throat cancer aged 78.

When he was born it was the first time four royal generations were alive at the same time and his grandfather, who was Prince of Wales, was at a ball and stopped the dancing to propose a toast to the baby boy. Queen Victoria attended his christening where he was named Edward Albert Christian George Andrew Patrick David, but in the family he was called David. He found it hard to pay attention to his school lessons and was a poor scholar. In later life he could barely conceal his inattention at important meetings and he would suddenly go off on a tangent and start talking about something like horse racing.

After his great-grandmother Queen Victoria died in 1901 there was a huge circle of hedonistic friends who surrounded his grandfather. In contrast, Edward's parents were strict disciplinarians and as a baby he had a nanny who pinched him and twisted his arm, and a butler who spanked him if he was naughty. He was educated at Sandringham by a tutor called Hansell and his childhood was solemn, disciplined, and cheerless. His father, George V, was a family bully who had a foul temper made worse by indigestion. But when his father was away the little boy enjoyed visits to London with his mother and they went out and about together without the public knowing.

Destined for the Royal Navy, in 1907 he became a naval cadet at Osborne. But he was bottom of the class and only with extra tuition did he eventually climb to 46th out of 60 students. In his last term he was joined by his younger brother, Bertie, and they were both transferred to Britannia Royal Naval College at Dartmouth where they caught mumps and measles. As shown on the shore memorial at HMS Ganges in Mylor, young Royal Navy cadets were much more likely to die of infectious diseases than warfare, and the killer diseases were diphtheria and scarlet fever.

He attended his father's coronation in 1936 and when invested as Prince of Wales he managed to say a few words in Welsh which Lloyd George taught him. At 18 he became Duke of Cornwall and from getting one shilling a week from the Royal Navy, he became a very wealthy young man with the income from thousands of west country acres as well as properties in London. He was introduced to alcohol and tobacco and joined his father to shoot pheasants at Sandringham. He said that alcohol enabled him to view the world with the broad span of a king of England, but others were worried about his intake and he periodically sought a cure for heavy drinking.

His brother Bertie said that Edward's personality changed after adolescence and he became devoid of loyalty or affection and seemed to have no soul anymore. On safari in Kenya he received the news of his father's death with callousness and his staff were shocked. And when he became king he dismissed his father's staff without thanks or remorse. He was sent to Magdalen College Oxford where he failed to study and spent eight terms fox hunting, socialising, and pursuing women. When he left without a degree he joined the Grenadier Guards and when war broke out in 1914 he served on the Western front, though he was not allowed in the front line. He complained to Lord Kitchener that he had four brothers and it didn't matter much if he were killed. But Kitchener overruled him and said it would matter greatly if he were taken prisoner. His car was shelled and his driver killed, but after the war he suffered from survivor's guilt and was embarrassed about his Military Cross.

After a riding accident his father tried to stop him steeple chasing and he took to arguing with his father about inconsequential matters. As a result the king lost trust in him and excluded him from important duties. When he travelled abroad to Australia, New Zealand, Japan, and Egypt he was feted as a celebrity and subjected to public touching mania. Young women snatched his handkerchiefs and coat buttons and his adviser, Sir Frederick Ponsonby, advised him to become less accessible and remain on a pedestal.

Back home he enjoyed the life of a bachelor, playing polo, hunting, and disregarding advice if he fell from a horse. He became a fine golfer and he loved parties where new dances such as the Charleston and Black Bottom were popular. He visited Africa and South America and said that his education was completed on the trade routes of the world. During the General Strike he was in Biarritz recovering from a minor ear operation, and on his return from Africa in 1931 he fell ill with Malaria[79]. And at his first changing of the colour on horse guards parade a man in the crowd called George McMahon had a loaded revolver wrestled from him by a policeman and received a prison sentence.

He set up home at Fort Belvedere in Windsor Park and his celebrity lifestyle made him the most talked about bachelor in the world. He was besieged by female admirers and it was said he "specialised" in married women and preferred Americans. Among the legions of women who followed him around the party circuit, he had a widely publicised affair with Freda Dudley Ward, the wife of a Liberal MP, and in 1931 on his return from a romantic African safari with an American called Thelma Furness, she introduced him to Wallis Simpson at a hunt weekend a Melton Mowbray. Wallis was bubbling with all the latest ideas and Edward said she was the most independent woman he ever met.

But she was a commoner and a married American soon to be twice divorced, and Edward seemed not to grasp that the marriage of

---

[79] See Medical Appendix – 9. Malaria, page 322.

the heir to the throne was governed by the Royal Marriages Act and was in the gift of Parliament and the king. Divorce at that time was not even recognised by the Church of England, of which he was the titular head.

Wallis had had countless affairs throughout her life, including Von Ribbentrop and Ciano, the fascist Foreign Ministers of Germany and Italy. There were even rumours of an abortion which was later blamed for her inability to have children.

Malicious rumours abounded and when she was having an affair with a handsome married car salesman called Guy Trundle she came under the surveillance of the UK secret services. The king refused to invite her to court and Edward lied to him about the relationship and even sued a newspaper to substantiate his lying.

*Wallis Simpson*

*Ernest Simpson, Ribbentrop, Ciano, and Guy Trundle*

When his father died in 1936, Edward flew to Sandringham and his first act as king was to change all the clocks back to Greenwich Mean Time. But when Cosmo Lang, the archbishop, visited him after the funeral, their meeting was frosty.

He now became Edward VIII and his ability to mix informally with all strata of society raised eyebrows in the establishment. He announced his wish to become a modern king and he overruled the Royal Mint and the Royal Mail about his portrait on coins and stamps. He even suggested to astonished friends that he might abdicate in favour of a republic and elope with Wallis.

George V had left each of his children £1m, and Edward had another £1m in savings. When he became king he was childless so he remained Prince of Wales and he continued to receive the income of the Duchy of Cornwall. With the Civil List and privy purse incomes and life interests in Balmoral and Sandringham, he had more than enough money to do as he chose including giving Wallis the most expensive jewellery.

He quickly tired of reading the state papers which were delivered to him in the red boxes each day. And he began to return the boxes unopened and was heard to call them mostly bunkem. And they were sometimes returned marked with the stains of cocktail glasses. He would disappear for days so that no one could ask him about official business. In addition, he seemed to care little if he offended powerful lobbies and he unwisely tried to get important people sacked. He also rather foolishly toured the South Wales coalfields and gave hope to the unemployed when no hope existed.

As his relationship with Wallis Simpson became wider known, the anxiety of the British establishment deepened. Her husband, Ernest, had seen his shipping business ruined by the Great Depression and the Simpsons were viewed as social climbers and money grabbers. Then, continuing to burn all his bridges he let it be known he would no longer support his own relations and he intended to sell off their royal estates. In 1936 it became known to Prime Minister Stanley Baldwin and Archbishop Cosmo Lang that the Simpsons' divorce was imminent and Wallis would be free to remarry. And when this was leaked to the newspapers by the Bishop of Bradford a constitutional crisis exploded.

In that age the views of the upper classes about divorce were rigid, and some like the Foreign Minister Lord Halifax would not even sit next to a divorced woman. People were shocked when Wallis' name began to appear on court invitation lists, and Edward's relationship with his brother and sister-in-law plummeted. Wallis' divorce from Ernest Simpson was eventually granted on the grounds of his adultery and there was public and family horror at the prospect of her now becoming queen. The British and Commonwealth governments said the marriage was not acceptable, and when even a morganatic arrangement was rejected, Edward told the Prime Minister he would abdicate. The Commonwealth heads were consulted and the view from Canada proved decisive. Edward was very popular in Canada but Canadians had Victorian views about divorce and they hated the fact that Wallis was American.

At the height of the crisis Edward's alcohol intake became worrying and the secret service were alarmed when he consulted a mysticist called Alexander Cannon. This man practiced on the Black shirt fringe of the German Nazi party and knew Oswald Moseley, von Ribbentrop, and a banker called Drummond who funded the British Union of Fascists. The secret services knew that Cannon was an eccentric and Edward was consulting him for a drying out cure, but they also worried he might be hypnotising the king. They kept Cannon under surveillance but allowed him to meet fascists interned on the Isle of Man and to operate high powered radiotelephony equipment capable of communicating with foreign governments. The security papers on Cannon will not be released until 2030 and it is possible he was recruited by the secret services as a double agent to monitor Edward's Nazi contacts.

Wallis was out of the UK when her decree nisi became absolute and the financial details of the abdication were being negotiated. With the growing tension, she tried to dissuade the king from abdicating. But his mind was made up, he broadcast to the nation and his brother, George, accepted the throne as George VI. The new Queen Elizabeth resented her husband, being asked to take on public duties for which he was ill suited, and much of what subsequently happened to Edward and Wallis was at the new queen's instigation. George found it impossible to speak in public because of his stammer and was horrified at the prospect of becoming king. As a result he broke down over the haggling about money and begged his brother not to abdicate. Edward and Wallis were created Duke and Duchess of

Windsor but she was denied the title of Royal Highness. They were not granted a grace and favour residence or any civil list income and after their wedding in France, they went to live in Paris as a rich couple but no longer fabulously wealthy. There was a good deal of romantic public sympathy for Edward who said in his abdication radio broadcast that "he could not carry out the duties of king as he would have wished, without the love and support of the woman he loved". About 60 MPs supported an anti-government Kings Party in Parliament and in Edward's inner circle there was great resentment towards Prime Minister Baldwin and to Archbishop Cosmo Lang.

Edward abdicated in December 1936 and was the first King of England to do so since James II in 1688. In exile in Paris, he would telephone to advise his brother about affairs of state but this sometimes ran counter to government policy and the secret service eventually blocked his calls. As World War II approached, the British and American governments were alarmed at the pro-German speeches he tried to make without government clearance and at visits he and Wallis made to Germany to meet prominent Nazis. Churchill and Roosevelt believed he was undermining the Anglo-American alliance and had him closely surveilled by the secret services. When the American FBI deciphered the secret Italian military codes, it was confirmed that Wallis had fascist sympathies and had been passing high level intelligence to the Germans. There was also evidence of illegal currency dealing with prominent Nazis, and of Edward being groomed by the Germans as the British Ambassador in Paris. Worst of all the pair disclosed allied plans to defend France which enabled the Germans to switch their Blitzkrieg attack from the Ardennes. And then infamously they told the Germans that continued bombing of British cities would soon incline the people towards a peace settlement. These were treasonable acts and in war they were punishable by death.

There was much in Wallis Simpson's private life which constituted a blackmail risk, especially her affairs with Ribbentrop and Ciano and her abortion. And in exile in Paris it was determined they should attend no more official functions. When France fell, they were at risk of being kidnapped by German paratroopers and were ushered back to Britain via Portugal. The pair were then sent to the Bahamas where he was safely out of the way and in an irrelevant job for the rest of the war.

After the armistice they were not invited to court and lived out their long lives in Paris. They visited England rarely, in 1951 for Wallis to have an operation to remove uterine fibroids, in 1952 for the funeral of George VI, and in 1965 for Edward to have eye surgery. With the help of a ghost writer he published three sentimental best-selling books about his life. But in 1972 he developed throat cancer caused by heavy lifelong tobacco smoking[80] and for this he received Cobalt radiotherapy.

Queen Elizabeth II relaxed the royal veto and visited him in Paris, and all the tubes and needles were removed from his arms and it took four hours to dress him for him to receive her. Wallis welcomed the queen but the visit was short and within a week he died with only his doctor and pet pug beside him.

The queen sent a royal aircraft to bring the body back to England, and for the funeral Wallis was invited to stay briefly at Buckingham Palace. His body lay in state at Windsor and he was buried at Frogmore with a coffin plate reading "Prince Edward Duke of Windsor, King Edward VIII, 1936".

Wallis lived the rest of her life as a recluse, and in 1980, she had a stroke and lost the power of speech. Towards the end, she was bed-ridden and apart from her doctor she did not receive visitors. When she died in Paris in 1986, her funeral was held in St. George's Chapel at Windsor and she was buried next to Edward as "Wallis, Duchess of Windsor". Most of her estate was bequeathed to the Pasteur Institute and in an auction at Sotheby's in 1987 her fabulous collection of jewels was sold for $45 million.

---

[80] See Medical Appendix – 18. Tobacco Diseases, page 342.

# George VI

George VI was the son of George V and Princess Mary of Teck and was born at Sandringham in 1895. He became king in 1936 when his brother abdicated, and he ruled for 16 years. He died of lung cancer at the age of 57.

He married a Scottish commoner called Elizabeth Bowes Lyons and their older daughter became Queen Elizabeth II. His reign spanned World War II, the transformation of the British Empire into a Commonwealth of Nations, and the British transfer of world dominance to the United States and communist Russia.

George was introverted and quiet by nature but his father was a family bully and George was tutored at home by a martinet called Henry Hansell.

In response he developed a stammer[81] which was to dog him for

---

[81] See Medical Appendix – 22. Speech Impediments, page 356.

the rest of his life. "Get it out boy, get it out," his father would thunder, and the humiliation, anguish, and exhaustion felt by the little boy were made worse by the teasing of the other children. He became intensely sensitive and from the age of five he sought refuge in the silence of his own company.

He was also forced to wear leg irons to straighten his slightly knocked knees and this further damaged his self-esteem. His schooling went badly, especially when he was made to recite German poems by Goethe. But he learned to ride at hounds, shoot pheasants, and ice skate on the lake in winter, and he was good at golf. In 1907 his brother Edward left for the Royal Navy at Osborne and in 1909 George followed him.

Here they both contracted Mumps and The Times referred to Mumps orchitis as a complication. In post-puberty males, orchitis affects 25% cases and when the disease is bilateral it can lead to sterility which may have been the case with Edward who remained childless, but not with George.

People contrasted him to his "brilliant" brother and though George put on a brave face, he minded deeply. In 1912 Edward went up to Oxford University and George continued at Dartmouth. He did well at everything outdoors but his academic studies went badly and in his last term he was 61st in the class of 67 students. He went to Cambridge University very briefly with his friend, Lord Louis Mountbatten, and he acquired a lasting Christian faith but no university degree.

On a cruise to the West Indies on HMS *Cumberland* he made his first public speech and stammered his way through the whole ordeal. In the next speech he had a stand-in deliver it for him. As Prince Albert he launched the Duke of York Camps which tried to break down class barriers, and he loved for everyone to sit cross-legged by a camp fire to sing together.

In 1913 he was 18 and he began to smoke the tobacco[82] which would eventually kill him. Three weeks after war broke out he was a midshipman on HMS *Collingwood* using the name of Johnson, but in the course of his duties he developed abdominal pain and his flotilla was accompanied by two destroyers to Scapa Flow where Sir James

---

[82] See Medical Appendix – 18. Tobacco Diseases, page 342.

Reid diagnosed appendicitis. He underwent a surgical appendectomy but despite a good recovery he was judged unfit to rejoin his ship.

And when he developed vomiting and lost weight, a peptic ulcer was diagnosed. In an age of tobacco smoking before any real understanding of the cause of peptic ulcers, there were none of the non-surgical treatments available today and which include Histamine antagonists to reduce gastric acid secretion and antibiotics to eradicate infection with *Helicobacter pylori*. His treatment initially centred around controlling his indigestion with milk and bicarbonate antacids, and to this was added complete bed rest and extraordinary enemas of bland beef solutions and digested milk. Under this regimen he became fit enough for shore duty and was posted to the Admiralty in London. For the Battle of Jutland he returned to HMS Collingwood which sank a German cruiser. But by 1917 he was stressed again, smoking heavily, not eating properly, and in constant pain from his peptic ulcer.

For these persistent symptoms and to exclude a malignant ulcer, he underwent a surgical gastrectomy, and following this he was transferred to Cranwell where he ended WW1 in the Royal Flying Corps.

After the war there was unrest in the heavy industries and calls by some socialist MPs to fly the red flag over Buckingham Palace. In response George visited factories and went to football matches with his father and gradually the republican sentiments in England waned. He became an enthusiastic and knowledgeable Freemason and progressed to become Principal of the Royal Arch Chapter. In addition, he was a talented sportsman and he and Louis Grey won the RAF tennis doubles championship in 1920, and they entered the Wimbledon tournament but lost to the eventual champions.

*Elizabeth, the Queen Mother*

He had courtships with Phyllis Monkman and Lady Londonderry but he then met Elizabeth Bowes Lyon. She was descended from Robert the Bruce and was the 4th daughter of the Earl of Strathmore. Her wealthy family had land and mining interests and she was attractive, intelligent, played the piano, and spoke fluent French. She was launched as a debutante and originally the queen viewed her as a suitable bride for Edward. But it was George who fell in love with her and he proposed three times before she accepted him. When they married in 1923 fusty old George V declined to have the service broadcast on the BBC as this would have enabled some citizens to listen with their hats off.

In later life Elizabeth said she had loved Bertie but could not face the responsibilities of royal life when he unexpectedly became king. She was much admired and was an excellent mimic who could make everyone laugh. But she also had a resolute character and insisted she and the king should remain at Buckingham Palace during the London blitz. She was the first queen consort since Queen Charlotte and the first commoner to give birth to a monarch since Ann Hyde.

As Duke and Duchess of York they lived at Royal Lodge at Windsor where they were neighbours to George's bachelor brother at Fort Belvedere and witnessed his worrying lifestyle. Their first child, Princess Elizabeth, was born by caesarean section at the Strathmore's

London home in Bruton Street and in 1930 a second girl was born, Princess Margaret Rose. Choosing to be known as the Queen Mother, she survived George by 50 years and took on a huge workload of public engagements until old age. During her long life she underwent surgery for appendicitis, colon cancer, and eye cataracts, and at the age of 97 she underwent bilateral hip replacements.

When George became king in 1936 his public life was made nearly impossible by his stammer[83], and he struggled through speeches. He did not improve after consulting an Italian speech therapist but was then contacted by Lionel Logue, a fellow Freemason from South Australia. Logue had helped shell-shocked soldiers and he taught George relaxing his jaw muscles, better diaphragmatic breathing and vocal exercises. He pointed out to George that he did not stammer when speaking to himself, or when he was angry, or when he was reading aloud or singing.

This boosted the king's confidence and there was an immediate improvement. Logue also used tongue twisters to help George rehearse for his coronation, and for his radio broadcasts to the British Empire. For the king's first Christmas radio broadcast this was delivered into a microphone with music playing and only Logue in the room, so the king spoke directly to him and not to the 100 million people who were listening. The two men remained friends until the king's death, and Logue went on to found the College of Speech Therapists and become a Commander of the Royal Victorian Order.

From then on George's public speaking was difficult but no longer impossible. He was daunted at the prospect of the coronation but took additional lessons from Robert Wood at the BBC on lip formation and voice intonation. On the day his voice was without any trace of a stammer and to prepare for the opening of Parliament he was helped by his wife, who was a natural actress.

By the time of his accession to the throne there were 28 ruling monarchs in Europe and he was related to them all. As war approached there was talk of a German plot to assassinate him and when his personal security was stepped up he reacted to the stress with symptoms of indigestion. On a visit to France every French policeman was called up to duty and when he visited President

Roosevelt in the USA the FBI foiled an IRA plot to assassinate him. In the lead-up to war he came to represent the spirit of the nation and when war was declared he donned military uniform and became Commander in Chief of the Armed forces of Great Britain and the Empire.

He had preferred Lord Halifax as a Prime Minister but accepted Winston Churchill who became his firm friend. They shared every war secret and were two of only four people in England who knew of the development of the atomic bomb.

His first Christmas radio broadcast to the empire struck a chord when it included the lines from the poem by Minnie Louis Haskins which were later inscribed on his tomb at Windsor –

> *I said to the man who stood at the gate of the Year*
> *Give me a light that I may tread safely into the unknown.*
> *And he replied, go out into the darkness*
> *And put your hand into the hand of God.*
> *That shall be to you better than light*
> *And safer than a known way*

As the disasters of the early war years unfolded he refused to send his daughters to Canada for their own safety. The Queen took to carrying a loaded revolver in her handbag and said the children would not leave without her and she would not leave without the king. The Battle of Britain raged in the skies above London and during the blitz Buckingham Palace was bombed by the Luftwaffe. Two German bombs went off in the quadrangle near where George was talking to his private secretary and the Queen Mother said that now they could look the East End in the face.

George was resolved to be seen doing his public duty, and in Buckingham Palace they shared the public deprivations by turning off the central heating and rationing the hot bathwater to a depth of five inches. He instituted the George Medal for civilian gallantry and awarded it to the entire island of Malta for resisting German bombing. In his turn he was awarded the gold medal of the Trades

Union Congress for being the country's hardest worker.

He did what he could to draw the USA into the war on Britain's side but this duty fell mainly to Churchill. The king's concern also focused on the PM's sobriety and his naval humour came to the rescue during one of Churchill's failed periods of abstinence when he presented him with some vintage wine smuggled to England by the Secret Services.

In 1942 his brother, the Duke of Kent, was killed in a Sunderland flying boat on a secret visit to Iceland. From then on George had to rely more on Henry, Duke of Gloucester, who had such a bad memory for names he called him the unknown soldier. In 1943 George visited Malta under the nom de guerre of General Lyon, where he knighted Field Marshal Montgomery after the battle of El Alamein. In 1944 he visited General Alexander's Eighth Army in Italy and George's security men arrested two suspicious characters in a small boat near his villa, but who turned out to be the King and Queen of Italy. On D-Day Churchill and the king forbad each to visit the Normandy beachheads and they both broke their promises.

By VE day in 1945 he was exhausted; his speech impediment returned and he wore artificial suntan to appear fit in public. After the defeat of Churchill in the General Election George didn't particularly like Atlee's socialist plans for nationalising major industries, but he did his duty and got on well with Aneurin Bevan who also stammered, and with Ernest Bevin who told earthy jokes and kept one hand in his pocket when shaking hands. But in 1947 after a peacetime visit to South Africa he lost 17 pounds in weight and was just about done in. He developed crowd claustrophobia and was greatly upset by an apparent assassination attempt which just turned out to be someone in the crowd attempting to give Princess Elizabeth a 10/- postal order for her birthday. He grew pessimistic about the future of the monarchy and thought the royal palaces would end up in the hands of the National Trust.

As his health weakened he had increasing fits of bad temper which the family called his gnashes. His jaws would work, his blue eyes would blaze and a stream of expletives would follow which the family called his Hanoverian spleen. In 1948 he developed a thrombosis in his leg and an amputation was considered. He was told he had Buergers Syndrome which is a vascular disease seen only in tobacco smokers and which causes severe leg cramps. Sir Martin Smart, Sir Maurice Cassidy, Sir Thomas Dunhill, and Sir James Learmonth were consulted and they all predicted gangrene if he did not cancel his engagements and stop smoking.

After two weeks bed rest they recommended a surgical lumbar sympathectomy to sever the nerves of the lower spine to reduce the spasm in the blood vessels in the legs. An operating theatre was set up in Buckingham Palace and in March 1949 he successfully underwent the operation. His exercise tolerance improved but after two years the symptoms returned and this time he consulted homeopathic doctors who he later knighted. In 1951 he became ill after an inauguration ceremony and was discovered to have inflammation of the lung and a shadow on his chest x-ray. Sir David Davies took tomographic chest x-rays which confirmed a tumour at the root of the lung and a bronchoscopic biopsy was taken which confirmed lung cancer. This is just one of the serious diseases caused by tobacco smoking[84] which was a family habit since Edward VII. Lord Moran, the President of the Royal College of Physicians, discussed the implications with Churchill and there were no public bulletins until after he had had his left lung removed by Clement Price Thomas.

The surgery in an operating theatre set up in Buckingham Palace lasted two hours and necessitated the severing of the recurrent laryngeal nerve which meant George could never speak again above a whisper. His Christmas broadcast to the nation was pre-recorded and quite extraordinarily it was decided he would not be told his diagnosis.

He was still in bed when Churchill was re-elected to power but he was able to travel to Heathrow airport to bid farewell to Princess Elizabeth and Prince Philip on an official tour to Australia and New Zealand, which George was not fit to carry out.

On 5th February he took himself to bed at 10:30pm and at midnight a police watchman in the garden saw him fiddling with the latch on his bedroom window. But that night he died in his sleep and he was found in the morning when his valet took him a cup of tea. Motorists across the UK got out of their cars and stood to attention

---

[84] See Medical Appendix – 18. Tobacco Diseases, page 342.

as a sign of respect, and at a stopover in Kenya, Princess Elizabeth was told the news as she sat in a fig tree at the Treetops Hotel watching wild animals drinking at a waterhole. And it was then she opened the sealed envelope containing her Accession Declaration. Churchill said the king had often walked with death as a companion and did not fear dying, and in the USA the House of Representatives adjourned for the day. The French ambassador called him a great king who had steered Britain through WW2 and had left the monarchy more stable than at any time in history.

His body lay in state at Sandringham guarded by estate workers and then at Westminster Hall where 300,000 people filed past in tribute. He was buried in St George's Chapel in Windsor and the wreath from Churchill bore the tribute, "For Valour". Elizabeth the Queen Mother lived for a further 50 years and died in 2002 aged 102.

# MEDICAL APPENDIX

## 1. Two Millennia

*Hippocrates*

In ancient Greece it was Hippocrates who described the four body humours of yellow bile, black bile, blood, and phlegm. He taught their imbalance led to illness, and health could be restored by restoring the balance using diet, blood-letting, sweating, purging, or vomiting.

*Aesculapius*

Sick patients flocked to the temples of Aesculapius the god of medicine, where they were treated by dream healing. They slept in temple dormitories surrounded by snakes which the Greeks used because venom was thought to be remedial and skin-shedding was a symbol of renewal. The healing occurred during dreams or after patients had followed the advice they dreamed about. When they woke they bathed, offered prayers and sacrifices, received herbal medication, and were advised to diet and take exercise. Astrological charts were then used to predict outcomes.

The Greeks absorbed medical knowledge from across the ancient world and despite having no empirical basis their ideas formed the basis of western medicine for a thousand years.

*Galen and Hildegard of Bingen*

Around 200AD, Galen of Pergamon described the four signs of inflammation, which are redness, pain, heat, and swelling, which are still used today. But he also taught that blood circulated from the arteries to the veins through a porous wall in the heart. And whilst this was wrong, it was not questioned for 1,400 years.

In medieval England most people believed that destiny, sin, and astral influences caused their diseases and only God could heal them. Physicians used herbal remedies from pagan folk sources, and the nun, Hildegard of Bingen, catalogued these in her *Causae et Cura*. She gave detailed instructions about blood-letting and advocated this was best done when the moon was waning, and the best veins to use were those nearest the diseased body part. From a strong patient, she advised to take "the amount that a thirsty person can swallow in one gulp" and from a weak patient, "the amount that an egg of moderate size can hold". Afterwards she advised patients to rest for three days and drink wine.

With the growth of the medieval church the monasteries cultivated physic gardens and offered medicinal herbs to local towns and passing travellers. Many family homes stocked their kitchens with herbs, and written Herbals advised about their use. Prayers and religious rituals were used by monks and nuns, but herbs were seen as gifts from God as natural healing aids. Latin herbal texts were translated into English and the monks added tables of contents to help find information more quickly. New herbs were added and ineffective ones were discarded, and drawings helped the reader to identify different plants, herbs were exchanged between physic gardens and new methods of cultivation were shared.

*Paracelsus*

The success of herbal remedies was ascribed to their effect on the four humours and their use drew on the Doctrine of Signatures described by Paracelsus von Hohenheim. He taught that God had provided herbs for every ailment, and carried a mark or signature upon them to indicate their usefulness. Eye bright was good for eye infections, skull cap seeds for headaches, lung wort for Tuberculosis, and tooth wort for tooth ache. The Herbals were widely plagiarised and one of the most famous was the *Red Book of Hergest*. This was written in Welsh in about 1382 and for centuries it passed through various families and is now in the Bodleian Library.

Superstition was widespread in medieval times and the kings and queens of England claimed the divine gift of curing patients by touching or stroking them. This was thought to be evidence of God's high esteem for anointed kings and queens, and in England, Edward the Confessor and Henry III were the first to claim this power. Edward IV gave gold touch pieces to hang on the necks of the afflicted and Henry VII read passages from the Bible and offered prayers. The royal touch was used mainly for skin Tuberculous which was called the King's Evil, but it was also used to cure other ailments which had a high spontaneous cure rate.

*The Royal Touch of Charles II*

Edward I applied the royal touch to about 1,700 patients a year, but other monarchs tended to perform the ritual according to their Protestant or Catholic beliefs. Elizabeth I stopped doing it but resumed it in 1570 after the Pope excommunicated her and alleged she had lost her healing powers. The ritual reached its climax during the reign of Charles II who touched over 92,000 patients. But William and Mary refused to take part in what they considered a pagan superstition and Queen Anne was the last to perform it in 1712.

After the Crusades, the idea of charitable hospitals, poor houses, and orphanages was brought back from the Middle East, and Santa Maria della Scala in Siena became the first hospital in Europe. These institutions spread from Italy, and the larger ones started to provide teaching in medicine and surgery. During the 13th century the world's first medical school opened in Salerno and its Latin medical texts were transcribed in the nearby monastery of Monte Cassino. The Salerno masters established a canon of writings, known as the *ars medicinae* and this remained the basis of European medicine in the centuries that followed.

In Paris in the 13th century, the Provost appointed experienced surgeons to assess the performance of trainees, and the new French universities taught surgery as a uniform discipline which was learned systematically and communicated to others. And in its famous anatomical theatre, the University of Padua started to dissect human cadavers in order to teach surgical anatomy.

*Anatomy theatre at Padua*

One of the duties of army surgeons was to survey the battlefields after a battle, to declare which soldiers were dead and assess the wounds of the survivors. They became skilled at removing arrowheads and after the Battle of Shrewsbury a surgeon called John Bradmore removed an arrow from Henry V, both saving his life and altering the course of history.

Non-university trained barber surgeons were only expected to perform minor surgery, dental extractions, and blood-letting. And in the 14th century, legal restrictions defined which injuries they were allowed to treat and made them accountable for any mistakes. But the Church still taught that God sent illness as a punishment, and repentance offered the only lasting cure. The mortal remains of the saints were still held to be incorruptible and their tombs emanated healing vapours which passing pilgrims could inhale. And even when medical training moved into the universities, the church still dictated when the spirit left the dead body and medical dissection was permitted.

The 12th and 13th centuries saw the ascent of medical universities in Paris, Bologna, Oxford and Montpelier. The training to become a licensed physician varied and Montpelier required six years of study and eight months of practical experience, whilst Bologna required three years of philosophy, three years of astrology, and four years of medical lectures.

There evolved a medical hierarchy with university educated physicians at the top, followed by craft-trained surgeons; barber surgeons, itinerant dentists and oculists, midwives, clergy and, finally, village wise women. Physicians trained in the universities usually attended wealthy families whilst apothecaries from the Grocers' Guilds dispensed herbal medicines to the poor. There was very little regulation and this medieval medicine embraced a diverse world of 'quacks', and 'sham' doctors.

During the 13<sup>th</sup> century more hospitals were built and Milan had a dozen and Florence had 30. These were originally built to isolate lepers and plague victims, but later they served passing pilgrims and eventually whole communities. From 1450 there were more advances in medical knowledge. Girolamo Fracastoro proposed that epidemics were transmitted by body contact. Andreas Vesalius wrote the first textbook on human anatomy and in 1628 William Harvey demonstrated the correct circulation of blood through the veins and arteries.

*William Harvey*

But expanding trade routes became the perfect channels for contagious diseases, and when bubonic plague spread from Asia in 1348 it killed a third of the population of Europe. The concept of physical contagion developed and in the earliest example at biological warfare, the Mongols in their siege of Kaffa loaded the dead or dying bodies of infected soldiers onto catapults and launched them over the city walls to infect those inside.

In the 19th century the concept of infectious contagion was proved conclusively when Dr John Snow brought an epidemic of Cholera to an end by closing a contaminated public water well in Broad Street in Soho. Semmelweiss then started to eliminate Puerperal fever by introducing labour room hygiene, Lister brought surgical infections under control by using antiseptics and Pasteur heralded the end to Tuberculosis by heat sterilising cows' milk. Medicine became taught as a science based on empirical evidence and advances were only adopted after scientific peer review. New technologies such as anaesthesia, blood transfusion, x-rays and antibiotics were discovered, doctors developed specialist skills and professional disciplinary committees like the General Medical Council were set up to protect the safety of patients.

In Victorian and Edwardian Britain the expanding population made it difficult for local boroughs and charities to fund sufficient growth in medical care. As a result there was a growth of medical insurance through industrial works committees and local medical societies, and in 1911 National Insurance was introduced by Parliament. But many of the poor were still unable to obtain medical cover and in 1945 William Beveridge proposed a free National Health Service funded from taxation and which Aneurin Bevan launched in 1948. The first NHS hospital was the Trafford General Hospital in Manchester and the first patient treated by the NHS was 13-year-old Sylvia Beckingham.

*Sylvia Beckingham*

As regards mental illnesses, mad people in the Middle Ages were often cast out by their families and wandered the city streets and country lanes where they were taunted, exploited and eventually starved to death or murdered.

*Skull Trepanning*

It was believed the brains of schizophrenics and epileptics were occupied by devils and the only treatment was trepanning a hole in the skull to let the devils out. Female hysteria on the other hand was thought to be brought on by internal wanderings of the womb in response to different phases of the moon. The temporary cure for this was to massage the external genitalia and the permanent cure was pregnancy.

Psychotic delusions and hallucinations were viewed as an imbalance of the four body humours, so that too much black bile caused melancholy and too much blood caused mania. Bleeding, vomiting, and purges were used to achieve a re-rebalance, in addition to which lunatics who behaved badly were manacled in strait jackets and flogged.

The first asylum for lunatics was built in London in 1247 during the reign of Henry III. As the Priory of St Mary of Bethlem it was established by the Bishop of Bethlehem, Goffredo de Prefetti, using the donation of a city alderman called Simon FitzMary. The Hospital of St Mary of Bethlehem (later contracted to Bethlem and then Bedlam) was outside the city walls in Bishopsgate and at first housed only six inmates.

*Bedlam*

The families of inmates were required to supplement any charitable support from their parishes and this was eventually enshrined by statute. The public curiosity about mad people was easily aroused, and Bedlam lunatics became a popular London tourist attraction. Voyeurs came in large numbers to be entertained and the 1p they paid became an important source of income for Bedlam hospital.

Inmates were treated harshly for any perceived moral weakness or wickedness, and it was not unusual for inmates to be to be stripped naked if they were incontinent, and to be manacled in solitary confinement. One patient called James Norris was locked in a tiny cage for 10 years.

All sorts of quacks boasted an expertise in mental disorders and made a corrupt living. Among these the Munroe family ran Bedlam for several hundred years and barred all others from the living. Strict discipline was enforced by staff with army backgrounds, and the church contributed with prayers and incantations to exorcise and cast out devils. Most of the staff were hired to restrain the inmates, and the physicians only visited occasionally. Some patients like epileptics were confined in special wards for incurables and whilst a few recovered sufficiently to be discharged, the majority served a life sentence.

In 1636 a new Bedlam hospital was constructed in Moorfields and was opened by Charles II. A more humane regimen was introduced and patients were provided with alms. At this time, Willis in Oxford made studies of the anatomy of the brain and Descartes described the concept of the mind. St Luke's hospital became a rival to Bedlam in 1751 and encouraged medical students to visit the wards and learn mad doctoring from first experience. From then on, a board of lunatic commissioners was appointed to regulate Bedlam and the physicians were required to be resident. A private asylum called the York Retreat was set up by Quakers in 1792 with a regimen of kindness, rest, and recreation. And sedation with Valerian and Opium replaced physical restraint and flogging. In the 19th century more mental hospitals were built, and in the 20th century the new science of psychology was developed by Freud, and psychotherapy was introduced.

In the 1850s chemicals like Choral Hydrate became available to sedate patients. And in the 1950s, new psychotropic drugs like

Phenothiazines provided a big advance in managing the most distressing symptoms of schizophrenia. As a result, it became safe for patients who would have spent their lives in mental institutions to be discharged back into the community.

Against this background, Richard II and Henry VI were deposed and murdered when they went mad. And when George III went insane he was restrained by force and given quack remedies which made him worse. In the end, he was deposed by a Regency council and lived to old age in the comfortable isolation of Windsor Castle. In contrast, in 1786 a mad woman called Margaret Nicholson tried to stab George III, and was committed to Bedlam and was never seen again. And when Harriette, the wife of Sir Charles Mordaunt, was allegedly seduced by Edward VII and became pregnant, a physician called Sir William Gull testified she was insane and she was committed to an asylum for the rest of her life. In contrast Princess Alice of Greece, the mother-in-law of the present monarch developed schizophrenia in 1930 and was committed to a sanatorium in Switzerland where she largely recovered. And she devoted her remaining years to charity work and lived at Buckingham Palace.

# 2. Porphyria

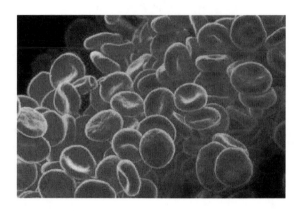

The term *porphyria* is from the Greek πορφύρα meaning "purple pigment" and is a reference to the purple colour of Porphyric urine when it is oxidised by sunlight. Porphyria is a rare inherited disease and most affected families can be traced to a single individual in whom the original genetic mutation took place. There was no way to confirm the diagnosis until the 19th century when Paul Ehrlich invented the urine test for Porphobilinogen. Nowadays the diagnosis is made by DNA analysis and eight different gene mutations are recognised.

The mechanisms which cause the symptoms remain unclear but are related to a block in the synthesis of the haemoglobin pigment in red blood cells. The disease is present from conception and can cause stillbirth or neonatal death. In birth survivors, however, the symptoms do not begin until adult life and usually start with unexplained fever, vomiting, diarrhoea, and abdominal pains. Fleeting joint pains are commonly confused with rheumatism and gout. And psychological symptoms are present in about half of cases including depression, anxiety, mania, hysteria, delusions, and personality changes. The neurological symptoms include limb pains, paralysis, muscle contractures, limb deformity, strokes, blindness, fainting, and epileptic convulsions. And in the variegate Porphyrias there are blistering skin rashes following exposure to sunlight. The acute episodes are often life threatening, and their damage accumulates and becomes permanent. Patients can, however, survive to old age, and George III lived until he was 82 years old.

Porphyria is often worse in pregnancy, with maternal mortality rates as high as 40%, as in the case of Princess Charlotte. The babies are often stillborn, and Queen Anne lost 17 pregnancies in this way. The biochemical defects are in the synthesis of haemoglobin in blood cells. Haem is produced from the amino acid glycine in a series of reactions controlled by different enzymes. The pigment is built into a molecule that binds oxygen in the lungs and carries it around the body. There are eight enzymes in the pathway and defects of the different enzymes lead to different forms of Porphyria. Each mutation reduces enzyme activity and allows chemical precursors to accumulate and cause the disease.

Some enzymes like ALA–Synthetase affect the process more than others, and external factors such as alcohol, heavy metals, and drugs are powerful inhibitors of this enzyme.

Various patterns of inheritance transmit the mutations from one generation to the next, and the royal disease was passed across 17 generations from James V of Scotland to a nephew of George VI. Some Porphyrias are inherited in an autosomal dominant pattern, in which half the male and female children inherit the disease, as in the Acute Intermittent Porphyria which affected the British royal family. The rarest Porphyrias are inherited in an autosomal recessive pattern, in which two copies of the mutated gene must be inherited from the father and the mother. Cousin marriages increase the chance of these Porphyrias but were not a factor in the British royal family. Some other rare forms of Porphyria have an X chromosome-linked pattern of inheritance in which males suffer from symptoms and females act as asymptomatic disease carriers.

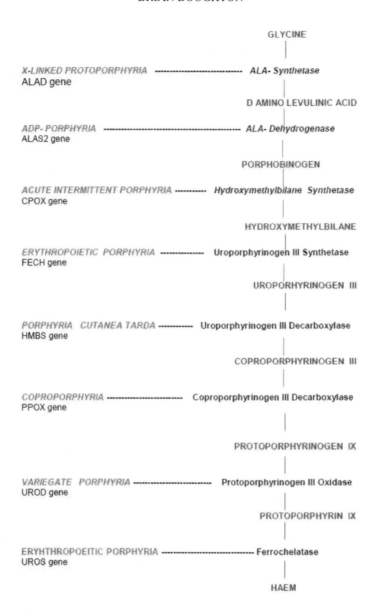

The disease can be asymptomatic for the entire life of the patient and inherited unknowingly by their children and detected only by laboratory tests. In others there are episodes of purple urine but no other symptoms. Yet others have recurrent abdominal pains and these patients are often subjected to unnecessary surgery for suspected appendicitis. The worst cases have serious symptoms often leading to death. Medical intervention often worsens the disease, as when George was forced by his physicians to drink alcohol. And with the life-long prospect of recurrent disease, some patients become depressed and commit suicide.

The first suggestion that Porphyria was the cause of George III's mental problems was in a 1966 paper in the British Medical Journal, "The Insanity of King George III". There was a follow-up paper in 1968, "Porphyria in the Royal Houses of Stuart, Hanover and Prussia". And this was followed by the "Purple Secret" which documented Porphyria in the extended royal family over several centuries.

The disease was symptomatic in some of George III's descendants but not in others. The latter must, however, have carried the Porphyria gene as their children or grandchildren developed the disease. One reason for this was clarified by the analysis of a surviving lock of George III's hair which showed high levels of Arsenic. This can precipitate attacks in otherwise asymptomatic patients and we now know that George was exposed to Arsenic in creams for his skin rashes and in his wig powder.

His physician, Sir James Baker, also prescribed "Dr James' Fever Powder" which was contaminated with Arsenic.

George III's Porphyria can be traced back to James V of Scotland who had a full range of symptoms and died of the disease when he was young. His daughter, Mary Queen of Scots, had a lifetime of suffering from Porphyria and displayed most of the symptoms. Her son, James I, showed a similar picture and periodically passed coloured urine. His eldest son, Henry, Prince of Wales, died of Porphyria at the age of 18. Henry's brother, Charles I, was an obligate carrier of the disease but was asymptomatic, and his daughter Henrietta died of it. Charles I's son, Charles II, was asymptomatic and his brother, James II, was also unaffected but must have been an obligate carrier since his daughter, Queen Anne, suffered lifelong symptoms and had 17 failed pregnancies which brought the Stuart dynasty to an end.

The Porphyria gene was re-introduced into the English monarchy by the Hanoverians who became affected through James I's daughter, Elizabeth of Bohemia. She and her daughter Sophia were asymptomatic carriers who passed the disease to Frederick the Great of Prussia and George I of England. And George I's son, George II, and his son, Frederick, Prince of Wales, were obligate carriers, whose abnormal personalities were probably caused by the disease.

George III was seriously affected and this led to the loss of the American colonies. His son, George IV, had symptoms of the disease and his sister, Queen Caroline of Denmark, was affected. His daughter, Princess Charlotte, died following a stillbirth which was probably Porphyria related. And his brother, the Duke of Kent and father of Queen Victoria, was a sufferer. Queen Victoria was an obligate carrier because the mutated gene was passed via her daughter, Princess Victoria, to Princess Charlotte of Meiningen, and her daughter, Princess Feodora, both of whom suffered symptoms. Feodora could not face further attacks of the disease and committed suicide in 1945, and her exhumed remains were examined in the 1990s by DNA analysis which confirmed a mutation of the gene for the enzyme Protoporphyrinogen oxidase.

*Princess Feodora and Prince William*

The last royal family member known to have suffered from Porphyria was Prince William of Gloucester, the grandson of King George V and nephew of George VI. In 1968, Prince William was examined at the request of his mother, Princess Alice of Gloucester, after he suffered unexplained fevers and skin blistering in sun light.

And specialists in Cambridge and Tokyo used DNA analysis to confirm he had variegate Porphyria. He was killed in an air accident in 1972.

DNA testing can now detect all eight Porphyria gene mutations, and modern patients now wear bracelets to alert medical attendants in an emergency. This is important because many modern medications can make the disease much worse and hospital treatment now includes antidotes which are only supplied from medical reference centres.

# 3. Haemophilia

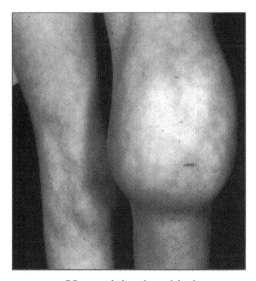

*Haemophiliac knee bleed*

Haemophilia is a rare hereditary blood deficiency of clotting factors VIII or IX which impairs the body's ability to arrest bleeding. There are 2,000-year-old descriptions of male babies who bled excessively after circumcision, and the disease affects mammals which evolved much longer ago than man. The disease is present in about 1 in 10,000 births and in the 20th century it was discovered that Haemophilia was caused by the deficiency of blood clotting factors VIII and IX.

It is an inherited sex-linked recessive disorder which only affects males. This is because the defective gene is carried on the X chromosome and in normal females with two X chromosomes, the normal gene compensates for the defective one. Males, on the other hand, have only one X chromosome and if it carries the Haemophilia mutation then factor VIII is reduced.

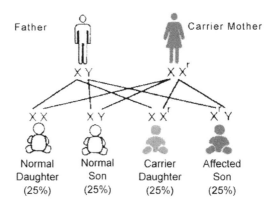

*Sex-linked recessive inheritance of Haemophilia*

Until 50 years ago, most haemophilic males did not survive long enough to produce children and the incidence of the disease was maintained by spontaneous new mutations of the Haemophilia gene. As a result, about 30% of affected individuals have no family history of the disease, as was the case with Queen Victoria. The disease severity depends on the factor VIII levels in the blood, so that individuals with less than 1% normal factor VIII have severe Haemophilia, those with 1-5% have moderate disease, and 5-40% factor VIII is associated with a mild form. Patients with severe disease suffer frequent, large, spontaneous bleeds. And often the first episode is when the umbilical cord is cut at birth or when circumcision is carried out. As children start to walk, haemorrhages into weight-bearing joints become common and lead to acute painful swellings and eventual arthritis. Bleeding into the brain or abdomen, is much more serious and is frequently fatal. As a result, patients with severe Haemophilia had short lives and prior to the 1950s their average life expectancy was only 10 years. By the 1970s, however, factor VIII transfusions became available and the average lifespan increased to 60. In contrast, patients with moderate or mild Haemophilia suffer minor symptoms and their bleeding only occurs after injuries and surgical or dental operations.

Until recently Haemophilia could be controlled with transfusions of factor VIII or IX from normal blood. But this carried the risk of transfusion-associated Hepatitis C and HIV. And much factor VIII is now produced by genetic engineering and is free of these viruses.

With more than 1,200 different mutations of the Haemophilia F8 gene, modern DNA technology now permits prenatal screening of embryos at risk from the disease, and if the pregnancies are affected the mother can be offered termination of the pregnancy. In addition, gene editing can now be used to replace Haemophilia genes in embryos, and Haemophilia gene replacement using virus vectors has been successfully carried out in adult haemophiliacs.

After their marriages to Queen Victoria's descendants, Haemophilia appeared in the royal families in Europe; and every case can be traced back to Queen Victoria. The disease played an important role in world history and was of the severe variety which caused numerous deaths. But it did not affect Edward VII and has not been passed to the present British royal family.

Queen Victoria transmitted Haemophilia to her son, Prince Leopold, who suffered severe episodes of bleeding. This was wrongly blamed on the chloroform anaesthesia she received during his birth and led to its withdrawal from use. The Queen wrote to Disraeli that Leopold never went for more than a few months without being laid up and he had four or five times been at death's door. He led a quiet life at Osborne and Balmoral but survived to adulthood when he married Helen of Waldeck and had two children. At the age of 31, however, he died of a cerebral haemorrhage after accidentally striking his head. His daughter, Alice, was a carrier who passed Haemophilia to her son, Rupert, and he died at the age of 21 from a cerebral haemorrhage.

Queen Victoria's daughter, Princess Alice, was born in 1843 and married Louis IV, Grand Duke of Hesse. Their son, Frederick, died of bleeding at the age of three and their daughter, Irene, married Henry of Prussia and had two haemophiliac sons, Henry and Waldemar. Irene's daughter, Alix, was a disease carrier who married Tsar Nicholas II of Russia, and their son, the Tsarevich Alexei, became the most famous of all haemophiliacs. He suffered as a newborn from umbilical cord bleeding and had painful bleeding after minor injuries. On several occasions his life was in danger and he received the last rites of the church. But when the mystic monk Rasputin became involved he managed to calm the boy with fairy stories and folk tales and he may also have used homeopathy, prayer, and hypnosis. Rasputin became trusted by the Tsarina, though not by the Tsar, and eventually he was the only person who was able to control the boy's pain. He advised the Tsarina not to let doctors bother the boy and since they were prescribing aspirin pain relief which made the bleeding worse, Rasputin's advice was sound in this respect. But he tried to influence the Tsar's domestic and foreign policy and was eventually murdered by Russian and British secret service agents. He was first poisoned with cyanide, then shot twice and finally drowned in the River Nera. As for the Romanovs, the Tsarevich's bleeding severely limited their ability to travel during the Russian revolution and this eventually led to their capture by the Bolsheviks and the execution of the whole family.

*Tsarevich and Alexei Rasputin*

Queen Victoria's youngest daughter was Princess Beatrice, who was a disease carrier who married Prince Henry of Battenburg, and two of her sons were haemophiliacs who died aged 23 and 33. Her daughter Eugenie married Alphonso XIII of Spain, and her sons, Alfonso and Gonzalo, both bled to death after minor accidents aged 19 and 31. And the girls in the family must have been carriers as their decendents are haemophiliacs and are alive and well as a result of modern treatment. Queen Victoria's heir, Edward VII, and her other sons, Alfred and Arthur, were not affected by Haemophilia and her daughters Victoria, Helena, and Louise were not carriers of the disease.

It was assumed for 150 years that the royal Haemophilia was due to factor VIII deficiency, but in 2009 genetic analysis of the remains of the Tsarevich Alexei, revealed his disease was Factor IX deficiency. This is called Christmas Disease after its discovery in 1952 in a patient called Stephen Christmas.

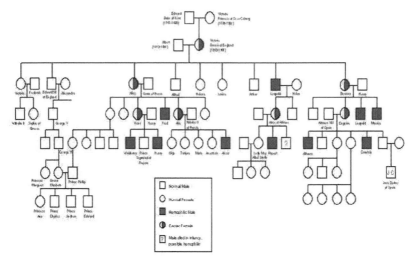

*The family Haemophilia of Queen Victoria*

# 4. Smallpox

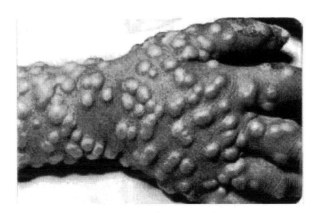

Smallpox is an extremely contagious infection caused by Variola viruses and it carries a high mortality. It was known in China 2,000 years ago, and there are Smallpox scars on the mummified head of the Pharaoh Rameses V who died in 1160 BC.

It was a seasonal disease which spread when people crowded indoors in winter, and it spread to Europe from Asia during the Middle Ages along the Silk Road. It was transmitted by close bodily contact with contaminated clothes and bedding, and was common in hospitals and sick rooms where those nursing infected patients were particularly at risk. Like modern Ebola infections, it was also caught by mourners at the funerals of infected bodies.

In medieval times the common variant of the disease was called Variola Minor or Alastrim, and in 1519 millions of Native Americans caught it from the Spanish conquistadors and died. Such people had no previous exposure and no immunity to the infection and were highly susceptible to Alastrim. And this allowed the virus to be used as a biological weapon during the American War of Independence, when the British army distributed free infected sleeping blankets to hostile tribes of native people.

In the 17th century a variant called Variola Major became the dominant form of the disease and with a high fever, severe skin pustules, and a deadly encephalitis, the mortality rate exceeded 60%. During the European epidemics there were hundreds of thousands of deaths, and in some cities the disease accounted for virtually all fatalities.

The only so-called treatment originated in Japan and involved draping the sickroom with red curtains. This was totally without benefit but was still used up until 1900.

But it was known since ancient times that Smallpox survivors were immune to further attacks, and after an epidemic the increased immunity of the population prevented further epidemics. Only sporadic cases were then seen for decades, until immunity fell again and more epidemics broke out. Voluntary protection against the disease was called Variolation, and was carried out in India and China by inhaling purulent material from the skin lesions of infected victims, or by exposing children to infected patients. In 1717 this practice was brought to England by the wife of the Ambassador to Constantinople, and after trials on prisoners in Newgate prison, King George II's wife, Queen Caroline, had her children variolated. But this was extremely risky and when it caused cases of fatal disease it fell from favour. But the genetic code of Variola Major has long sequence homologies with other pox viruses, and this explains the success of vaccination against Smallpox using the much less dangerous Vaccinia or Cowpox virus.

A Gloucestershire physician called Edward Jenner had noted how dairymaids infected with Cowpox were less likely to contract Smallpox, and in 1796 he successfully vaccinated a boy called James Phipps with the Cowpox lymph from an infected dairy maid called Sarah Nelmes. Within five years hundreds of thousands of vaccinations were carried out in England, and by 1853 Smallpox had declined to such a level that compulsory vaccination was considered though not enforced.

*Edward Jenner*

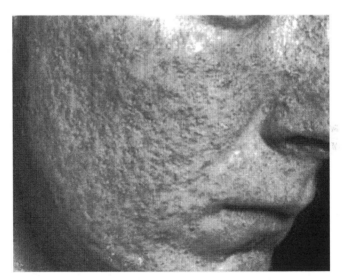

*Smallpox scarring*

Some patients die of Smallpox whilst others survive, and susceptibility to the virus is partly controlled by an inherited CD32 virus receptor on white blood cells which varies from person to person. Skin scarring in survivors also varies and Elizabeth I had to wear a lot of facial make up to hide her Smallpox scars whereas Mary Queen of Scots had none.

In the Tudor courts Henry VIII, Mary Queen of Scots, Edward VI, and Elizabeth I survived Smallpox. And in the Stuart court James II and Queen Anne survived the disease, but Queen Mary II, Mary of Orange, and William Duke of Gloucester died of it.

The last epidemic in 1870 caused 44,000 deaths in London. But in 1948 vaccination became compulsory in England and in 1967 the World Health Organisation set up a global vaccination campaign. The last wild case of Smallpox occurred in Somalia in 1977 and the final fatal case occurred in a laboratory worker called Janet Parker in Birmingham in 1978. The last case of all was her mother and she survived. Since then there have been no other cases and the only Smallpox viruses in existence are stored in biological weapons laboratories in the USA and Russia.

# 5. Tuberculosis

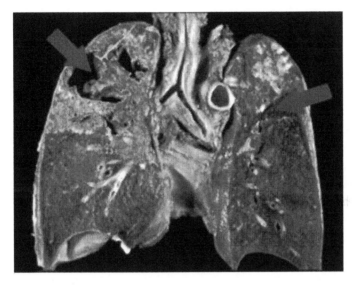

*TB cavities in the lungs*

Tuberculosis, or TB, is caused by the *Mycobacterium tuberculosis* bacterium and has been isolated in the 3,000-year-old mummies of Egyptian Pharaohs. It is not highly contagious but is spread by coughing aerosols or spitting sputum, particularly when people are crowded together and hygiene is poor. The less serious *Mycobacterium bovis* strain of the bacterium causes local infections in the gastrointestinal tract and before cattle were tested for Tuberculosis and milk was sterilised by pasteurisation, Bovine TB was transmitted from infected cows' milk. A non-fatal form of this disease is called Scrofula, and causes swollen lymph nodes in the neck and ugly scarring.

Most healthy subjects are exposed to the TB at an early age and develop an immunity which prevents clinical disease developing. These patients have no symptoms but may have a small scar in the lungs which is visible on chest X-rays. These so-called Ghon lesions become calcified and contain persistent TB bacteria which can be reactivated years later and progress to clinical disease.

Subjects with lesser immunity get worse infections, which can cause cavities in the lungs and shed large amounts of infectious sputum. They are a major infective risk to others and are subject to massive lung haemorrhages which cause sudden death.

In patients with no immunity the initial infection can spread quickly to every organ of the body, causing rapidly fatal miliary Tuberculosis. In these cases, the body wasting is extreme and it was commonly called Consumption.

In medieval times Tuberculosis was usually fatal, as in the case of Henry VII and Edward VI, but in those who survived there was often damage to the spine which was a common cause of the kyphoscoliosis seen in hunchbacks like Richard III. It also spread to the joints and was a common cause of the hip arthritis, suffered by Edward VII's wife, Queen Alexandra. A 20th-century form of management was to quarantine patients in sanitoria in the countryside where they could receive nutritious food and rest from hard physical labour.

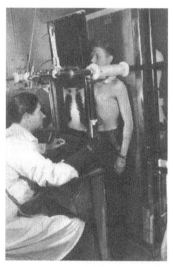

*Chest X-ray screening for TB*

After WW2, mobile chest X-ray mass screening programmes were introduced to detect cases at an early stage of the disease, and an attenuated live vaccine called BCG was developed for mass vaccination programmes. In addition, antibiotics such as Streptomycin and Isoniazid became available to treat active infections, and as a result of these measures TB became less common after the 1950s. More recently, however, decreased immunity caused by Aids/HIV infections has led to a recurrence of TB, and the development of antibiotic resistance threatens to make it a major killer again.

# 6. Plague

Plague is caused by the bacterium *Yersinia pestis* and is transferred to humans who are bitten by infected rat fleas. Black rats from city sewers are more susceptible to fleas and at one time there were more rats than people living in London, and a rat lived within 10 feet of every London inhabitant. Added to this, most rats were covered in fleas and the fleas were commonly infected with Plague bacteria.

The filthy poor parts of cities were ideal breeding ground for rats and the city tenements were grossly overcrowded. The cobbled roads were slippery with animal dung, rubbish slops were thrown out of the houses on to the streets, and the City Corporation rakers were only able to remove the worst of the filth to rotting mounds outside the city walls. The stench was overwhelming and many people walked around with handkerchiefs and nosegays pressed to their noses.

The infected flea bites were followed by painful lymph node enlargement in the armpits and groins, and these swellings or buboes become gangrenous and broke through the skin and bled. Before modern treatment Bubonic Plague had a mortality of 60% and these cases excreted the bacteria in their sputum and spread the Pneumonic form of disease which passed directly from man to man and was fatal in virtually all cases.

At the time, the bacterial cause of Plague was unknown and the credulous blamed bad air, sewage, bad weather, livestock sickness, or even increased numbers of moles, or frogs or mice. When cats were blamed these were culled and the rats bred even faster and the epidemics worsened. It was not until 1894 that *Yersinia pestis* was identified by Alexandre Yersin and the transmission by rat fleas was discovered.

The Justinian Plague swept across Europe in 540 AD, the Black Death arrived here in 1348, and the Great Plague in 1665. Plague caused 30,000 deaths during outbreaks in 1603 and 1625, and at the height of the Great Plague there were 7,000 deaths a month in London. And with a total death toll of 100,000 in the capital and 200,000 in the whole country, normal life stopped and trade ground to a halt. Wealthy residents and the royal family fled to the safety of the countryside and severed all connections with Plague towns. No commoners were permitted anywhere near the monarch and supplies to the royal kitchens were only allowed from towns which were known to be Plague free. Charles II's court moved from London to Salisbury, and when Plague broke out in Salisbury, it moved to Oxford.

The cause of the disease was unknown, but the benefits of quarantine were understood and poorer families were padlocked in houses marked by red crosses on the doors and guarded by sentries. Whole neighbourhoods were turned into no-go areas, and the dead bodies were left out for collection each night so as to minimise alarm. Each parish appointed body searchers and the streets rang to the carters' cry of "bring out your dead". The searchers and carters lived apart from the community for fear of spreading the disease and they carried a white stick to warn others of their dangerous occupation.

As the Great Plague spread, neighbourhood quarantine was increased from 30 to 40 days and the Privy Council quarantined ships coming to London and assigned naval frigates to intercept vessels entering the Thames estuary. Bills of Mortality were posted regularly but there was no obligation on families to report their dead and the official figures grossly under-reported the real numbers.

The Lord Mayor issued proclamations that householders must clean the streets and constables were instructed to inspect everyone wishing to travel, especially vagrants. And since these were required to produce certificates signed by the mayor it became impossible for poor people to leave London. As the numbers mounted, graveyards quickly filled, and mass burial pits turned into mounds of decomposing corpses. When there were too few carters to remove the bodies, they stacked them against the houses and left them to decay. Plague doctors patrolled the streets diagnosing new victims, and the authorities ordered bonfires to be burned in the streets to cleanse the air. Church services were a common way in which the disease was spread and when villages were burned and rebuilt on new sites, the churches were the only buildings left standing in the old village. In Eyam in Derbyshire, the Plague arrived with a merchant carrying a parcel of cloth from London, and the villagers imposed a quarantine on themselves to stop the spread of the disease. This prevented it from spreading to surrounding villages but Eyam lost 80% of its own inhabitants.

The 1665 disaster in London slowly waned and was finally brought to an end by the Great Fire of 1666. After this, London streets were widened, pavements were created, open sewers abolished, and the use of brick or stone became compulsory. As a result, the capital became cleaner and much less infested with rats, and Plague epidemics ceased.

The Black Death killed one third of the population of Europe and in Italy Petrarch described abandoned towns, the countryside littered with corpses and everywhere an eerie silence. The effect on European history was far reaching. Feudalism ended because of the shortage of farm labour, Jews were accused of poisoning the drinking water and suffered savage pogroms, the Church of Rome ran out of priests and became vulnerable to new Protestant ideas, and the Church monopoly on medicine was lost to the universities.

No English monarch died of Plague, but Edward III's daughter died of it and the royal courts forever moved to keep away from the disease. The last outbreak occurred in Glasgow in 1900 but effective antibiotics became available in 1945 and there have been no cases in England since that time.

# 7. Influenza

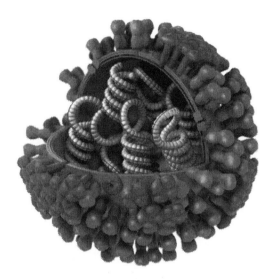

Serious respiratory infections due to Influenza virus have been known since ancient times, and were described by Hippocrates in 400 BC. It was called Influenza because it was thought to be spread by the influence of the stars. The disease is caused by a sub-microscopic RNA virus, which was described as a filterable agent in 1928 and first viewed by electron microscopy in 1950. The human virus also infects pigs and birds in which the unstable structure of the virus continuously mutates into new variants. Since the immunity of the population is only effective for about a year, these new variants cause new outbreaks of sporadic, epidemic and pandemic disease.

At 10-20 year intervals, major mutations of the Haemagglutinin and Neuraminidase virus antigens give rise to virulent new strains which sweep across the world and cause millions of deaths. Many victims are fit but non-immune young people, and the 1918 Flu pandemic killed 20 million with viral pneumonia. As a result, the death toll from this was higher than all those killed in military action in WW1.

An epidemic in England in 1730 killed 1,000 people each week, and the Influenza from Bukhara in 1890, was responsible for the death of Prince Eddie. And since he was heir to the throne it was responsible for the accession of Edward VII. Much less is known about the outbreak which killed Prince Arthur in 1509 and resulted in the accession of Henry VIII.

The illness is spread by coughing or sneezing and is highly contagious. There is a systemic viraemia with fever, headaches, muscle pains, and a cough with sputum. In a high proportion of cases this 3-4 day viral illness is prolonged for another 7-10 days by bacterial superinfections. In virulent pandemics there is little or no immunity to the virus, which can infect every organ of the body and is rapidly fatal.

Symptomatic relief for patients is needed for a few days but antibiotics are not effective against the virus. Nowadays new viral mutations are monitored across the world, especially in animal reservoirs in poultry and pigs, and new vaccines are rapidly manufactured using molecular engineering. These are now administered annually to keep pace with mutations in the virus and to maintain the immunity of the population.

# 8. Sweating Sickness

*Ann Boleyn, the Duke of Suffolk, and Cardinal Wolsey*

In Henry VII's reign, a new illness appeared in England, called the Sweating Sickness. Some saw it as retribution on the Tudor usurper, Henry VII, and in Europe it was called the English Sweat.

It was first reported before the Battle of Bosworth Field in 1485, when Lord Stanley used it an excuse for withholding his army's support from Richard III. This proved decisive to the outcome of the battle and it brought the Wars of the Roses, the Plantagenet dynasty, and the Middle Ages to an end. The sickness was then conveyed by Henry VII's victorious troops to London, where compared to the 1,100 deaths on the battlefield at Bosworth Field, it killed 15,000 Londoners in six weeks.

The origin and nature of the infection were unclear but the mercenaries who fought at Bosworth may have brought it to England after campaigning against the Ottomans in 1480. English outbreaks occurred between 1485 and 1553, and during one London epidemic, the mortality rate exceeded 4,000 a day. It spread to Denmark, Scandinavia, and Russia, and struck cities like Hamburg, Danzig and Lübeck before apparently disappearing forever.

Because of their living conditions, the poor were very susceptible to the disease and it instilled terror because the victims died so quickly. As a result, it was said that a man could be merry at dinner and dead by supper. The disease began suddenly with fever, aches, and vomiting, followed by intense chills and sweating. There was then an intense desire to sleep and death quickly followed.

The homeopathic remedies of the day included treacle, herbs, powdered sapphire, and powdered gold. But these were expensive as well as useless and during the 1517 epidemic Henry VII fled to secret houses and left the country to run itself. Having moved his court, only the queen and his physician, Dr Linacre, had access to the king, and foreign ambassadors were forbidden to come to court. Henry would not accept household goods from towns with Sweating Sickness, and he sent for safe supplies from as far afield as Holland.

In 1528 when Henry VIII was courting Ann Boleyn, one of her Ladies in Waiting contracted the disease and died. Ann herself contracted it, and in quarantine at Hever Castle the king sent his doctor, William Butts, to attend her. Her relatives, Thomas and George Boleyn, caught Sweating Sickness but survived, and Cardinal Wolsey fell ill with it and nearly died. But others like Mary Boleyn's husband, William Carey, Henry VIII's Groom of the Stool, William Compton, and the king's Latin secretary, Lord Grey, all died of the disease. And in 1551 Henry and Charles Brandon who were the second and third Dukes of Suffolk and both in line to the throne, died of it.

The cause has always remained a puzzle and a variant of European Relapsing Fever has been suggested. This is caused by the spiral bacterium *Borrelia recurrentis* which is spread from rats by lice and ticks. A more likely cause, however, is the Hantavirus. This is transmitted by mice and rats, and the clinical manifestations of present-day Hantavirus Pulmonary Syndrome (HPS) are similar to those described by Sweating Sickness. The USA still has about 50 cases of HPS each year and the last outbreak began in Yosemite National Park and had mortality rate of 38%. There is no effective treatment.

Whatever the cause, Sweating Sickness was not seen again in England after 1578, though a similar illness known as the Picardy Sweat occurred in France until 1861. The cause of its disappearance is debated. Viruses are intracellular parasites which cannot live outside animal cells and if all the infected patients were killed by the disease the virus would die out as well. But many cases survived the disease and there are also survivors from the modern Hantavirus syndrome. Alternatively, the virus could have become less virulent and continue to pass from person to person without causing recognisable disease. Finally, the human population may have developed cell-mediated immunity to the disease so that exposure to the virus no longer results in clinical disease.

# 9. Malaria

*Anopheles mosquito*

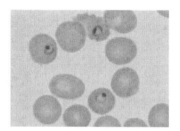

*Parasites in blood cells*

The association of fever with bad air from swamps (Mal-aria) was known in 400 BC, and the ancient Greeks knew the benefit of draining stagnant swamps around their cities. They did not, however, understand these were the breeding grounds of mosquitoes. Benign Tertian Malaria was common in England in medieval times when the summers were hot enough for Malarial parasites to complete their life cycle in Anopheles mosquitoes. This form of the disease causes a three-day cycle of fever and is an infection with the Plasmodium Vivax malarial parasite. It is transmitted to man by the bite of the female Anopheles mosquito which needs human blood to incubate its fertilised eggs. The fever is caused by the release of Malarial parasites from inside the circulating red blood cells and is accompanied by shivering, sweating, vomiting, headaches, anaemia, and jaundice. It is rarely fatal but the parasites persist in the liver and the disease can relapse for many years without further mosquito bites. As a result, Benign Tertian Malaria recurred in soldiers returning to England from the Crusades and in modern times from fighting in tropical countries during WW1 and WW2. And the last epidemic in England originated in such troops and was transmitted by mosquitoes to residents on the Isle of Sheppey in 1952.

Richard I and his Crusaders suffered from Malaria which they caught in the Middle East, and Henry VIII, Elizabeth I, and Cromwell caught Malaria from mosquitos breeding in the undrained swamps and fishponds of Southern England. In Cromwell's case it interfered with his military campaigns and he refused quinine powder because of its association with the Jesuits. In modern times Edward VIII suffered from Malaria which he caught during his royal visits to tropical countries. And the only Malaria seen in England today are sporadic infections brought back from tropical countries by tourists.

The more serious form of the disease is called Malignant Tertian Malaria and has a three-day cycle of fever caused by the Plasmodium Falciparum parasite. It is commonly fatal because it infects the brain and it is the commonest cause of death in the world. However, it has never been transmitted from man to man in England because the parasites require tropical temperatures to complete their life cycle in the mosquito.

There was no known specific treatment until 1600 when a Jesuit priest called Juan Lopez was cured by the powdered bark of the Cinchona tree. Called Jesuits' Powder, it was obtained from Peruvian Indians and was introduced to England in 1637 by Morton and Sydenham. Its active ingredient is quinine, and this was isolated in 1820. Using his microscope in 1878, Patrick Manson discovered the Malarial parasite in blood, and in 1924 Ronald Ross established the parasite's life cycle in the mosquito and in man.

For many years the treatment emphasis was preventing the disease by draining swamplands, killing mosquitos with insecticides, and using mosquito nets to prevent insect bites. Modern drugs were then introduced and were effective in the treatment of acute attacks and the prevention the disease. But increasing drug resistance is now a major public health problem and some parasites have become resistant to all drugs. As a result, the emphasis has switched back to the prevention strategies of the past. In addition, a Malaria vaccine is about to begin clinical trials, and genetic engineering is being used to create infertile male mosquitoes for release into the wild.

# 10. Syphilis

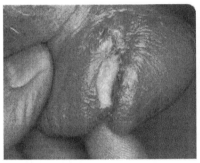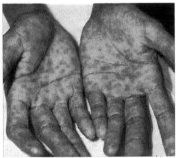

*Primary genital chancre and secondary skin rash*

Syphilis was once extremely common and was called the Great Pox. It is a serious sexually transmitted infection caused by the spiral bacterium *Treponema pallidum*, and it progresses from a localised infection on the genitalia to a generalised disease which can kill its victims years after it is first contracted.

The primary infection presents with a firm, painless skin ulcer on the penis or vulva called a chancre. In a secondary phase some months later there is a diffuse rash which characteristically includes the palms of the hands and soles of the feet. And after a symptomless phase of up to 20 years there is a tertiary phase in which growths called gummas appear in different organs. Gummas in the nasal cartilage cause a characteristic collapsed nose and in the aorta they lead to aneurysms which rupture and cause sudden death. In the spinal cord a tertiary infection called Tabes Dorsalis can cause loss of balance, and in the brain an encephalitis can lead to insanity.

During pregnancy the disease can be transmitted from an infected mother to her baby, resulting in congenital Syphilis. And many of these babies die in utero or soon after birth. The survivors fail to thrive and have misshapen teeth, eye inflammation, deafness, and deformities of the skull, nose, palate, and legs.

Syphilis can mimic many other diseases and is known as the great imitator. It can now by diagnosed using laboratory blood tests for Treponemal antibodies and by specialised microscopy to visualise the spiral bacteria.

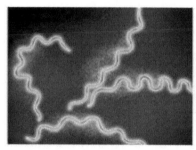 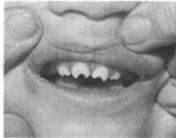

*Spiral bacteria and Syphilitic teeth*

The disease originated in the Americas and was brought to Europe around 1500 by the voyages of Christopher Columbus. Syphilis was common among the soldiers of all countries and the different armies and navies named it after their worst enemies. The French called it the Neapolitan disease, the Italians and Germans called it the French evil, and the Russians called it the Polish disease. The Persians called it the Turkish disease, the Turks called it the Christian disease, the Tahitians called it the British disease, and in Japan it was called the Chinese pox. According to the Diurnal of Occurents Henry Lord Darnley, the husband of Mary Queen of Scots, was struck down with the Great Pox, and modern examination of his skull in the Royal College of Surgeons of London confirms the characteristic bony pit marks of Syphilis. In his last years he demonstrated serious mental changes which led to his estrangement from Mary and his eventual murder. The consequences for Anglo-Scottish relations were far reaching and extended from Edinburgh to London and across Europe.

Cardinal Wolsey's physician, Augustine Agostini, said that Wolsey and Henry VIII had both contracted the Great Pox, and Henry's frightening temper was sometimes attributed to this. He was sexually promiscuous and one of his mistresses, Mary Boleyn, was also a mistress of Francis I of France, who was treated with Mercury and died of Syphilis. A portrait of Henry in Hever Castle is supposed to show he had a collapsed nose, but no other portraits showed the same feature and if he did have a saddle nose this would more easily have resulted from a physical injury. His severe headaches were also attributed to Syphilis but these occurred after a serious head injury in 1526 when he may have fractured his skull. Likewise, a persistent sore on his leg was treated by Thomas Vicary but was caused by a jousting injury and not Syphilis. Even the repeated miscarriages of Catherine of Aragon and Ann Boleyn are sometimes said to have been caused by Syphilis, but there is no evidence that these two women or their dead children contracted the disease. Medical records describing treatment for Syphilis are a sure sign that a patient may have had the disease, as was the case of William IV who travelled the world as a bachelor in the Royal Navy. But Henry VIII never received treatment for Syphilis and there is no objective evidence that he ever had Syphilis or transmitted it to others.

The disease was commonly treated with Mercury which gave rise to the adage that a night with Venus could lead to a lifetime with Mercury. In 1496 Giorgio Sommariva of Verona used Mercury against Syphilis and in 1536 Paracelsus proclaimed it was the only proper cure. In the form of Mercuric Chloride (Calomel) it was administered by mouth, rubbed into the skin or injected into the urethra using a wooden syringe. In addition, a curious method was fumigation in which the patient was placed in a closed box with his head sticking out. Mercury was placed inside the box and a fire started under it, causing the Mercury to vaporise. This was used to cure many diseases as well as Syphilis but it slowly poisoned the patients and its side effects included mouth ulcers, bone erosions, loose teeth, and kidney failure. The gruelling regimen was often worse than the diseases being treated and in the 17th century it fell from use.

It was also observed that Syphilis improved when the patients developed other infections, and this led to the development of Fever Therapy. This was performed by deliberately infecting the patient with Malaria, which benefitted the Syphilis and could then be cured with Quinine. Other agents like Guaiacum and Sarsaparilla were also used but there is no evidence they were effective. In the 19th century Syphilis became treatable with the Arsenical drug Salvarsan and in 1928 it became curable with penicillin.

# 11. Dysentery

*Dysentery in a prison camp*

Most vomiting and diarrhoea which lasts for 4-5 days is caused by food contamination with *Salmonella typhimurium* or *Campylobacter*, or viruses such as *Norovirus*. It is commonly caught from undercooked, infected poultry and the food poisoning requires no specific treatment and is rarely life threatening.

Dysentery, on the other hand, is a potentially fatal diarrhoea caused by the bacterium *Shigella dysenteriae*. It is highly contagious and the bacterium can persist in asymptomatic disease carriers who can cause repeated outbreaks of the disease. Another form of Dysentery is caused by *Entamoeba histolytica* but this is confined to tropical countries and is spread from crops fertilised with contaminated human sewage. Cholera is indistinguishable from Dysentery and is caused by the bacterium, *Vibrio cholerae*.

Dysentery victims have voluminous bloody diarrhoea which was called the bloody flux, and was accompanied by abdominal cramps and high fever, and led quickly to death from dehydration. In medieval times Dysentery was common in military camps when it was spread by soldiers defecating in the open or using crude latrines. It decimated many military campaigns, and at Crecy the French called the English the bare bottom soldiers. Half of Henry V's troops caught Dysentery from infected shellfish at Harfleur, and 9,000 men-at-arms and 5,000 archers died of it before the Battle of Agincourt. The Earl of Somerset and the Bishop of Norwich were among the victims, and the Duke of Clarence survived but was sent back to England. Dysentery during military campaigning caused the death of King John, Edward I, Edward the Black Prince, and Henry V. And it was responsible for many deaths in the Crimean and Boer wars, and in prisoner of war camps in WW1 and WW2.

Medieval armies on the move rarely justified camp latrines or washing facilities, and everything touched by infected hands transmitted the disease. And when men defecated in the open it became possible for flies to transmit the disease to food. The routes of marches were littered with the dead bodies of Dysentery victims and to combat this, Genghis Khan ordered his army's drinking water to be boiled to sterilise it. If it became tasteless it was flavoured with plant leaves and it was this which began the custom of brewing tea.

Domestic cleanliness was often no better than in the army and the peasant classes defecated anywhere they found convenient. In the cities of the 19th century the chamber pots were emptied out of the windows onto the streets, and cess pits were hardly ever cleaned out because the work was filthy and workmen called gongfermors charged high prices for the work. As a result, when rivers like the Thames flooded, the cess pits overflowed into the cellars and contaminated the water wells. It was then that many discovered that drinking beer was safer than drinking well water. For wiping material, the Romans used running water and wet sponges, and in medieval times the richer classes had cotton and linen rags. The poorer classes on the other hand used moss or the leaves of a plant known as Common Mullein.

In 1388 Parliament issued a statute to clean up London and the Crusaders brought soap to Europe from the Middle East. Larger households built stone lavers for people to wash their hands, and the lavatories were positioned away from the diners and with double doors to control smells. Chutes were provided for the discharges and

But epidemics of Dysentery and Cholera continued to kill large numbers until it became clear that the outbreaks were waterborne and new control methods were necessary. In 1854 Dr John Snow closed down the contaminated Broad Street public water pump in Soho, and brought a cholera epidemic to an end. And Tawton Council in Devon achieved a similar result by treating an infected well with quicklime. But the River Thames continued as an open sewer and in summer the smell outside the Palace of Westminster was overpowering. As a direct result of its impact on MPs in Parliament, the Chadwick Report in 1847 set up a General Board of Health and commissioned Sir Joseph Balzagette to build a vast new sewage system to divert sewage out of London on the ebb tide of the River Thames.

In the 19th century Dysentery and Cholera numbers fell dramatically but infected victims were still likely to die until the advent of modern antibiotics and vaccines. During WW1, the damage to London public water supplies and sewers by German bombers led to the compulsory chlorination of drinking water. This effectively eliminated epidemic Dysentery, and was retained after the war finished and adopted by other countries around the world.

# 12. Typhoid

Typhoid Fever is caused by the *Salmonella typhi* and *Salmonella paratyphi* bacilli and was spread to drinking water from rivers contaminated with raw sewage or from wells infected by leaking or flooded sewage systems. In these cases it usually occurred as epidemics. Many cases were contracted from shellfish harvested from sea water which was polluted by raw sewage, and from unhygienic food handling. Initially the bowel is infected and if it bleeds or perforates this can be fatal. A systemic infection follows, and the brain, lungs, bones, kidneys, and heart can become involved with serious consequences. If the gall bladder is infected these patients become chronic carriers of the disease. And since they often have no symptoms and escape detection, they cause further epidemics if they work in school or hospital kitchens.

Patients develop a high swinging fever, with sweating, headaches, abdominal pain, nausea, anorexia, and constipation, and this eventually lead to delirium and exhaustion. There is a skin rash of rose pink spots, and the spleen becomes enlarged.

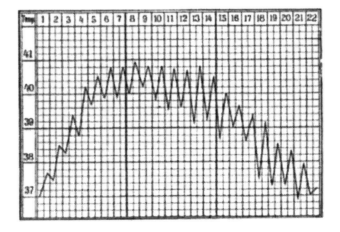

*Typhoid temperature chart*

The modern diagnosis is confirmed from bacterial cultures of the stools, urine, and blood, and by using the Widal Test to identify the bacteria in the laboratory.

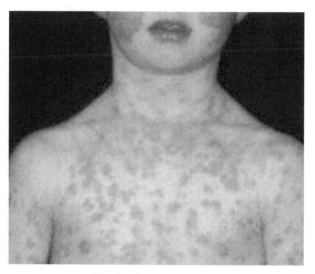

*Typhoid rose pink spots*

Henry Prince of Wales in 1612, and Albert the Prince Consort in 1861, were both suspected of dying from Typhoid, though both are now known to have died from other causes. But Edward VII and George V contracted Typhoid Fever and both survived.

Modern sanitation and hygiene have reduced the incidence of the disease in Britain and most of the 200 cases a year are contracted abroad. The last epidemic in Britain occurred in Aberdeen in 1964 and was traced to tins of imported meat. The mortality in untreated cases is 25% and large numbers still die in third world countries. A TAB vaccine has been developed to provide immunity against the infection, and antibiotics such as Ampicillin and Chloramphenicol can reduce mortality rates to 1%. In chronic disease carriers, however, antibiotics are less effective.

# 13. Puerperal Fever

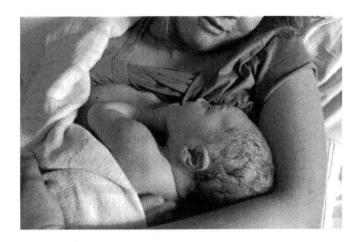

Puerperal or Childbed Fever starts with the infection of the birth canal after childbirth and was extremely common before the advent of modern hygiene. As a result, it was the major cause of maternal mortality until the 20th century.

If the vagina or perineum are injured during a baby's delivery, bacteria can gain entry to the pelvic soft tissues and can easily spread to cause peritonitis and septicaemia. The most serious organism to cause this is the Gas Gangrene bacterium, *Clostridium welchii*, and there was no cure for this before the advent of penicillin.

When records began around 1900, 1 in 200 mothers died in childbirth, and the mortality from Puerperal fever was 35%. In the preceding centuries this was much higher and the royal deaths from it included Elizabeth of York the wife of Henry VII, Jane Seymour the wife of Henry VIII, and Queen Catherine Parr the widow of Henry VIII. Any complications of labour made infection more likely and the unassisted 48-hour labour of Jane Seymour left her seriously traumatised and susceptible to the infection which killed her.

Queen Victoria was the first royal mother to be delivered by a skilled obstetrician, and before this, only women were allowed to act as midwives These were self-trained and they were able to manage normal deliveries but not any complications which might arise. In addition, village midwives had wide experience but royal Ladies in Waiting often had no experience at all. Midwifery was often run as a lucrative family business, handed from mother to daughter, and since the fee from a wealthy family could be as much as £100, any advances in labour management were carefully kept secrets. A good example was when assisted delivery forceps were invented by Dr Peter Chamberlen in 1616. His technique was a strict secret and in 1819, sets of his obstetric forceps were discovered hidden beneath the floor boards of his family home.

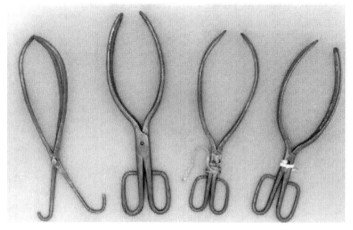

*Obstetric Forceps*

Puerperal Fever was particularly dangerous when caused by bacteria from the dirty surroundings of the labour room and transferred from the dirty hands of the midwife. And in the case of Jane Seymour's delivery of Edward VI we know the midwives were not accustomed to wash their hands and were affronted if asked to do so. In addition, Jane Seymour was draped in animal fur.

The infectious nature of Childbed Fever was first described in 1847 by Ignaz Semmelweis in Vienna, and it was he who implemented a regimen of hand washing with chlorinated lime solution. This reduced the incidence of the disease to under 1% but there was resistance to his findings and it was only after the work of

Pasteur and Lister that his methods were widely adopted. Semmelweis became known as the saviour of mothers but was dismissed from his university and ended his days in a lunatic asylum. Since 1902 antibiotics have largely eliminated death from Puerperal Fever and by 1970 British maternal mortality fell to 1 in 5,000.

# 14. Habitual Abortion

The miscarriage of three or more pregnancies is called habitual abortion and in many cases an underlying cause can now be identified. About 1% of couples are affected nowadays, and thorough investigations can reveal a treatable cause.

Lifestyle factors include smoking, alcohol, and drugs, and women with diabetes mellitus are also at increased risk. In addition, some infections can lead to abortion, including Rubella and Measles. Another cause is Polycystic Ovary Syndrome in which a defect of steroid hormone metabolism increases male testosterone production in the mother. Uterine malformations cause some cases and the most common abnormalities are uterine fibroids or cervical malformations. In some cases, chromosomal abnormalities in one of the parents can lead to pregnancy loss, and preimplantation genetic diagnosis can now be used to identify affected embryos.

Habitual abortions are common in women with an excessive blood clotting tendency called thrombophilia in which blood clots in the placenta obstruct the flow of blood to the foetus and deprive it of oxygen and nutrients. As a result, the baby fails to thrive and eventually dies in the womb or soon after birth. The most common causes of Thrombophilia are the blood clotting factor mutations called Factor V Leiden and Prothrombin 20210A. And in 70-80% of such cases, treatment with anticoagulants such as Aspirin and Heparin can lead to a successful pregnancy.

Another group of disorders involve abnormal maternal immunity. All foetuses inherit half of their body makeup from their father, and this is foreign to the mother's immune system and would normally lead to immune rejection. The lining of the womb normally protects foetuses from this but in some cases the mechanism breaks down. The classic example is Rhesus Haemolytic Disease in which a Rhesus negative mother carries the father's Rhesus positive baby and produces Rhesus antibodies against the baby. This was an extremely common cause of habitual abortion until the 1960s when the use of Anti-Rhesus antiserum completely eliminated the disease. In some mothers there is maternal immunisation against male-specific histocompatibility antigens and in these cases the daughters survive but not the sons.

As regards the wives of Henry VIII, none of his first three wives had difficulty becoming pregnant. During her 22-year marriage to Henry, Catherine of Aragon had two stillbirths, two neonatal deaths of live-born infants, and a cot death of a healthy boy 52 days after birth. Only one of her daughters survived to adulthood. Ann Boleyn had two stillbirths, one neonatal death of a premature boy, and the only surviving child of her two-year marriage was a daughter. Jane Seymour had one pregnancy and delivered a healthy son but she died of Puerperal Fever two weeks later.

In comparison, none of Henry's last three marriages produced children. His marriage to Ann of Cleves was not consummated, and Henry was ill during his marriages to Catherine Howard and Catherine Parr. Catherine remarried after Henry's death and gave birth to a child by Thomas Seymour but then died of Puerperal Fever. It is also relevant that Henry had numerous mistresses and several illegitimate children, including a daughter by Mary Boleyn and a son by Ann Blount. His six wives produced three surviving children from 12 pregnancies, which represents an overall infant mortality of 75%. This seems appalling by modern standards but was not unusual at that time. Indeed, John Colet, who was Henry's Dean of St Paul's and became known for educational reforms, was the only one of his mother's 22 children to survive beyond the first year of life. Poor nutrition, hard physical work, and intercurrent disease accounted for the high infant mortality of the poorer classes, but in the case of the Henry VIII's wives additional causes seem likely. And it is sobering to think that something as simple as Aspirin may have solved the problems of Catherine of Aragon or Ann Boleyn, and changed the course of history.

In the case of Queen Anne, she had 17 pregnancies with only one live child who died aged nine from a probable birth injury. Her failure to produce an heir lead to the end of the Stuart dynasty and we know now that her abortions were due to hereditary Porphyria. And this was re-introduced into the English monarchy by George I.

# 15. Pseudocyesis

Pseudocyesis is a woman's firm but mistaken belief that she is pregnant and is distinguished from when a woman feigns pregnancy. It usually occurs in hysteria-prone women at the time of the menopause, when it is accompanied by signs that are confused with pregnancy. These include cessation of menstrual periods, morning sickness, tender breasts, mood swings, weight gain, and pelvic distension due to the contraction of the diaphragmatic muscles. In some cases the woman experiences foetal movements and a small number undergo a false labour.

The syndrome is part of a hysterical spectrum of symptoms, and occurs most commonly in those who have every whim gratified and sympathy lavished on every woe. Sir William Osler described how such patients can be completely incapacitated and how their behaviour can become irrational. They develop a morbid craving for sympathy, and are bed ridden for long periods.

Queen Mary I was under enormous pressure to produce a Catholic heir to the throne and she is the prime royal example of the disorder. Her court and the Church were constantly on alert because of her suspected pregnancies, and on the last occasion she had a serious underlying disease which appears to have been the ovarian cancer which killed her.

# 16. Liver Cirrhosis

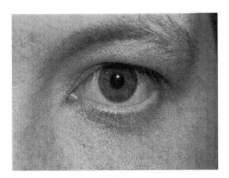

*Jaundice*

Chronic inflammation of the liver eventually leads to fibrous scarring and at that stage the damage becomes permanent.

The most common causes of liver inflammation are Hepatitis A, B, and C viruses, which are spread via the oro-faecal route by poor hygiene. Increasing numbers of cases are also due to chronic alcoholism.

The loss of normal liver function leads to jaundice, and altered blood flow through the liver causes fluid distension of the abdomen or ascites. Venous swellings called oesophageal varices appear in the gullet and if these burst, the bleeding is often fatal. The liver is important in many metabolic processes and when these are compromised it leads to episodes of coma called hepatic encephalopathy.

The modern diagnosis is made by examining a liver biopsy under the microscope, and the non-surgical management of cirrhosis can often slow the progress of the disease. Eventually, however, many patients undergo liver transplantation.

William I died following internal injury to his distended abdomen after a riding accident, and George IV bled to death from oesophageal varices. In both cases their cirrhosis was caused by alcoholism.

# 17. Urinary Tract Stones

Kidney stones are composed of calcium salts or uric acid and vary in size from small pieces of gravel to large stones. They are found in the kidney, the ureter, or the bladder and if less than 5mm in diameter they are passed down the ureters to the bladder and are expelled in the urine. This produces extremely painful colic and can also cause bleeding, infection, and kidney failure. Excessive meat consumption increases uric acid stone formation and the Tudors and the Hanoverians were renowned for this. An outdoor life and exposure to excessive sunlight alters calcium metabolism and increases vitamin D formation, and this was a possible factor in the case of Oliver Cromwell.

In Cromwell's case his renal colic led to severe depression and affected his judgment during his military campaigns in Ireland. From medieval times there were lithotomy surgeons who specialised in removing stones by cutting into the perineum and the base of the bladder. But before modern anaesthesia this was extremely painful and was often complicated by damage to the bladder, prostate gland, and penis. It was an operation which most patients declined and which Cromwell was offered but turned down.

Nowadays anti-uric acid drugs such as Allopurinol are able to prevent recurrences. And when surgical intervention is needed, fibre optic endoscopy and shockwave lithotripsy have revolutionised the surgical management.

# 18. Tobacco Diseases

Tobacco was brought to Europe from the New World around 1600, and smoking became popular in the next 100 years. In the 19th century cigar and cigarette manufacture was industrialised and smoking soared in WW1 and WW2 when free cigarettes were handed to the troops.

Tobacco smoke contains many harmful chemicals and it greatly increases the risk of fatal diseases such as lung cancer, bronchitis, emphysema, strokes, and heart attacks. It also contributes to a wide array of diseases such as and breast and bowel cancer and peptic ulcers, and a peripheral vascular disease of the legs called Buerger's Syndrome is only found in smokers.

In addition to Nicotine which is the addictive chemical in tobacco smoke, there are 40 chemicals known to cause cancer including Cyanide, Benzene, and Acetyline. The health risks were first suspected in Germany in the 1930s, but WW2 made it impossible to follow up on this and after the war the powerful worldwide tobacco industry made it difficult to reduce tobacco smoking through education. It was only when the Oxford epidemiologists Richard Doll and Austin Bradford Hill published the statistics about tobacco smoking that changes began.

After banning advertising, prohibiting smoking in public places, and increasing taxes on tobacco sales, a massive reduction in tobacco smoking took place, and was the single most important health measure in the 20th century. As a result, the average life expectancy increased by 25 years.

*Sir Richard Doll*                    *Austin Bradford Hill*

From the age of 13 Edward VII smoked 20 Egyptian cigarettes and 10 cigars a day and he died of a heart attack aged 69. His son, George V, began a life time of chain smoking as a naval cadet, suffered recurrent chest infections, and died of lung cancer aged 71. Edward VIII smoked all his life and died of throat cancer in 1972. And his brother, George VI, started smoking cigarettes from the age of 18 whilst serving in the Royal Navy and suffered from a gastric ulcer, Buerger's Syndrome, and lung cancer. His younger daughter, Princess Margaret, smoked cigarettes from the age of 15, had a lung removed and died of a stroke. But since that time the royal family have not been cigarette smokers and the Queen Mother lived to be 102 and her daughter, Queen Elizabeth II, is now 90.

# 19. Kypho-scoliosis

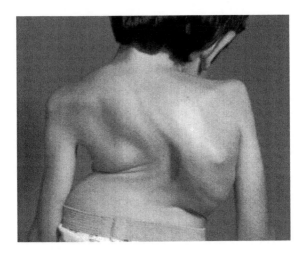

Kypho-scoliosis is a deformity of the spine due to vertebrae which have become wedge-shaped and misaligned. Most cases are due to Scheuermann's Osteochondritis, which is an inflammation of the intervertebral discs which begins in childhood and gets worse until bone growth stops. The cause of the inflammation is unknown but impaired blood supply to the vertebrae is one possibility. The condition can also be due to bone weakening from senile osteoporosis, or to wear and tear from spondylosis, or following spina bifida, in which the spine doesn't form properly in the growing foetus. Other secondary causes include Tuberculosis and physical injury.

There is no cure and the modern treatment is an external spinal support called a Milwaukee back brace, or orthopaedic surgery to implant metal rods to straighten the curvature. These relieve some of the deformity and discomfort but do not reverse the underlying disease or prevent the chest infections which are eventually fatal. After his death at Bosworth Field, Richard III was represented by his Tudor enemies as physically deformed by kypho-scoliosis, and his appearance was evidence of an evil character. In some cultures hunchbacks were put to death and Victor Hugo's Quasimodo was only able to find safety from the mob in the bell tower of Notre Dame Cathedral.

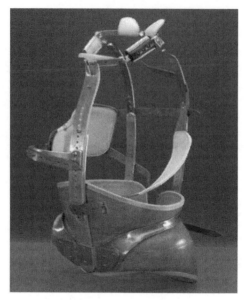

*Milwaukee Back Brace*

The deformed back and compensatory limp of "Richard Crookback" were said by Yorkists to have been Tudor propaganda put about by Thomas More and William Shakespeare. And on the battlefield Richard was not at all disabled but a fearsome warrior who came close to killing Henry VII in hand-to-hand combat. Lancastrians on the other hand said the hunchback was his true likeness, and when he appeared in public it was hidden by cleverly tailored clothes. None of Richard's portraits show a deformity but modern X-rays of the paintings confirm that some were altered so as to conceal it.

*Richard III's skeleton and its deformed spine*

This dispute continued for 500 years and was only settled recently when Richard's remains were located in a common grave in a Leicester car park. They confirm a serious kypho-scoliosis and it is unlikely that he could have survived to old age with this deformity.

# 20. Epilepsy

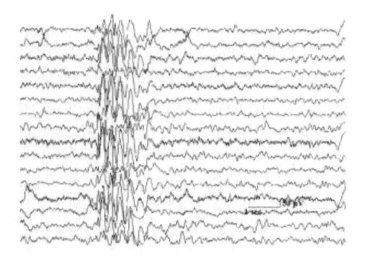

*EEG of a Grand Mal seizure*

In medieval times epileptics were thought to be possessed by devils and the treatment was to drill a hole in the skull to let the devils out. It was regarded as a form of madness and most patients spent the rest of their lives in lunatic asylums.

The major disease, Grand Mal epilepsy, is characterised by sudden seizures in which patients fall to the ground unconscious, foam at the mouth, bite their tongues and stop breathing. There is violent involuntary shaking of the arms or legs and the patients are incontinent and soil themselves with urine and faeces. Sometimes they can choke and die from inhaling vomit, but in most patients the seizure stops and they sleep for a period and wake without remembering what has happened. This post-ictal period lasts several hours and the patients can be temporarily paralysed or show psychotic behaviour. Sometimes a fit is brought on by external stimuli such as flashing lights, and is preceded by a feeling or aura in which the patients sense that a fit is imminent. And one of the features of worsening disease is Status Epilepticus in which seizures follow one another without consciousness being recovered, and which can be fatal.

Nowadays Grand Mal seizures can be recorded on an electroencephalogram (EEG) of the brain, and this shows that it begins at a focal point before spreading to the whole brain. In many cases the focus is a lesion in the cerebral cortex such as a birth injury scar or a brain tumour, and nowadays these can be surgically removed.

In many cases, however, no underlying lesion is located and the epilepsy is said to be idiopathic.

In most patients the modern treatment is with anticonvulsant drugs such as Phenytoin and Valproic acid and these suppress seizures in most patients but without removing the underlying cause. But seizures during activities like driving a car can have fatal consequences for more than just the patient and epileptics are banned by law from activities such as driving.

*Henry IV*                    *Prince John*

To develop epilepsy was devastating for Henry IV and he was forced to hand over the administration of the country to his son. In Prince John's case the Windsor family removed him from public life and he lived at a farm on the Sandringham estate where he was eventually found dead in bed after a seizure.

# 21. Mental Illness

| Richard II | Henry VI | George III | Victoria |

## Depression

Depression is the commonest mental illness and affects up to 15% of the population. The patients say they feel sad, anxious, empty, hopeless, helpless, worthless, guilty, irritable, angry, or ashamed. They lose interest in pleasurable activities, have no appetite, and have problems concentrating, remembering details or making decisions. They also find personal relationships increasingly difficult and they contemplate, attempt, or commit suicide. Depression occurs at all ages and may be a reaction to bullying, bereavement, unemployment, or divorce. In these instances it is said to be reactive and does not usually persist.

Patients prone to depression often have pre-existing negative emotions and low self-esteem, and some have problems with alcohol or drug abuse. Brain scans indicate that some have abnormal anatomical features in their brains. In addition, their brains have low levels of neurotransmitter serotonin, norepinephrine, and dopamine. In some cases depression may be part of Bipolar Disorder in which the patients experience episodes of mania interspersed with depression.

Mild depression often responds to counselling. But more severe cases need antidepressant medications to raise neurotransmitter levels in the brain. In the most serious cases, especially when suicide is a possibility, hospitalisation for psychiatric supervision is needed.

Queen Victoria was a vivacious young woman but later developed a melancholic personality. She experienced post-natal depression after her pregnancies and had a long period of depression in 1861 after the death of her husband. Following Prince Albert's death she withdrew from public life for three years, which alienated the public and generated an upsurge in republicanism. She did not open Parliament for five years and without modern psychiatric treatment she had to rely on the support from her family and friends, and particularly from John Brown and the staff at Balmoral. She only slowly improved and it was not until her Golden Jubilee in 1887 that she was able to entertain again on a grand scale.

The use of Cannabis is associated with depression and Queen Victoria's use of Cannabis as an analgesic is now thought to have been a factor. During pregnancy Cannabis crosses the placenta into the baby's circulation where it can retard the brain development of the foetus and cause Attention Deficit Disorder. This occurred in her eldest son, Edward VII, whose behaviour caused repeated social embarrassment and concern to the royal family and the government.

## Schizophrenia

About 0.5% of the population are affected by schizophrenia which is a serious psychosis characterised by delusional beliefs, paranoia, hallucinations, social isolation, reduced emotional expression, and a lack of motivation. Catatonic posturing is a particularly bizarre sign in which the patients sit silently for hours in strange adopted postures. Schizophrenics also have an increased incidence of anxiety, depression, and suicide.

It usually begins in young adults and is usually lifelong. No single cause is known and a range of genetic and environmental factors are implicated. Up until the 1960s schizophrenics were judged unfit or unsafe to remain in the community and were confined to institutions. As a result, most of the patients in the huge Victorian lunatic asylums were schizophrenics. Modern treatment, however, is now carried out in the community and comprises antipsychotic medication supported with counselling, job training, and social rehabilitation.

*Catatonic posturing*

Schizophrenia is now thought to have affected Richard II, Henry VI, and George III, in whom it severely reduced their ability to reign and had serious consequences. Richard II became narcissistic and self-obsessed and aware only of his own needs. He became socially awkward and eventually lost all touch with reality. Henry VI was seen singing and laughing on the battlefield at St Albans whilst his wife directed the troops. And like Richard II he was deposed and eventually murdered by rivals for the throne. There is a strong tendency for schizophrenia to run in families and Henry VI inherited schizophrenia from his mother, Catherine of Valois, who in turn inherited it from her father, Charles VI of France.

George III was totally incapacitated with symptoms of psychosis caused by the rare disease hereditary Porphyria. He would walk about and talk non-stop for days on end and he had to be restrained for his own safety, and not allowed to shave with a razor. And also for the safety of his wife, who he was deluded into thinking was unfaithful to him. Eventually George's ministers found him unmanageable and a Regency Act was passed by Parliament which removed him from power and allowed him to live at Windsor whilst his son ruled as Regent.

In modern times by contrast, Princess Alice, the mother of the Duke of Edinburgh, was diagnosed with schizophrenia and spent her life in a Swiss sanatorium and at Buckingham Palace where she was successfully treated with modern antipsychotic medications.

## Anxiety Neurosis

George V's sons all suffered from anxiety neurosis which is now ascribed to the strict moralising of their bullying father and to the sadistic nannies and tutors who were employed to help raise them. George VI developed a severe stammer, and the Duke of Gloucester looked at his feet when spoken to. The Duke of Kent retreated into a life of cocaine and heroin abuse, and Edward VIII chain smoked and drank too much alcohol.

George VI found being king a severe strain and his temper often snapped. His family were very supportive and tried to make light of what they called his gnashes but for comfort he smoked cigarettes and these eventually led to his death from lung cancer.

## Personality Disorders

Personality disorders are ingrained patterns of maladaptive behaviour which usually begin in adolescence and cause difficulties in personal relationships. About ten different types are recognised including paranoid, obsessive-compulsive, narcissistic, and psychopathic variants.

Feeling angry is a natural response to being attacked, insulted, deceived, or frustrated. The adrenalin creates a lot of nervous energy and letting off steam releases the tension.

The Plantagenets were a dynasty who habitually violated others without remorse and easily fulfil the DSM-5 diagnosis of the American Psychiatric Association for Psychopathic Personality Disorder. Edward I was an **extraordinarily** violent example but Richard I, John, Edward IV, and Richard III were not men to be trusted or crossed. Ruthlessness was what enabled the Plantagenets to win the throne and keep their empires secure, and this was tolerated so long as the king's malevolence protected other powerful interests as well. As a result there was a medieval expectation for the king to rule ruthlessly and the requirement was passed from father to son.

The condition remains poorly understood but modern targeted MRI brain scans show that psychopaths fail to employ parts of the brain which integrate the emotions in normal subjects. Psychopaths comprise about 5% of the population and studies of identical twins raised apart from each other indicate there is a strong familial predisposition. There is also a link between psychopathy and interbreeding. But nurture also plays an important role since psychopathic behaviour can be mitigated in a growing child by loving parents who teach impulse control. If, on the other hand, children are exposed to a manipulative, deceptive, bullying parent, they grow to believe sociopathic behaviour is normal and develop it for their own use.

Overt psychopaths lack remorse and feel only shallow emotion. In extreme cases, they do not care whether someone lives or dies. They view the world in a very different way to normal people and are quite unable to understand other people's emotions. They have superficial charm, emotional shallowness, and a grandiose sense of self-worth. And pathological lying, cunning manipulativeness, a tendency to boredom, impulsive lack of control, juvenile delinquency, criminal versatility, multiple marriages, and promiscuous sexual behaviour.

Successive generations of Plantagenets were easily angered and used their anger to control those around them. And they discovered it was more effective if their anger was frightening. It was said that Henry II could roll around on the floor in a purple fury and foam at the mouth. Their behaviour usually benefitted the king's family, and their nepotism could reach extreme proportions. In a civilized society psychopathic behaviour eventually harms everyone and after killing all their opponents, it was not surprising that the Plantagenets eventually killed themselves as well.

Psychopaths are attracted to power and often rise to the top of politics, business, and journalism. Psychologists now say that Hitler was abused by his tyrannical father and scapegoated the Jews for his residual fury. He was vengeful towards any wounding of his narcissism and the need to suppress his aggression led to obsessive-compulsive behaviour. He suffered from insomnia and irritable bowel syndrome, and used sedative and stimulant drugs. During WW1 he developed hysterical mutism and blindness and in later life his barely controlled attacks of anger were frightening. From adolescence he showed syphilophobia towards women and he may have resented his mother not protecting him from his abusive father. Ultimately he developed a Messiah Complex with alternating periods of despair and rage which are typical of Bipolar Disorder. The Plantagenets' behaviour can be explained along similar lines and when as young boys they appeared at their father's side on the battlefields, they witnessed their fathers' atrocities and grew to believe this was normal.

Psychopaths shows a spectrum of severity and whilst extreme cases have a cluster of psychopathic traits, even civilised leaders have to make decisions which may require a psychopathic mind-set. On the grand scale these can cause the deaths of hundreds of thousands of innocent people, as when Churchill and President Truman ordered the carpet bombing of Dresden and the nuclear attacks on Hiroshima and Nagasaki.

Even civilised leaders are required to take decisions which most normal men could not deal with, and whether some of these have psychopathic elements is an area for debate. As a result it is difficult to decide if the Plantagenets were overt psychopaths or normal men who periodically drifted into psychopathy when the circumstances demanded.

# 22. Speech Impediments

So far as can be ascertained, five monarchs had speech impediments. Edward I and James I spoke with a lisp, William II and George VI struggled with a stammer for most of their lives, and James II developed a stammer in old age. Public speaking exaggerates speech difficulties and for those required to speak a lot in public, a speech impediment is a severe handicap.

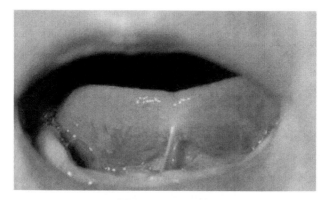

*Tongue Frenulum*

With lisping the person misarticulates sibilant sounds like "s" and "z", because the tongue and front teeth are misaligned. In some cases the tongue is tied by a frenulum to the floor of the mouth and in James I it was debated whether his should be surgically divided. Speech therapy is the main modern treatment in which a therapist uses exercises to position the tongue correctly behind the incisor teeth. Once success is achieved, continued practice is important and subjects are taught to monitor their own impediment. Speech therapy is usually sufficient, but some cases may require orthodontic braces or minor oral surgery.

With stammering the patients have a struggle to get words out. The words are repeated or prolonged, or get stuck, or extra sounds are uttered. Some pick their way around difficult words and most avoid speaking in public. Many are fluent one minute and struggle to speak the next and most admit to strong frustration, anger, embarrassment, and shame.

They stammer especially on words of several syllables and it is more difficult for them to speak fluently when they are feeling ill, stressed, tired, excited, or upset. Remarkably, however, they are often fluent when singing, whispering, or talking to themselves.

For children who stammer it can undermine their confidence and self-esteem, and they are likely to be teased and bullied. More than 5% of children go through a phase of stammering at some stage, and without intervention a quarter of these become persistent. About 1% of adults stammer and more men stammer than women.

Speech and language therapy are most effective in children under five years of age, and in many cases the child becomes able to speak fluently if the problem is treated early enough. Stammering is partly a neurological condition and there are differences in the anatomy and functioning of the brains of those who stammer. The speech area of the cerebral cortex is called Broca's area and in patients who stammer its vascular circulation is impaired. Many sufferers are naturally left handed but were forced to use their right hand, and this "misplaced sinister" is because the speech area is in the "wrong" side of the brain. Someone with stammering in the family is more likely to stammer themselves, and the genes GNPTAB and GNPTG are linked to stammering.

The main focus of speech therapy is the dysfunctional diaphragmatic breathing and insufficient air flow over the epiglottis. This is often brought on by anxiety and is reinforced by failed attempts to present oneself as a non-stammerer. During speech therapy patients are trained to use costal rather than diaphragmatic breathing and to bolster their self-confidence by meeting former stammerers who have been treated successfully. But patients are never cured permanently and when they relapse they need further treatment.

Adults with established stammering must learn to reduce its impact on their lives. Many find that self-help groups enable them to be more open about their stammer and embrace situations they previously avoided. An outcome of therapy may be that the person's stammer is actually more apparent, because they now say what they want to say and do not hold back because of the stammer. Renowned stammerers like Aneurin Bevan and Winston Churchill even learned to use their stammer to good effect when speaking in public.

# 23. Poison

*Belladonna*

Poisoning was always suspected when a king's death was unexplained and Henry I was said to have been poisoned by a surfeit of lampreys even though they are not poisonous. In his case it is more likely he died of accidental food poisoning caused by poor kitchen hygiene. There was speculation about the death of Prince Arthur, the eldest son of Henry VII, and there are modern historians would like to analyse his mortal remains for poison.

Henry VIII employed food tasters more than any other monarch. And after one attempt to poison his food the cook was threatened with being boiled alive before the sentence was commuted to being hanged, drawn, and quartered. When Henry's son Edward was born, Henry even had the food tasters test the breast milk of the wet nurse. And after Catherine of Aragon was removed from Henry's court she greatly feared being poisoned and would not eat any food that had not been tasted before her. Edward VI died of Tuberculosis but his sudden death was unforeseen and followed the intervention of a quack healer who was later accused of poisoning him. In this case, however, it was likely he succumbed to poisoning from the overenthusiastic use of a tonic containing Arsenic.

Since ancient times, rulers employed food tasters and in many instances they also prepared and served the king's food and drink. Some like Halotus, the food taster of the Roman Emperor Claudius, became famous and wealthy. In modern times Hitler's food taster, Margot Woelk, tried the Fuhrer's food at 8:00 am every day, and only if she did not fall ill was Hitler allowed to eat it. In more recent times Presidents Barack Obama and Vladimir Putin hired food tasters as part of their security staff and it is said our modern monarchs have a system in operation when they dine out.

Hemlock is famous as the poison that Socrates drank when he was sentenced to commit suicide, and it is a paralytic agent which causes death by asphyxiation. A variation was the meat of larks, which are resistant to hemlock but eat so many of the berries their flesh becomes poisonous to humans.

Aconite comes from the plant Monkshood and the emperor Augustus was said to have been poisoned by his wife, Livia, who used Aconite in a plate of mushrooms. It causes vomiting and diarrhoea, and then fatal heart arrhythmias.

Belladonna gets its name because peasant women used to rub it in their eyes to constrict their pupils and flush their faces so as to give them an attractive dreamy look. But in excess it causes nausea, hallucinations, and fatal heart arrhythmias.

The fruit of the Mandrake is edible but its roots are poisonous and extracts are strong enough to remove skin warts. As a poison, it causes liver and kidney failure.

Cyanide is a more modern poison which induces unconsciousness followed by convulsions, and an inability to absorb oxygen. It was used to kill millions of concentration camp prisoners in WW2 and was swallowed by Herman Goering when he was under sentence to be hanged for war crimes.

Strychnine was used as a poison in China for centuries, but only made its way to Europe in the late 1700s. It originates in the *Strychnos nux-vomica* tree and is still used widely as an agricultural poison for bird pests and rats. It causes muscle spasms and death from asphyxiation.

Poisoning with Mercury was usually accidental and was common among those who dabbled in alchemy. The alchemists Blaise Pascal and Michael Faraday both died this way and Charles II's final illness may have been due to him refining Mercury for medicinal purposes. He and his Chemical Physician operated a basement laboratory in Whitehall where they distilled Mercury from Cinnabar without any safety precautions. In 1967, however, his hair was analysed by nuclear mission spectroscopy and showed high levels of Lead but not Mercury. Fits from acute Mercury poisoning were called Erethrism and were once common among industrial workers who used Mercury to soften felt for the hatting industry, so-called Mad Hatter's Disease. It was also seen as a side effect when Mercury was used to treat Syphilis. Arsenic was called the King of Poisons by the Romans and was the favourite of the Borgias in Renaissance Italy.

It was implicated in the death of Edward VI and George III, in whom hundreds of years later the laboratory analysis of his hair confirmed high Arsenic levels. in George III's case, however, it was administered unknowingly in creams to treat his skin Porphyria and in his wig powder. Arsenic is tasteless, colourless, and odourless, and is a potent poison of important intracellular enzymes. It causes sweating, confusion, muscle cramps and stomach, pains and just a few grains can cause unconsciousness and death.

# SELECTED BIBLIOGRAPHY

A vast amount of information is accumulating on the Internet and for medical information about individual diseases the reader is also referred to the US Library of the National Institutes of Health.

*Henry II. A Prince among Princes*, Richard Barber, Penguin Random, UK, 2015

*Eleanor of Acquitaine*, Alison Weir, Jonathan Cape Publishers, 1999

*England in the Late Middle Ages*, AR Myers, Penguin Books, 1952

*Wars of the Roses*, Hubert Cole, Ludovic Kennedy editor, Granada Publishing, 1973

*King Richard II*, Bryan Bevan, Rubicon Press, 1990

*The Wars of the Roses*, Hubert Cole, Hart Davis, MacGibbon Ltd, 1973

*Richard Duke of Gloucester King of England*, Caroline Halsted, Longman Brown Green Publishers, 1844

*England under the Tudors*, GR Elton, Methuen and Co Ltd, 1955

*The life and times of Henry VII*, Neville Williams, Weidenfeld and Nicolson, 1973

*Arthur Tudor*, Worcester News, 2009

*Henry VIII, King and Court*, Alison Weir, Jonathon Cape, 2007

*The Reign of Edward VI*, James A Stroude, JM Dent Publishers, 1907

*Edward VI*, Jennifer Loach, Yale University Press, 1999

*Lady Jane Grey*, David Matthew, Eyre Methuen, 1972

*The Lady in the Tower*, Alison Weir, Cape Publishers, 2010

*Elizabeth and Leicester*, Milton Waldman, WM Collins Sons and Co Ltd, 1946

*Mary Queen of Scots*, Antonia Fraser, Panther Books Ltd, 1970

'The Skull of Lord Darnley', Sir Arthur Keith, *British Medical Journal*, 1928. Sept 8th, 456-458

'Porphyria and the Royal Houses of Stuart, Hanover and Prussia', I. McAlpine, R Hunter, & C Rimington. *British Medical Journal*, 1968. Jan 6; 1(5583): 7-18

'Porphyria in the royal houses of Stuart, Hanover and Prussia.' I. McAlpine, R. Hunter, and C. Rimington. *British Med. J.*, 1966. 1. 65-71.

*The Sickly Stuarts*, Frederick Holmes, Sutton Publishing, 2003

*The Isles. A History*, Norman Davies, Macmillan Publishers, 1999

*King Charles II*, Antonia Fraser, Wieldenfeld and Nicholson Publishers, 1979

*King James II*, FMG Higham, Hamish Hamilton, 1952

*The Stuart Princesses*, Alison Plowden, Sutton Publishing, 1997

*Cromwell Our Chief of Men*, Antonia Fraser, Weidenfeld and Nicolson, 1997

*The Two Protectors*, SW Partidge and Sons, 1899

*The First Four Georges*, JH Plumb, Batsford, 1956.

*King George III*, John Brooke with a foreword by HRH the Prince of Wales, London Constable, 1972

*Frederick the Great*, David Fraser, Penguin Press, 2000

*George IV Regent and King*, Christopher Hibbert, Allen Lane Publishers, 1973

*Victoria's Daughters*, Jerrold M Packard, Sutton Publishing Ltd, 2000

*The Fenian Five: the plot to assassinate Queen Victoria*, Christy Campbell, Harper Collins, 2002

*Edward VII, a portrait*, Christopher Hibbert, JP Lippincott Publishers, 1976

*King George V, his life and times,* Harold Nicholson, Constable and Co., 1952

*King Edward VIII,* Philip Zeigler, Alfred Knopf Publishers, 1991

*A King's Story,* HRH the Duke of Windsor, The Reprint Society 1951 and Castell & Co Ltd. 1953

*George VI,* Sarah Bradford, Fontana, 1989

*Diseases of infancy and childhood,* R.E.B Ellis, Livingstone, 1963

*Disorders of haemostasis,* Ratnoff O.D. and Forbes C.D., WB Saunders Publishers, 1991

'The History of Haemophilia', G.I.C. Ingram, *Journal of Clinical Pathology.* 1976.29.469-479

*Disease and History,* PF Cartwright, Sutton Publishing, 2000

*Textbook of Human Virology,* RB Belshe, PSG Publishing, 1984

*The Principles and Practice of Medicine,* William Osler, Appleton and Co., 1892

*Essential Malariology,* LJ Bruce-Chwatt, W. Heinemann Medical Books, 1986

*The Royal Way of Death,* Olivia Bland, Constable London, 1986

*The Death of Kings,* Clifford Brewer, Abson Books London, 2002,

*Kings and Queens of England & Great Britain,* Eric R Delderfield, David & Charles Publishers, 1990

*The Lives of the Kings and Queens of England,* Anatonia Fraser, Wieldenfeldt & Nicolson Publishers, 1993.

# COVER PHOTOGRAPH

This portrait of George III is by Allan Ramsay and shows the king in his coronation robes. It was painted in 1761 and is one of numerous replicas which were sent to Britain's new colonies to represent royal authority across the British Empire.

Ramsay was trained in Rome and Naples and was appointed Painter to the King in preference to Joshua Reynolds. He painted over 100 important portraits but gave up in 1770 to follow literary pursuits.

Printed in Great Britain
by Amazon